exponential and logarithmic functions

with calculator commentary

kenneth f. klopfenstein

the davies group, publishers

aurora, colorado usa

 The Davies Group, Publishers
P.O. Box 440140
Aurora, CO 80044-0140

ISBN 1-888570-29-6

Library of Congress Catalog Card Number: to come

edition for the academic year 2003-2004
printing for august, 2003

cover art: reprinted with the generous permission of nasa's hubble space telescope.
interior illustrations: the davies group
editors: the davies group
design: the davies group

preface

At Colorado State University, precalculus mathematics is taught in a flexible, mastery oriented instructional system called the Individualized Mathematics Program. This system is based on the belief that, given proper organization and sequencing of content, appropriate learning resources, adequate time, and sufficient positive feedback and encouragement, virtually every student can master the content of a course. These materials are written primarily for students studying exponential and logarithmic functions in the Individualized Mathematics Program and similar instructional programs, and for those learning independently. The selection and organization of content and style of presentation reflect principles of individualized instruction. Instructional objectives are carefully formulated and prominently displayed to tell student, teacher, and test writer what students are expected to be able to do as a result of studying each section. Short units of material provide manageable learning tasks and opportunities for frequent positive feedback and encouragement. The discussion, examples and exercises focus specifically on the stated objectives. I hope readers who are learning about functions as mathematicians know them and, in particular, about exponential and logarithmic functions, will find that these features make learning easier.

In this edition of Exponential and Logarithmic Functions the Texas Instruments TI-83® Graphing Calculator is fully integrated into the presentation. The calculator is presented as a tool to enhance learning and not as something additional to be learned. Concepts and ideas are presented without using the calculator in sections titled Discussion. Most Discussions are followed by a section titled Calculator Commentary, where graphing and programming features of the TI-83® are used to consider the ideas presented in the Discussion both graphically and numerically. When advanced features of the TI-83® can be used to solve problems, two solutions to the Examples are presented. One solution uses only basic features of the calculator and the other takes advantage of advanced features. Almost all Practice Problems can be done using the TI-83® only for arithmetic calculations and function evaluations, but some can be solved more easily and elegantly using advanced features of the TI-83®. One could master all the objectives in *Exponential and Logarithmic Functions* without learning any features of the TI-83® beyond the basic operations found on any scientific calculator. However, students who make intensive use of the TI-83® from the outset will acquire a more comprehensive understanding, expend less effort mastering the material, and enjoy their learning experience more.

In preparing this edition, I have benefited greatly from the comments of many students who learned from the preceding editions, from graduate and undergraduate course assistants who lectured and tutored from them, and from faculty colleagues who taught from them. I am sincerely grateful to all these people for contributions large and small, recognized and unrecognized.

My realization that I should acknowledge technological progress by incorporating advanced scientific/ graphing calculators into this text would not have been translated into action without the support of Robert Gaines, my department head during the time I was developing and writing this book, and the encouragement, enthusiasm, and vision of J. Keith and Elizabeth (B.J.) Baker Davies of The Davies Group. A special thanks to B.J. for her sensitive editing of my often ponderous writing and her appealing page design, and to Keith for the desktop publishing wizardry that transformed this work into print. The Davies' patience, skill, good humor, and professional commitment have made preparing this edition enjoyable and rewarding. I hope the reader will find learning from it enjoyable and rewarding.

Kenneth F. Klopfenstein
Colorado State University
Fort Collins CO 80523-1874
August, 2002

about the cover art

The photographic art work reproduced on this book's cover is provided courtesy of NASA's Hubble Space Telescope. The technology that makes this photograph possible could not have been developed without an understanding of mathematics. We hope that your life's journeys will be enhanced by mathematics.

If you wish to learn more about this photograph, and the annual archives in which others may be found, please visit the Hubble Space Telescope web site found at http://hubblesite.org/newscenter/.

special recognition

The author and publisher wish to thank Texas Instruments for their continued support of this textbook through their permission to reproduced certain material from the *Texas Instruments TI-83® Graphing Calculator Guidebook.*

The Davies Group, Publishers
August, 2003

contents

exponential and logarithmic functions

exponential and logarithmic functions

In this book, the positions of keys on the TI-83® keyboard are indicated by giving the row and column where a key is found. Rows of the keyboard are numbered from top to bottom and columns are numbered from left to right.

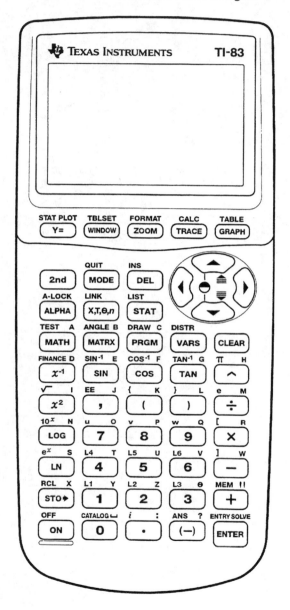

FUNCTIONS AND GRAPHS

OBJECTIVE 1.1

Given a function f specified by an equation $y = f(x)$ and given a number a, compute $f(a)$ or state that a is not in the domain of f.

OBJECTIVE 1.2

(a) Given a graph, determine whether it is the graph of a function.

(b) Given the graph of a function, determine the domain and the range of the function.

(c) Given the graph of a function f and given a number a, find $f(a)$ or state that a is not in the domain of f.

(d) Given the graph of a function f and given a number b, find all numbers a such that $f(a) = b$, or state that b is not in the range of f.

OBJECTIVE 1.3

(a) Given an exponential function $f(x) = b^x$, $b > 0$, $b \neq 1$, and given a number a, use a Texas Instruments TI-83® calculator to evaluate $f(a)$.

(b) Given a number a, use a Texas Instruments TI-83® calculator to evaluate $\log(a)$ and $\ln(a)$, or state that a is not in the domain of these logarithmic functions.

OBJECTIVE 1.4

(a) Given $b > 0$, $b \neq 1$, sketch the graph of $f(x) = b^x$.

(b) Given the graph of an exponential function $f(x) = b^x$, estimate b.

OBJECTIVE 1.5

(a) Given two functions f and g, and given a number a, compute $f(g(a)) = f \circ g(a)$, or state that $f \circ g(a)$ is not defined.

(b) Given two functions $y = f(x)$ and $y = g(x)$, find an expression for their composition and simplify it.

UNIT 1
FUNCTIONS AND GRAPHS

OVERVIEW

The abstract notion of a function, which was first articulated by L. Euler in the mid-seventeen hundreds, is central to much of mathematics and, of course, to this book. Much of pure mathematics is concerned with discovering and understanding the properties of various functions and classes of functions. Much of applied mathematics is concerned with discovering functions which describe phenomena in the world around us and then using these functions to understand the phenomena they describe. In this book we are concerned with both kinds of questions; with understanding the properties of the exponential and logarithmic functions and with using these functions to describe phenomena we see in the world around us.

In Unit 1 we will examine the idea of a mathematical function and study various ways functions can be specified. We will use the TI-83® graphics calculator to investigate exponential and logarithmic functions as examples of mathematical functions and to graph exponential functions. Finally, we will study composition as a process for combining two functions to form another function. In Unit 2 we will use composition of functions to describe the fundamental relationship between exponential and logarithmic functions.

FUNCTIONS AND GRAPHS

OBJECTIVE 1.1

Given a function f specified by an equation $y = f(x)$ and given a number a, compute $f(a)$ or state that a is not in the domain of f.

DISCUSSION

In mathematical language, a **function** has been specified when the following two things are given:

- a **collection D** of numbers and
- a **procedure** for determining exactly one number (often denoted y) from each number (often denoted x) in the collection D.

The collection D is called the **domain** of the function.

In many discussions involving a function it is not necessary, or even important, to know specifically either the domain of the function or the procedure for the function. It is important only to know that there is a domain and there is a procedure. The phrase y *is a function of* x and the function notation $y = f(x)$ (read y *equals f of x*) are used to say that there is a domain D and there is a procedure for determining exactly one number y from each number x in D.

In the function notation $y = f(x)$, the symbol f is thought of as a **name** for the function or as a name for the procedure for the function. The notation implies nothing about what the procedure f or the domain D might be. Capital letters, lower case letters, Greek letters, and even combinations of letters are often used in place of the letter f in function notation. Other letters (usually, but not always, lower case) are often used in place of x and y.

The symbols x and y in the equation $y = f(x)$ are also called **variables**. The symbol in the position occupied by x is the **independent variable**. Any numerical value from the domain of the function can be assigned to the independent variable. The symbol in the y position is the **dependent variable** because the numerical value of y is determined by and depends on the numerical value assigned to x.

Another use for function notation is to give an equation or expression for a **computational procedure** which specifies a function. For example, the equation $f(x) = x^2$ (read f *of x* *equals x squared*) says that **squaring** is the procedure used with the function f to determine a number y from each number x. Similarly, the equation $g(t) = \sqrt{4 - t^2}$ says that with the function g the procedure for determining a number y from a number t in the domain of g is to square the number t, subtract the result from 4, and take the square root.

A third use of function notation is to denote the number obtained by applying the procedure used with the function to a specific number from the domain. As an example, consider the function $g(t) = \sqrt{4 - t^2}$ again. The notation $g(0)$ (read *g of zero*) denotes the number y obtained from $t = 0$ by applying the procedure used with g.

Thus,
$$g(0) = \sqrt{4 - (0)^2} = \sqrt{4} = 2,$$

$$g(-2) = \sqrt{4 - (-2)^2} = 0,$$

and
$$g(1) = \sqrt{4 - (1)^2} = \sqrt{3}.$$

The process of finding the numerical value $f(a)$ from a particular number a is called **evaluating f at a** and the resulting number $f(a)$ is called **the value of f at a** or, more simply, **f at a**. When the number a is not in the domain of the function f, we say that $f(a)$ **is not defined**.

The domain of a function is sometimes given explicitly. More often the domain must be inferred from the procedure for the function. When the domain of $y = f(x)$ is not specifically stated, it is understood to be the collection of all real numbers to which the procedure for the function can be applied to produce another real number. When the procedure for the function involves division, the numbers that would require division by zero are excluded from the domain. When square roots are involved, the numbers that would require taking the square root of a negative number are excluded.

CALCULATOR COMMENTARY

Many familiar functions are pre-programmed into advanced scientific calculators and can be accessed by a single keystroke or a simple combination of keystrokes. On the Texas Instruments TI-83®, the key labeled $\boxed{x^2}$ (row 6, column 1 on the calculator keyboard) is the square function $s(x) = x^2$ and the key labeled $\boxed{x^{-1}}$ (row 5, column 1) is the reciprocal function $r(x) = \dfrac{1}{x}$. The square root function $\text{sqrt}(x) = \sqrt{x}$ is also pre-programmed, but there is no key labeled $\sqrt{}$. The square root symbol $\sqrt{}$ is printed above the $\boxed{x^2}$ key to indicate that the square root function is accessed through this key by first pressing the $\boxed{\text{2nd}}$ key (row 2, column 1). We will indicate that a calculator function or operation is accessed through the [2nd] key by enclosing it in square brackets. Thus, the sequence of keystrokes for the square root function is given as [2nd] , [$\sqrt{}$].

On the TI-83® numbers, operations, and expressions are entered and displayed, as nearly as possible, in the same way you would write them on a page. Thus, to evaluate the square function for a particular number, say 12.397, first enter the number, and then press [x^2] . The calculator will display

$$12.397^2$$

Press [ENTER] (row 10, column 5). The calculator will display the result of squaring 12.397:

$$12.397^2$$
$$153.685609$$

Since we write $\sqrt{3}$ to denote the square root of 3 and the TI-83® displays expressions in the same way we would write them, the sequence of keystrokes for the square root of three is [2nd] , [$\sqrt{}$] (row 6, column 1) followed by [3] .

We understand the domains of $r(x) = x^{-1}$ and $sqrt(x) = \sqrt{x}$ to be all of the numbers to which these calculations can be applied to produce another real number. Thus, the domain of $r(x) = x^{-1}$ is all real numbers other than zero and the domain of $sqrt(x) = \sqrt{x}$ is all non-negative real numbers.

When the TI-83® is asked to evaluate x^{-1} or $\sqrt{x}$ for a number not in the domain of the function, the machine displays an error message. For example, when asked to evaluate 0^{-1}, the TI-83® displays the error message **ERR:DIVIDE BY 0** and a special error menu. When it is asked to evaluate $\sqrt{-3}$, the TI-83® displays the error message **ERR:NONREAL ANS**. (Consult the *Texas Instruments TI-83® Graphing Calculator Guidebook* for the meanings of various error messages.) Experiment by evaluating the square, reciprocal, and square root functions for numbers a that you choose.

There are several ways to use the TI-83® to evaluate a function specified by an equation. The calculation can be entered directly, a previously entered calculation can be edited, or the equation can be programmed. These procedures are illustrated in Examples 5, 6 and 7.

SUMMARY

1. A function has been specified when the following two things are given:
   - a **collection** of numbers D called the **domain** of the function and
   - a **procedure** for determining exactly one number y from each number x in the domain D.

2. The function notation $y = f(x)$ means that there is a domain D and a procedure f for determining exactly one number y from each number x in D.

3. When a is a number from the domain of a function f, the notation $f(a)$ denotes the number obtained by applying the procedure for f to the number a. When a is not in the domain of f, we say that $f(a)$ **is not defined**.

4. When the domain of a function is not explicitly stated, it is understood to be the collection of all real numbers to which the procedure for the function can be applied to obtain another real number.

EXAMPLES

Example 1: What is the domain of the function $f(x) = \dfrac{1}{x - 3}$?

Solution 1: The domain of f is not given explicitly. It must be inferred from the procedure for the function. The computational procedure for f can be applied to all numbers except $x = 3$, which would require division by zero. The domain of f is the collection of all real numbers other than 3.

Example 2: What is the domain of the function $g(t) = \sqrt{4 - t^2}$?

Solution 2: The domain of g is not given explicitly. It must be inferred from the procedure for g. The computational procedure for g can be applied to all numbers which do not require taking the square root of a negative number. These are the values of t for which $4 - t^2 \geq 0$. The domain of g is all numbers t such that $-2 \leq t \leq 2$.

Example 3: Let $f(x) = \dfrac{x + 3}{2x - 1}$ and $a = 5$.

Find $f(a)$ or state that a is not in the domain of f.

Solution 3: The computational procedure given by the equation for f can be applied to the number $a = 5$ to obtain a real number. Therefore, 5 is in the domain of f and

$$f(5) = \frac{5 + 3}{2(5) - 1} = \frac{8}{9}.$$

Example 4: Let $h(s) = 1 - \sqrt{s}$ and $b = -9$.

Find $h(b)$ or state that b is not in the domain of h.

Solution 4: Since negative numbers do not have square roots which are real numbers, the computational procedure given by the equation for h cannot be applied to the number $b = -9$. Therefore, $b = -9$ is not in the domain of the function h and $h(-9)$ is not defined.

Example 5: Let $f(x) = \dfrac{x + 3}{2x - 1}$ and $a = 5$.

Find $f(a)$ or state that a is not in the domain of f.

Solution 5: In this example, we will evaluate $f(5)$ by using the TI-83® to calculate $\dfrac{5 + 3}{2(5) - 1}$ directly. Enter this numerical expression into the TI-83® as you would write it with numerator and denominator enclosed in parentheses. When this expression is correctly entered, the display will show

$$\boxed{(5+3)/(2*5-1)}$$

Press ⌈ENTER⌉. The display will show

$$\boxed{\begin{array}{l}(5+3)/(2*5-1)\\ \hspace{3em}.8888888889\end{array}}$$

Thus, $f(5) = 0.8888888889$ which is $\dfrac{8}{9}$ rounded to 10 decimal places.

Example 6: Let $f(x) = \dfrac{x + 3}{2x - 1}$.

Find $f(3.7)$ or state that 3.7 is not in the domain of f.

Solution 6: In this example, we will find $f(3.7)$ by editing a previous calculation. Press ⌈2nd⌉ , [ENTRY] (row 10, column 5) to recover the numerical expression $\dfrac{5 + 3}{2(5) - 1}$ from Example 5 (provided this was the last entry made). The display will show

$$\boxed{(5+3)/(2*5-1)}$$

Now use the arrow keys to move the cursor over the 5. Press [DEL] (row 2, column 3) to delete 5. Press [2nd], [INS] (row 2, column 3), [3], [•], [7] to insert 3.7. Move the cursor over the second 5 and repeat the deletion and insertion. Press [ENTER]. The display will show

```
( 3.7+3 ) / ( 2*3.7−1 )
                1.046875
```

Thus, $f(3.7) = 1.046875$. Press [MATH] (row 4, col. 1), [1], [ENTER], to convert this decimal into a fraction and find that $f(3.7) = 1.046875 = \dfrac{67}{64}$.

Choose several numbers a and compute $f(a)$ by editing previous calculations.

Example 7: Let $f(x) = \dfrac{x + 3}{2x - 1}$. Evaluate f at -3.79, -1.24, 0.03, 2.57, and 0.5.

Solution 7:   In this example, we will evaluate the function by programming. A program is a sequence of instructions that is stored in the calculator's memory to be carried out on command.   An equation $y = f(x)$ for a function is also a sequence of instructions for computing a number y from any given number x from the domain of the function. To program the calculator to follow the instructions contained in the formula $y = f(x)$, we enter the expression for the function into one of the calculator's memories in almost the same way one would write the equation.

The TI-83® has ten memories for storing expressions or formulas. Press [Y=] (row 1, column 1) to display the **Y =** edit screen that provides access to these memories. If there are no expressions already stored in these memories, the TI-83® will display

```
Plot 1   Plot 2   Plot 3
\Y1 =
\Y2 =
\Y3 =
\Y4 =
\Y5 =
\Y6 =
\Y7 =
```

Expressions stored in these memories can be deleted by using the up and down arrow keys to position the cursor anywhere on the expression to be deleted and pressing $\boxed{\text{CLEAR}}$ (row 4, column 5). Space for three more expressions can be accessed by pressing the down arrow key repeatedly.

TI Tip

> If your **Y**= edit screen doesn't look like the screen shown above, your calculator is not set to function mode. To set your TI-83® to function mode, first press $\boxed{\text{MODE}}$ (row 2, column 2). Move the cursor to **Func** (fourth line), and press $\boxed{\text{ENTER}}$. Finally, press $\boxed{\text{2nd}}$, [QUIT] (row 2, column 2) to return to the home screen and try again.

Enter the expression for $f(x) = \dfrac{x+3}{2x-1}$ after **Y1**=. Press $\boxed{\text{X,T,}\theta,n}$ (row 3, column 2) to enter the variable x. Be sure to enclose numerator and denominator in parentheses. When the expression is entered correctly, the display will show

> **Y1=(X+3)/(2*X−1)**
> **Y2=**

The TI-83® interprets **2X** to mean 2 multiplied times x, so the multiplication operation symbol * could be omitted. However, none of the parentheses can be left out. Press $\boxed{\text{2nd}}$, [QUIT] (row 2, column 2) to return to the home screen. (This sequence of key strokes almost always returns the TI-83® to the home screen.)

To execute the calculations to evaluate $f(-3.79)$, first select the formula **Y1**. Do this by first pressing $\boxed{\text{VARS}}$ (row 4, column 4) to display a menu of categories of variables. Press the right arrow key to select the category **Y-VARS**. Select the category **Function** by pressing $\boxed{1}$. The calculator will display a menu of the ten variables **Y1** through **Y0**. Select **Y1** by pressing $\boxed{1}$. The display will show

> **Y1**

Immediately to the right of **Y1**, type (-3.79) so the display shows

> **Y1(-3.79)**

Press $\boxed{\text{ENTER}}$.

TI Tip

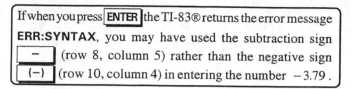

If when you press ENTER the TI-83® returns the error message **ERR:SYNTAX**, you may have used the subtraction sign − (row 8, column 5) rather than the negative sign (−) (row 10, column 4) in entering the number −3.79 .

The calculator immediately evaluates the formula **Y1** for the number −3.79 and displays

```
Y1(-3.79)
             .0920745921
```

Thus, rounded to 10 decimal places, $f(-3.79) = .0920745921$. Press MATH (row 4, column 1), 1 , ENTER to convert this decimal into a fraction and find

$$f(-3.79) = .0920745921 = \frac{79}{858}.$$

To evaluate $f(-1.24)$, press 2nd , [ENTRY] several times to recall **Y1(-3.79)**. Use the left and right arrow keys to position the cursor over the negative sign and then type −1.24. The display will show

```
Y1(-1.24)
```

Press ENTER . The calculator immediately evaluates the formula **Y1** for the number −1.24 and displays

```
Y1(-1.24)
              -.5057471264
```

Thus, rounded to 10 decimal places, $f(-1.24) = -0.5057471264$. Follow similar procedures to find that $f(0.03) = -3.223404255$, $f(2.57) = 1.345410628$, and 0.5 is not in the domain of f. Use DEL (row 2, column 3) to delete unwanted characters.

Example 8: Let $f(x) = 5x^2 + 11x - 23$, $a = 3.7$ and $b = -31.5$. Find $f(a) - f(b)$.

Solution 8: First press Y= to display the **Y =** edit screen. Enter $5x^2 + 11x - 23$ as **Y1**. Press 2nd , [QUIT] to return to the home screen.

Now follow the procedures from the previous example and enter

$$\boxed{\text{Y1(3.7)} - \text{Y1(-31.5)}}$$

Press $\boxed{\text{ENTER}}$. The calculator immediately evaluates $\text{Y1(3.7)} - \text{Y1(-31.5)}$ and determines that

$$f(a) - f(b) = f(3.7) - f(-31.5) = -4505.6.$$

PRACTICE PROBLEMS

In problems 1 - 6, find the domain of the given function.

1. $f(x) = \dfrac{1}{x - 2}$

2. $g(x) = \sqrt{5 - 3x}$

3. $h(x) = x^2 - 4x + 3$

4. $f(x) = \dfrac{1}{\sqrt{2x + 9}}$

5. $g(x) = \dfrac{\sqrt{9 - x^2}}{x - 2}$

6. $h(x) = \dfrac{x + 3}{x^2 - 6x + 5}$

7. Let $f(x) = 1 - 3x + x^3$.
   (a) Let $a = -2$. Find $f(a)$ or state that a is not in the domain of f.
   (b) Find $f(3)$ or state that $f(3)$ is not defined.

8. Let $h(x) = \dfrac{x^2 - 3x - 10}{x + 1}$.

   (a) Let $c = 4$. Find $h(c)$ or state that $h(c)$ is not defined.
   (b) Find $h(-1)$ or state that -1 is not in the domain of h.
   (c) Evaluate h at 23.76.

9. Let $g(x) = \dfrac{1}{\sqrt{2x + 7}}$.

   (a) Find $g\!\left(\dfrac{-19}{4}\right)$ or state that $\dfrac{-19}{4}$ is not in the domain of g.
   (b) Let $s = -1$. Find $g(s)$ or state that $g(s)$ is not defined.
   (c) Evaluate g at 0.013.

10. Let $F(x) = \dfrac{\sqrt{x^2 - 7}}{x - 1}$.

    (a) Find $F(2)$ or state that 2 is not in the domain of F.

    (b) Let $a = 4$.   Find $F(a)$ or state that $F(a)$ is not defined.

    (c) Find $F(1)$ or state that $F(1)$ is not defined.

11. Let $H(x) = \dfrac{x + 2\sqrt{5 - x}}{2x - 1}$.

    (a) Find $H\left(\dfrac{1}{2}\right)$ or state that $\dfrac{1}{2}$ is not in the domain of H.

    (b) Let $t = 5$.   Find $H(t)$ or state that $H(t)$ is not defined.

    (c) Let $q = 1$.   Find $H(q)$ or state that q is not in the domain of H.

    (d) Calculate $H(2.1) - H(1.2)$.

12. Let $R(x) = \dfrac{2x - 1}{x^2 - 4x - 5}$.

    (a) Find $R(5)$ or state that $R(5)$ is not defined.

    (b) Find $R\left(\dfrac{1}{2}\right)$ or state that $\dfrac{1}{2}$ is not in the domain of R.

    (c) Let $R(-2)$ or state that $R(-2)$ is not defined.

13. Let $f(x) = 4 - x^2$, $a = -3$ and $b = 5$. Find $f(a) - f(b)$.

14. Let $g(x) = \dfrac{2x + 1}{x - 3}$. Find $g\left(-\dfrac{1}{2}\right) + g(2)$.

15. Let $h(x) = \dfrac{\sqrt{x + 2}}{x^2 - x - 6}$. Find $h(2) - h(-2)$.

16. Let $K(x) = \dfrac{3}{\sqrt{x - 4}}$, $a = 13$ and $b = 40$. Find $K(a) - K(b)$.

17. Let $F(x) = 8 - x^3$. Find $F(-1) + F(3)$.

18. Let $G(x) = \dfrac{x + 3}{\sqrt{5 - 2x}}$, $a = \dfrac{5}{2}$ and $b = \dfrac{3}{2}$. Find $G(a) - G(b)$.

19. Find $F(19.7) - G(0.25)$ when F is the function from problem 17 and G is the function from problem 18.

20. Find $g(1.25) + h(3.47)$ when g is the function from problem 14 and h is the function from problem 15.

AUTHOR'S NOTE

The Cartesian Coordinate system (see page 14) derives its name from the 17th-century philosopher René Decartes. Descarte was a thinker, mathematician, scientist, soldier and teacher. He was as caustic, ill-tempered, and arrogrant as he was brilliant.

As a thinker Decartes formulated his famous axiom *Cogito ergo sum*, which he took to be irrefutable evidence of the existence of the mind. From this he postulated the existence of matter. As a mathematician Decartes deivsed new systems of algebraic notation and is widely regarded as the originator of analytic geometry. As a scientist he is credited with the development of the scientific method. His philosophical theories provided the basis for 17th-century Rationalism, in that he accepted certain *a priori* truths and sought to develop a system of philosophic thought based methods of deduction and what he called "methodical doubt." As a soldier, Descartes enlisted under the Elector of Bavaria and was engaged in the fighting at the battle of Prague. Mathematics historian Howard Eves tells us that once, while armed only with a sword, Descartes forced the captors who planned to kill him, to return him, unharmed and by boat, to safety. Additionally, he served under, and fought with, the Duke of Savoy and the King of France. After finding himself in wide disfavor in his native France, he accepted a commission and became the teacher to Sweden's Queen Christina. Descartes died suddenly and swiftly in Stockholm of what was probably pneumonia.

When, seventeen years after Descartes' death, his remains were returned and re-entombed in Paris, Carl Gustav Joseph Jacobi remarked, "It is often more convenient to possess the ashes of great men than to possess the men themselves."

Recommended reading - Science and Philosophy: *Discourse on Method* (1637) and *Principles of Philosophy* (1644) by René Decartes.

OBJECTIVE 1.2

    (a) **Given a graph, determine whether it is the graph of a function.**

    (b) **Given the graph of a function, determine the domain and the range of the function.**

    (c) **Given the graph of a function f and given a number a, find $f(a)$ or state that a is not in the domain of f.**

    (d) **Given the graph of a function f and given a number b, find all numbers a such that $f(a) = b$ or state that b is not in the range of f.**

DISCUSSION

To specify a function one must give the domain of the function and a procedure for determining a number from each number in the domain. In Objective 1.1 we used equations to specify functions. In this Discussion we show how a graph is used to specify a function.

Figure 1.1 is a **rectangular**, or **Cartesian, coordinate system**. It consists of perpendicular number lines that intersect at their **zero points**. Their common zero point is called the **origin**. The horizontal number line is called the **x-axis**. The vertical number line is called the **y-axis**. Points are located by ordered pairs of numbers (a, b). The first member of the ordered pair is the **x-coordinate** of the point. The second member of the ordered pair is the **y-coordinate** of the point.

A collection of points in a rectangular coordinate system is called a **graph**. A graph is given by marking or shading the points in the collection. In previous courses you have constructed graphs from equations.

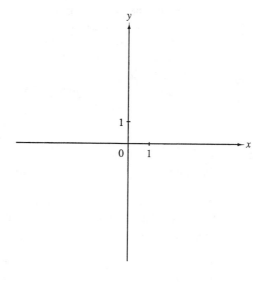

Figure 1.1 A Cartesian coordinate system

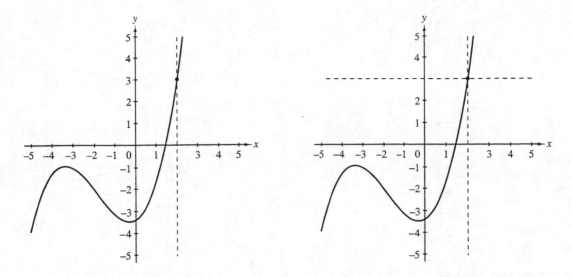

Figure 1.2 The graph of a function (see Step 1)   *Figure 1.3* The graph of a function (see Steps 2 - 3)

Figure 1.2 is the graph of a function $y = f(x)$. This graph gives both the domain of f and a procedure for determining a number y from each number x in the domain. The procedure for using a graph to evaluate a function is the reverse of the procedure used to construct a graph from an equation for the function. To illustrate, we evaluate f at 2.

Step 1.   Locate the number $x = 2$ on the x-axis and draw a line perpendicular to the x-axis through it, as shown in Figure 1.2.

Step 2.   Locate the point where the vertical line drawn in Step 1 intersects the graph. Draw a line parallel to the x-axis through it, as shown in Figure 1.3.

Step 3.   Locate the point where the horizontal line drawn in Step 2 crosses the y-axis. The y-coordinate of this point is $f(2)$. Therefore, $f(2) = 3$, as shown in Figure 1.3.

The **domain** of a function which is given by a graph is the collection D of numbers on the x-axis to which the procedure just illustrated can be applied to get another number. Thus, the domain is the collection of numbers x on the x-axis such that the vertical line through x intersects the graph. In geometric language, it is the projection of the graph onto the x-axis. The domain of the function given by the graph in Figure 1.4 is the shaded portion of the x-axis.

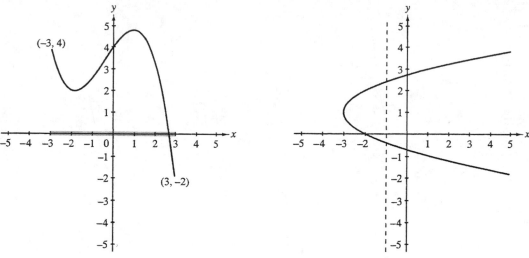

Figure 1.4   Figure 1.5 This graph is not a function.

Recall that the procedure for a function must produce exactly one number y from each x in its domain. Indeed, when the procedure just described is applied to any number x in the domain of the function in Figure 1.3, only one number y is produced. This is due to the special shape of the graph and its position in the coordinate system. Think of applying this same procedure, based now on the graph in Figure 1.5, to the number $x = -1$. Two y values result because the vertical line through $x = -1$ intersects this graph in two points. Therefore, the graph in Figure 1.5 is **not** the graph of a function.

We can identify the graph of a function by applying the VERTICAL LINE TEST:
   A graph in a Cartesian coordinate system specifies a function if and only if every
   line perpendicular to the x-axis intersects the graph in no more than one point.

To apply the VERTICAL LINE TEST to a graph, imagine moving a vertical line from left to right across the graph. If at every position the line cuts the graph at no more than one point, then the graph is the graph of a function. If there is even one position where the line cuts the graph at more than one point, then the graph is not the graph of a function.

The collection of numbers obtained by applying the procedure for a function f to every number in its domain is called the **range** of the function. The range of a function given by a graph is the collection of numbers on the y-axis obtained by applying the procedure for evaluating the function to all of the numbers in the domain. Thus, the range consists of the numbers y on the vertical axis such that the horizontal line through y intersects the graph. In geometric language, it is the projection of the graph onto the y-axis. The range of the function given by the graph in Figure 1.6 is the shaded portion of the y-axis.

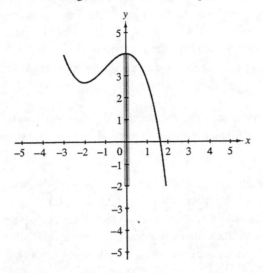

Figure 1.6

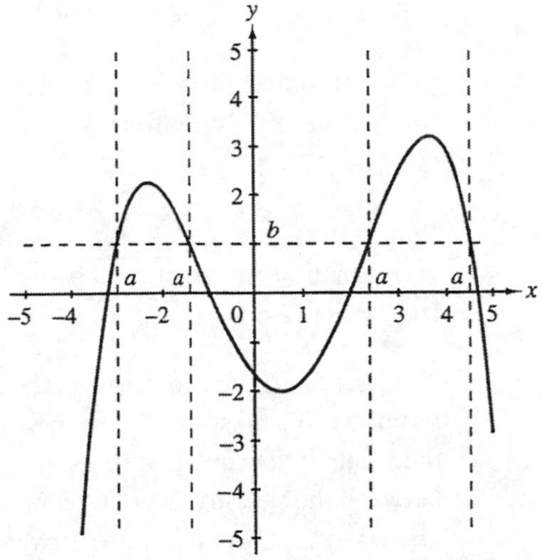

Figure 1.7 Graphical procedure for finding all numbers a such that $f(a) = b$ (see Steps 1 - 3)

If a number b is in the range of f, then there are one or more numbers a such that $f(a) = b$. These numbers can be found from the graph of f by reversing the procedure for evaluating a function from its graph. Given b in the range of f, find all numbers a such that $f(a) = b$ by following these steps as shown in Figure 1.7.

Step 1.   Locate the number b on the y-axis and draw a line perpendicular to the y-axis through it. If the line drawn does not intersect the graph, then the number b is not in the range of the function.

Step 2.   Locate the point or points where the horizontal line drawn in Step 1 intersects the graph. Draw a line parallel to the y-axis through each one of these points.

Step 3.   Locate the points where the vertical lines drawn in Step 2 intersect the x-axis. The x-coordinates of these points are the numbers a such that $f(a) = b$.

CALCULATOR COMMENTARY

In the past, you have graphed equations by making tables of x and y values which satisfy the equation, plotting these points in a coordinate plane and, finally, connecting these points with a smooth curve. Graphic calculators construct graphs in the same way. Because calculators are fast and tireless, they can calculate many more points than any person ever would want to, plot these points on their screen, and connect them to display a detailed graph. To illustrate the procedure for graphing a function on the TI-83®, let's generate the graph of $f(x) = x^3 - 4x^2 - x + 4$.

First, enter $x^3 - 4x^2 - x + 4$ as **Y1** (or any one of the **Ys**) on the **Y=** screen. Use the cube function from the MATH (row 4, column 1) menu to enter x^3. Delete all other expressions from this screen.

The portion of the coordinate system on which the graph will be drawn is called the **viewing window**. We must specify the viewing window. Press WINDOW (row 1, column 2) to display the menu used to designate the smallest and largest allowable x- and y-values and the distance between the tick marks on the coordinate axes in the viewing window. Use the up and down arrow keys to move the cursor between lines of this menu. Enter -10 for **Xmin**, 10 for **Xmax**, 1 for **Xscl**, -10 for **Ymin**, 10 for **Ymax**, 1 for **Yscl** and 1 for **Xres**. When these values are entered correctly, the display will show

```
WINDOW
Xmin = -10
Xmax = 10
Xscl = 1
Ymin = -10
Ymax = 10
Yscl = 1
Xres = 1
```

This coordinate system is called the **standard viewing window**. It can also be chosen by pressing ZOOM (row 1, column 3) and selecting **6** from the **ZOOM** menu.

Finally, press GRAPH (row 1, column 5). The graph will appear in the display. The graph of $f(x) = x^3 - 4x^2 - x + 4$ is actually a smooth curve. The "segmented" appearance of the graph generated by the calculator is a limitation of the calculator screen .

In function mode (**Func** on the MODE screen), the calculator generates a graph by using a single equation to calculate y values from a succession of x values and plotting the points (x, y).

In **parametric mode** (**Par** on the MODE screen) the calculator generates a graph by using a third variable (customarily denoted t for time) and two equations that express x and y each in terms of this third variable. The calculator uses these two equations to calculate an x value and a y value for a succession of t values specified on the WINDOW screen and then plots the points (x, y).

To illustrate the procedure for graphing parametric equations the TI-83®, let's generate the graph determined by the parametric equations $x(t) = 8 \sin t$ and $y(t) = 2 + 6 \cos t$. First, set the calculator to parametric mode. Press MODE (row 2, column 2). Move the cursor to **Par** (fourth line of the **MODE** menu). Press ENTER to select this option. If **Dot** is highlighted on the fifth line the **MODE** menu, move the cursor to **Connected** and press ENTER .

Second, enter the equations to be graphed. Press Y= (row 1, column 1). Notice that in parametric mode the **Y=** edit screen has a different form and accepts pairs of equations involving the variable t. Enter $8 \sin t$ as **X1T** and $2 + 6 \cos t$ as **Y1T** on this screen. Press the SIN (row 5, column 2) and COS (row 5, column 3) keys to enter the sine and cosine functions. Press X,T,Θ,n (row 3, column 2),) to enter t.

Next, set the viewing window. Press ZOOM (row 1, column 3) and select **6** to establish the **standard viewing window** and standard interval of values for the parameter t. The graph, which should be an ellipse displaced upward from the origin, will be generated immediately. To see the intervals of x and y values in this standard viewing window and the interval of t values used to calculate the x and y values plotted to obtain this graph, press WINDOW . Press GRAPH to return to the graph.

According to the Vertical Line Test this graph is not the graph of a function. To implement the Vertical Line Test on the calculator screen, move the cursor to a point near $x = 3$ on the horizontal axis. The coordinates of the point where the cursor is located are displayed at the bottom of the screen. The calculator can only display discrete points. The points that are displayed depend on the viewing window. The standard viewing window does not happen to include the point with x-coordinate 3 and y-coordinate 0. Settle for a nearby point.

The up and down arrow keys move the cursor along the line perpendicular to the y-axis and positioned at this x value. By moving the cursor up and down, you see that this vertical line intersects the graph at two points. One intersection point has y-coordinate about 7.4 and the other has y-coordinate about -3.5. Since two y values correspond to this x value (and to others), this is not the graph of a function.

The domain and range of a function given by a graph on the calculator screen can also be found by using the moving cursor to find the projections of the graph onto the coordinate axes. Graph the parametric equations $x(t) = t$ and $y(t) = \dfrac{\left(t^3 - 2t^2 - 5t + 6\right)}{5}$ on the **Y=** screen. Use the following WINDOW settings and then press GRAPH.

```
WINDOW
Tmin  = -2.1
Tmax  =  3.8
Tstep = .1
Xmin  = -4.7
Xmax  =  4.7
Xscl  =  1
Ymin  = -3.1
Ymax  =  3.1
Yscl  =  1
```

To find the domain of the function specified by this graph, position the cursor at the left most point of the graph. Now use the up and down arrow keys to move the cursor from this point to the horizontal axis. This point on the x-axis is the left endpoint of the domain. Its x-coordinate is displayed at the bottom of the screen and is −2.1. To find the right endpoint of the domain, position the cursor at the right most point of the graph and use the up and down arrow keys to move the cursor to the horizontal axis. This point is the right end point of the domain. Its x-coordinate is displayed at the bottom of the screen and is 3.8. Thus, the domain of this function is the interval from −2.1 to 3.8.

To find the range of the function, position the cursor at the lowest point of the graph. Then use the left and right arrow keys to move the cursor from this point to the vertical axis. This point on the y-axis is the left endpoint of the range. Its coordinate on the y-axis is displayed at the bottom of the screen and is approximately −0.8. To find the right endpoint of the range, position the cursor at the highest point of the graph and then use the left and right arrow keys to move the cursor to the vertical axis. This point is the right endpoint of the range. Its coordinate on the y-axis is displayed at the bottom of the screen and is approximately 2.6. Thus, the range of this function is (approximately) the interval from −0.8 to 2.6.

Notice that this procedure for finding the domain and range must be modified when the function is given by a graph that has breaks or jumps such as in Example 4 and Practice Problems 2 and 4 which follow.

The procedure for using a graph to evaluate a function at a particular value of the independent variable x can be easily carried out on the TI-83® by using the cursor movement keys. First, display the graph. Then move the cursor to the point on the x-axis corresponding to the given value for x.

Next, use the up and down arrow keys to move the cursor vertically to a point on the graph. Finally, use the left and right arrow keys to move the cursor horizontally to a point on the y-axis. The coordinate of this point on the y-axis is the value of the function for this value of x.

The procedure for finding all numbers *a* for which a function has a specified value *b* from the function's graph can also be carried out the TI-83® by using the cursor movement keys. First, display the graph. Then move the cursor to the point on the vertical axis corresponding to the specified function value *b*. Next, use the left and right arrow keys to move the cursor horizontally to a point on the graph. If there is no such point on the graph, the number *b* is not in the range of the function. If there is such a point, use the up and down arrow keys to move the cursor vertically from this point on the graph to a point on the x-axis. The coordinate of this point on the x-axis is a number *a* such that $f(a) = b$. If there are several such points on the graph, then there are several numbers *a* for which $f(a) = b$.

SUMMARY

1. **VERTICAL LINE TEST.** A graph is the graph of a function if and only if every line perpendicular to the x-axis intersects the graph in no more than one point.

2. The **domain** of a function given by a graph is the projection of the graph onto the x-axis.

3. The **range** of a function is the set of numbers obtained by applying the procedure for the function to every number in its domain. The **range** of a function given by a graph is the projection of the graph onto the y-axis.

4. To find $f(a)$ from the graph of *f* follow these steps.
   Step 1. Locate *a* on the x-axis and draw a vertical line through it.
   Step 2. Locate the point where this vertical line intersects the graph and draw a horizontal line through it. If this vertical line does not intersect the graph, then *a* is not in the domain of *f*.
   Step 3. Locate the point where this horizontal line crosses the y-axis. The y-coordinate of this point is $f(a)$.

5. To find the numbers *a* such that $f(a) = b$ from the graph of *f* follow these steps.
   Step 1. Locate *b* on the y-axis and draw a horizontal line through it.
   Step 2. Locate the point(s) where this horizontal line intersects the graph and draw a vertical line through each one. If this horizontal line does not intersect the graph, *b* is not in the range.
   Step 3. Locate the point(s) where the vertical line(s) intersect the x-axis. The x-coordinates of these points are the number(s) *a* such that $f(a) = b$.

EXAMPLES

Example 1: Determine whether Figure 1.8 shows the graph of a function.

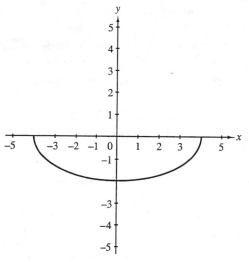

Solution 1:
Apply the Vertical Line Test. Imagine all possible lines perpendicular to the *x*-axis. Every one of them intersects the graph in no more than one point. Therefore, this is the graph of a function.

Figure 1.8

Example 2: Determine whether Figure 1.9 shows the graph of a function.

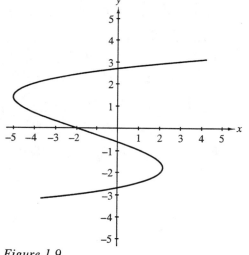

Solution 2:
Apply the Vertical Line Test. Imagine all possible lines perpendicular to the *x*-axis. The vertical line at $x = 1$, as well as others, intersects the graph in more than one point. Since there is at least one vertical line that intersects the graph in more than one point, this is not the graph of a function.

Figure 1.9

Example 3: The graph of a function is shown in Figure 1.10. What is the domain and what isthe range of this function?

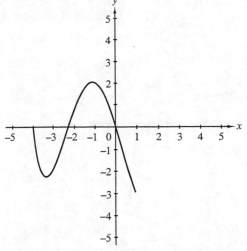

Solution 3:
The domain of the function is the projection of the graph onto the x-axis. Therefore, the domain is the interval from -4 to 1.

The range of the function is the projection of the graph on the y-axis. Therefore, the range is the interval from -3 to 2.

Figure 1.10

Example 4: The graph of a function is shown in Figure 1.11. What is the domain and what is the range of this function? (The open circle at $(0, -1)$ indicates this point is not part of the graph. The solid circle at $(0, 1)$ indicates this point is part of the graph.)

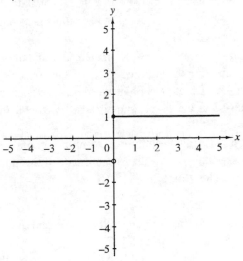

Solution 4:
The domain of the function is the projection of the graph onto the x-axis. Therefore, the domain is the interval from -5 to 5.

The range of the function is the projection of the graph onto the y-axis. Therefore, the range of the function consists only of the numbers -1 and 1.

Figure 1.11

Example 5: The graph of a function $y = g(x)$ is shown in Figure 1.12.
    (a) Find $g(2)$ or state that 2 is not in the domain of g.
    (b) Find all numbers a such that $g(a) = 1$, or state that 1 is not in the range of g.

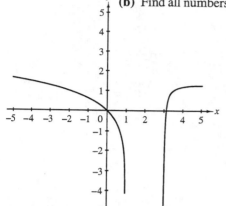

Figure 1.12

Solution 5: (a)

Step 1. Locate $x = 2$ on the x-axis and draw a vertical line through it.

Step 2. This vertical line does not intersect the graph. Therefore, $x = 2$ is not in the domain of g.

Solution 5: (b)

Step 1. Locate $y = 1$ on the y-axis and draw a horizontal line through it.

Step 2. Locate the points where this horizontal line intersects the graph and draw vertical lines through them.

Step 3. Locate the points where these vertical lines cross the x-axis. The x-coordinates of these points are $x = -2$ and $x = \frac{7}{2}$. Therefore, $g(-2) = 1$ and $g\left(\frac{7}{2}\right) = 1$.

Example 6: The graph of a function $y = f(x)$ is shown in Figure 1.13. (The dashed lines indicate asymptotes.)
    (a) Find $f(-1)$ or state that $f(-1)$ is not defined.
    (b) Find all numbers a such that $f(a) = 3$ or state that 3 is not in the range of f.

Solution 6: (a)

Step 1. Locate $x = -1$ on the x-axis and draw a vertical line through it.

Step 2. Locate the point where this vertical line inter-sects the graph and draw a horizontal line through it.

Step 3. Locate the point where this horizontal line crosses the y-axis. The y-coordinate of this point is 0. Therefore, $f(-1) = 0$.

Solution 6: (b)

Step 1. Locate $y = 3$ on the y-axis and draw a horizontal line through it.

Step 2. This horizontal line does not intersect the graph. Therefore, $y = 3$ is not in the range of f.

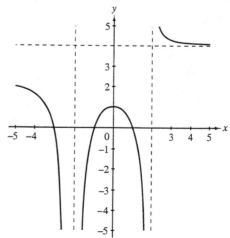

Figure 1.13

Example 7: Graph the parametric equations $x(t) = \sqrt[3]{t}$, $y(t) = \dfrac{\left(t^3 - 2t^2 - 5t + 6\right)}{5}$ on the TI-83® using the viewing window.

$$
\begin{aligned}
&\text{Tmin} = -2.1 \\
&\text{Tmax} = 3.8 \\
&\text{Tstep} = .1 \\
&\text{Xmin} = -2 \\
&\text{Xmax} = 2.7 \\
&\text{Xscl} = 1 \\
&\text{Ymin} = -1.2 \\
&\text{Ymax} = 3 \\
&\text{Yscl} = 1
\end{aligned}
$$

(Use the cube root function $\sqrt[3]{\ }$ from the $\boxed{\text{MATH}}$ (row 4, column 1) menu to enter $x(t)$.)
This graph passes the vertical line test and therefore specifies a function F.
(a) Find $F(-1)$, $F(1.25)$, and $F(2)$.
(b) Find all numbers a such that (i) $F(a) = 1$, (ii) $F(a) = -1$.
(c) Find the domain of F.
(d) Find the range of F.

Solution 7:   (a) To find $F(-1)$ from the graph on the TI-83®, move the cursor to the point $x = -1$ on the x-axis. (You can position the cursor exactly at this point because the viewing window happens to include this point. Most viewing windows will not include the point $x = -1$ exactly.) Next, use the up and down arrow keys to move the cursor vertically to a point on the graph. At the bottom of the screen, the calculator displays the coordinates of this point as $(-1, 1.6)$ (rounded to one decimal place). Now use the right arrow key to move the cursor horizontally to a point on the y-axis. The y-coordinate of this point on the y-axis is the value of the function for this value of x, so $F(-1) = 1.6$ (rounded to one decimal place). Similar procedure shows that $F(1.25) = -0.8$ (rounded to one decimal place). The number $x = 2$ is not in the domain of F because the vertical line through this point on the x-axis does not intersect the graph.

(b)(i) To find all numbers a such that $F(a) = 1$ from the graph on the TI-83®, move the cursor to the point on the vertical axis having y-coordinate 1. Since the calculator screen displays discrete points it cannot show every point. There is no point of the display on the y-axis that has y-coordinate exactly 1. Use a point that has *y*-coordinate near 1, say .9677 (rounded). Now, find all points on the graph that can be reached by moving the cursor horizontally from this point. There are three such points. Their coordinates are $(-1.15, 0.9677)$, $(0.6, 0.9677)$, and $(1.5, 0.9677)$.

Place the cursor at $(-1.15, 0.9677)$ and use the up and down arrow keys to move the cursor vertically from this point on the graph to a point on the *x*-axis. The coordinate of this point on the *x*-axis is -1.15. Therefore, $F(-1.15) = 0.9677$ (approximately 1). From the remaining two points, we find that $F(0.6)$ is approximately 1 and $F(1.5)$ is approximately 1. The numbers *a* for which $F(a) = 1$ are, approximately, -1.15, 0.6, and 1.5.

(*ii*) To find all numbers *a* such that $F(a) = -1$ from the graph on the TI-83®, move the cursor to the point on the vertical axis having *y*-coordinate approximately -1. Next, find all points on the graph that can be reached by moving the cursor horizontally from this point. There are no such points. Consequently, there are no numbers *a* for which $F(a) = -1$. That is to say, -1 is not in the range of *F*.

(*c*) The domain of *F* is the projection of its graph onto the *x*-axis. To find the domain of *F*, position the cursor at the left most point of the graph. Use the up and down arrow keys to move the cursor from this point to the *x*-axis. This point on the *x*-axis is the left endpoint of the domain. Its *x*-coordinate is displayed at the bottom of the screen and is -1.3. Now position the cursor at the right most point of the graph and use the up and down arrow keys to move the cursor to the *x*-axis. This point is the right endpoint of the domain. Its *x*-coordinate is displayed at the bottom of the screen and is 1.55. Since the graph of *F* has no gaps, the projection of the graph onto the *x*-axis is the interval from -1.3 to 1.55. The domain of *F* is the interval from -1.3 to 1.55.

(*d*) The range of *F* is the projection of its graph onto the *y*-axis. To find the range of the function, position the cursor at the lowest point of the graph. Now use the left arrow key to move the cursor from this point to the vertical axis. This point on the *y*-axis is the left end point of the range. Its coordinate on the *y*-axis is displayed at the bottom of the screen and is approximately -0.8. To find the right endpoint of the range, position the cursor at the highest point of the graph and then use the right arrow key to move the cursor to the vertical axis. This point is the right end point of the range. Its coordinate on the *y*-axis is displayed at the bottom of the screen and is approximately 2.6. Since the graph of *F* has no jumps or breaks, the projection of the graph onto the *y*-axis is the interval from -0.8 to 2.6. The range of *F* is the interval from -0.8 to 2.6.

PRACTICE PROBLEMS

In problems 1 - 6, determine whether each figure shows the graph of a function.

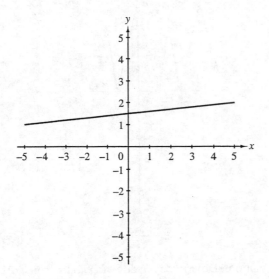

1. *Figure 1.14*

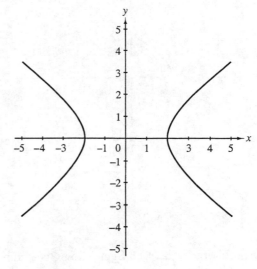

2. *Figure 1.15*

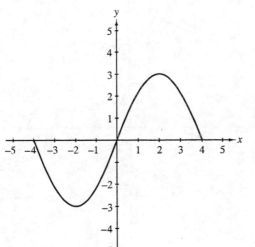

3. *Figure 1.16*

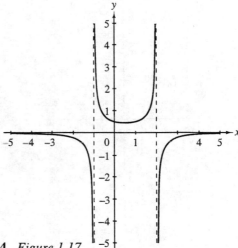

4. *Figure 1.17*

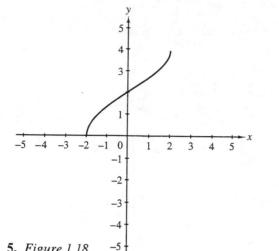

5. *Figure 1.18*

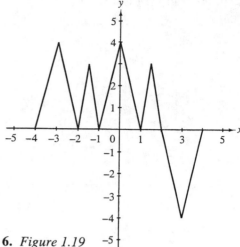

6. *Figure 1.19*

In problems 7 - 12, each figure shows the graph of a function. Determine the domain and the range of each function.

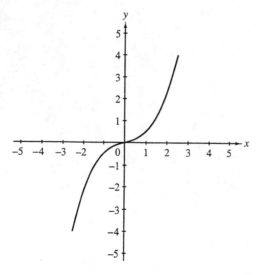

7. *Figure 1.20*

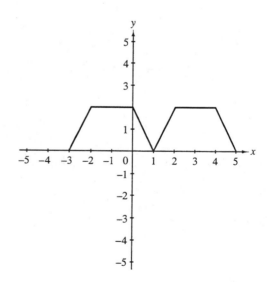

8. *Figure 1.21*

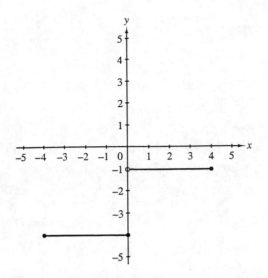

9. *Figure 1.22*

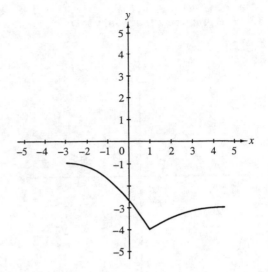

10. *Figure 1.23*

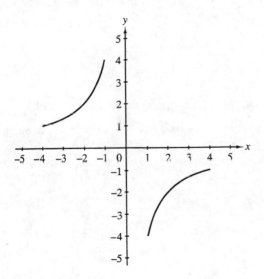

11. *Figure 1.24*

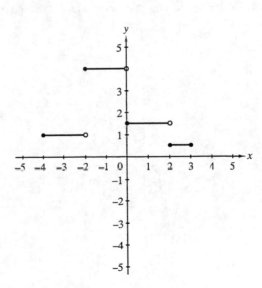

12. *Figure 1.25*

13. The graph of a function $y = f(x)$ is shown in Figure 1.26.

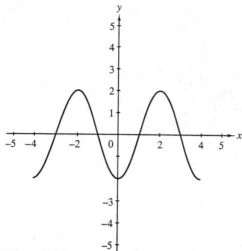

Figure 1.26

(a) Find $f(-3)$ or state that -3 is not in the domain of f.

(b) Find $f(0)$ or state that $f(0)$ is not defined.

14. The graph of a function $y = h(x)$ is shown in Figure 1.27. (The dashed lines indicate asymptotes.)

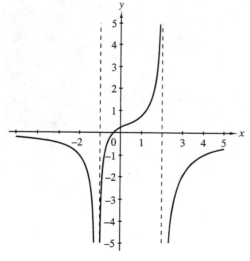

Figure 1.27

(a) Find $h(-1)$ or state that $h(-1)$ is not defined.

(b) Find $h(4)$ or state that 4 is not in the domain of h.

15. The graph of a function $y = F(x)$ is shown in Figure 1.28.

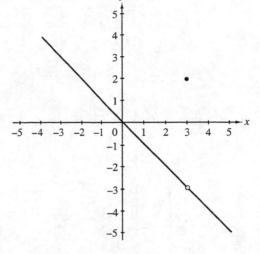

(a) Find $F(3)$ or state that 3 is not in the domain of F.

(b) Find $F\left(-4\dfrac{1}{2}\right)$ or state that $F\left(-4\dfrac{1}{2}\right)$ is not defined.

Figure 1.28

16. The graph of a function $y = f(x)$ is shown in Figure 1.29.

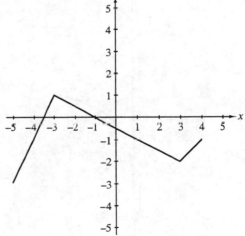

(a) Find all numbers a, such that $f(a) = -1$, or state that -1 is not in the range of f.

(b) Find all numbers such that $f(c) = 0$ or state that 0 is not in the range of f.

Figure 1.29

17. The graph of a function $y = g(x)$ is shown in Figure 1.30.

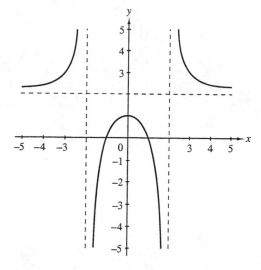

(a) Find all numbers a, such that $g(a) = 2$, or state that 2 is not in the range of g.

(b) Find all numbers c such that $g(c) = 3$, or state that 3 is not in the range of g.

Figure 1.30

18. The graph of a function $y = h(x)$ is shown in Figure 1.31.

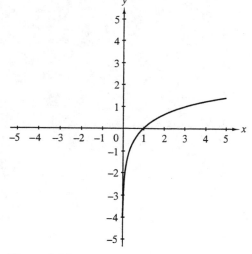

(a) Find all numbers a, such that $h(a) = 1$, or state that 1 is not in the range of h.

(b) Find all numbers c such that $h(c) = -1$ or state that -1 is not in the range of h.

Figure 1.31

19. Graph the parametric equations $x(t) = t - \sin t$, $y(t) = 1 - \cos t$ on the TI-83® using the viewing window

Tmin = 0
Tmax = 6π
Tstep = .1
Xmin = -3.5
Xmax = 20
Xscl = 5
Ymin = -.5
Ymax = 2.6
Yscl = 1

TI Tip

You can enter **6π** as it is printed; | 6 |, | 2nd |,
[π] (row 5, column 5).

(a) Verify that this graph passes the vertical line test and therefore specifies a function G.
(b) Find the domain and the range of G.
(c) Find $G(1)$, $G(5.75)$, and $G(14.5)$.
(d) Find all numbers a such that (*i*) $G(a) = 2$, (*ii*) $G(a) = -1$, (*iii*) $G(a) = 1$

20. Graph the parametric equations $x(t) = \tan\sqrt[3]{t}$, $y(t) = 1 + t^3$ on the TI-83® using the viewing window

Tmin = - π/3
Tmax = π/2.5
Tstep = .05
Xmin = -2.35
Xmax = 2.35
Xscl = 1
Ymin = -.6
Ymax = 3.3
Yscl = 1

(a) Verify that this graph passes the vertical line test and therefore specifies a function H.
(b) Find the domain and the range of H.
(c) Find $H(-1.35)$, $H(0)$, and $H(1)$.
(d) Find all numbers a such that (*i*) $H(a) = 2$, (*ii*) $H(a) = 0.4$.

OBJECTIVE 1.3

(a) **Given an exponential function** $f(x) = b^x$, $b > 0$, $b \neq 1$, **and given a number** a, **use a Texas Instruments TI-83® calculator to evaluate** $f(a)$.

(b) **Given a number** a, **use a Texas Instruments TI-83® calculator to evaluate** $\log(a)$ **and** $\ln(a)$ **or state that** a **is not in the domain of these logarithmic functions.**

DISCUSSION

To specify a function, one must give the domain of the function and a procedure for determining a number from each number in the domain. In Objectives 1.1 and 1.2 we used equations and graphs to specify functions. In this Discussion we use a scientific calculator to specify exponential and logarithmic functions.

Exponential Functions

Exponential functions are given by expressions of the form $f(x) = b^x$ (read *f of x equals b to the x*). In this equation b is a fixed positive number different from 1. It is called the **base** of the exponential function. The exponent, x, is the **independent variable**.

Consider the exponential function with base 4, $f(x) = 4^x$. We can evaluate $f(a)$ for integer values of a by using the definition of exponents.

$$f(3) = 4^3 = 4 \cdot 4 \cdot 4 = 64$$

$$f(1) = 4^1 = 4$$

$$f(0) = 4^0 = 1$$

$$f(-1) = 4^{-1} = \frac{1}{4}$$

$$f(-2) = 4^{-2} = \frac{1}{4^2} = \frac{1}{16}$$

We can use the definition of fractional exponents to evaluate $f(a)$ when a is a fraction.

$$f\left(\frac{1}{2}\right) = 4^{1/2} = \sqrt{4} = 2$$

$$f\left(\frac{3}{2}\right) = 4^{3/2} = \left(\sqrt{4}\right)^3 = 2^3 = 8$$

$$f\left(\frac{-5}{2}\right) = 4^{-5/2} = \left(\sqrt{4}\right)^{-5} = 2^{-5} = \frac{1}{2^5} = \frac{1}{32}$$

For any fraction $a = \dfrac{m}{n}$ we can, in principle if not in practice, evaluate $f(a) = 4^{m/n}$ by extracting the *nth* root of 4 and raising the result to the *mth* power. This computational procedure for f can be applied to any whole number or fraction, so the domain of f includes all rational numbers.

When a is an irrational number, such as π or $\sqrt{3}$, $f(a) = 4^a$ cannot be computed as powers of roots. Nevertheless, the irrational numbers are also in the domain of $f(x) = 4^x$. The function has definite values at $a = \pi$ and $a = \sqrt{3}$, but the limit process from calculus is needed to explain how to compute them.

In the Discussion to this point we have examined the particular exponential function $f(x) = 4^x$. Since the base b of an exponential function is required to be positive, the same discussion applies to any exponential function $f(x) = b^x$. Every exponential function has the collection of all real numbers as its domain. When $a = \dfrac{m}{n}$ is a fraction, we think of the procedure for evaluating $f(a) = b^{m/n}$ as *extract the nth root of b and raise the result to the mth power*. When a is an irrational number, the limit process from calculus is needed to interpret $f(a) = b^a$. In practice, in all but the simplest situations, we will think of the procedure for evaluating an exponential function as *pressing certain keys on a scientific calculator*. Examples 1 - 4 show how to do this.

The exponential function base e, $f(x) = e^x$, and the exponential function base 10, $f(x) = 10^x$, are used often. The number e is irrational and cannot be expressed exactly as a fraction. It is approximately 2.718281828. It is used as the base for an exponential function to simplify many operations in calculus. The number 10 is a convenient base for an exponential function because we use a base 10 number system. Scientific calculators have special keys for these two exponential functions. The Examples (see Examples 3 and 4) show how to use the Texas Instruments TI-83® to evaluate exponential functions.

Logarithmic Functions

Logarithmic functions are closely related to exponential functions. Just as there is an exponential function for every base $b > 0$, $b \neq 1$, there is a logarithmic function for every base $b > 0$, $b \neq 1$. The connection between logarithmic and exponential functions is explained in terms of their graphs in Unit 2. For the moment, however, we will think of logarithmic functions entirely in terms of the scientific calculator and study only those that appear as special calculator keys. These are the logarithmic functions base 10 and base e.

All logarithmic functions have the collection of positive real numbers as their **domain**. Scientific calculators will only accept positive numbers in evaluations of the logarithmic functions base 10 and base e. The reason for this will be apparent from the Discussion of the connection between logarithmic and exponential functions in Unit 2.

The logarithm function base 10 is called the **common logarithm** and is denoted log or $\log(x)$. The letters **log** are like the symbol f in the function notation $f(x)$. The common logarithm is important for historical and computational reasons. The procedure for using the Texas Instruments TI-83® to determine the number $y = \log(a)$ corresponding to a particular number a is illustrated in Example 5.

The logarithmic function base e is called the **natural logarithm** and is denoted ln or $\ln(x)$. The two letters **ln** are like the symbol f in the function notation $f(x)$. The natural logarithm is important because it simplifies many operations in calculus. The procedure for using the Texas Instruments TI-83® to determine the number $y = \ln(a)$ corresponding to a particular number a is illustrated in Example 6.

SUMMARY

1. Exponential functions are given by $f(x) = b^x$, where $b > 0$, $b \neq 1$. The number b is called the **base** of the exponential function. The domain of an exponential function is all real numbers. Exponential functions can be evaluated by using a scientific calculator.

2. The natural logarithm function $f(x) = \ln(x)$ and the common logarithm function $f(x) = \log(x)$ are closely related to the exponential functions $f(x) = e^x$ and $f(x) = 10^x$. Their domain is the positive real numbers. These logarithmic functions can be evaluated by using a scientific calculator.

EXAMPLES

These Examples show how to use the Texas Instruments TI-83® graphing calculator to evaluate exponential and logarithmic functions. Other makes and models of calculators may have keys labeled differently or may require a slightly different sequence of key strokes. Other calculators may also display more or fewer decimal places than the TI-83®.

Consult the instruction manual for your calculator and work these Examples yourself to be sure that you are using your calculator correctly. You will save time and improve accuracy by learning to use your calculator's memory to avoid having to re-enter numbers.

Exponential Functions

Example 1: Let $f(x) = 4^x$.

    (a) Find $f(1.236) = 4^{1.236}$ and round the answer to five decimal places.

    (b) Find $f\left(\dfrac{2}{7}\right) = 4^{2/7}$ and round the answer to five decimal places.

Solution 1: (a)

    Step 1. Enter the base, 4.

    Step 2. Press the power key ⌐ ∧ ⌐ (row 5, column 5).

    Step 3. Enter the exponent, 1.236.

            When these numbers and operations are entered correctly, the TI-83® screen will display

                     4^1.236

    Step 4. Press **ENTER** (row 10, column 5). The answer appears in the display.

                               5.548123877

    Step 5. Thus, rounded to five decimal places,

$$f(1.236) = 4^{1.236} = 5.54812.$$

Note that the numbers 5.548123877 and 5.54812 are both approximations for $f(1.236)$. It would be more accurate to use the symbol $\cong$ (for *approximately equal to*) in place of the symbol $=$ (for *equal to*). However, for simplicity we will use the symbol $=$.

Solution 1: (b)

    Step 1. Enter the base, 4.

    Step 2. Press the power key ⌐ ∧ ⌐ .

Step 3. Enter the exponent $\dfrac{2}{7}$ by pressing the following keys in order:

$$\boxed{(} \; , \; \boxed{2} \; , \; \boxed{\div} \; , \; \boxed{7} \; , \; \boxed{)} \; .$$

The parentheses direct the calculator to compute $\dfrac{2}{7}$ **before** computing the power.

When these numbers and operations are entered correctly, the TI-83® will display

$$\boxed{4\wedge(\,2/\,7\,)}$$

Step 4. Press $\boxed{\text{ENTER}}$. The answer appears in the display.

$$\boxed{1.485994289}$$

Step 5. Thus, rounded to five decimal places,

$$f\!\left(\frac{2}{7}\right) = 4^{2\!/\!7} = 1.48599.$$

Example 2: Let $f(x) = \left(\dfrac{7}{3}\right)^{x}$.

Find $f\!\left(\sqrt{2}\right) = \left(\dfrac{7}{3}\right)^{\sqrt{2}}$ and round the answer to three decimal places.

Solution 2: To evaluate $f\!\left(\sqrt{2}\right)$, enter $\left(\dfrac{7}{3}\right)^{\sqrt{2}}$ as it is written, complete with parentheses, inserting the operation symbol $\wedge$ to indicate exponentiation. When this expression is correctly entered, the TI-83® display will show

$$\boxed{(\,7/3\,)\wedge \sqrt{\;}(2)}$$

Press $\boxed{\text{ENTER}}$ to carry out the calculation. The answer appears in the display.

$$\boxed{3.314345358}$$

Thus, rounded to three decimal places,

$$f\!\left(\sqrt{2}\right) = \left(\frac{7}{3}\right)^{\sqrt{2}} = 3.314.$$

Example 3: Let $g(x) = e^{x}$. Find $g(-0.693147)$ and round the answer to one decimal place.

Solution 3: The exponential function e^{x} is pre-programmed into the TI-83® and is accessed by the sequence of key strokes $\boxed{\text{2nd}}$, $[\; e^{x} \;]$ (row 8, column 1). Enter the exponential function by pressing this combination of keys and then enter the exponent -0.693147 followed by a right parenthesis. The TI-83® will display

$$e\wedge(-.693147)$$

Press ENTER . The answer will appear in the display.

$$.5000000903$$

Thus, rounded to one decimal place,

$$g(-0.693147) = e^{-0.693147} = 0.5.$$

TI Tip

If when you press ENTER the TI83® returns the error message **ERR:SYNTAX**, you have used the subtraction sign $\boxed{-}$ (row 8, column 5) rather than the negative sign $\boxed{(-)}$ (row 10, column 9) in the exponent.

Alternately, $g(-0.693147)$ could be calculated as in Example 1 using 2.718281828 as the value of e.

Example 4: Let $f(x) = 10^x$. Find $f(0.30103)$ and round the answer to the nearest whole number.

Solution 4: The exponential function 10^x is pre-programmed into the TI-83® and is accessed by the sequence of key strokes $\boxed{\text{2nd}}$, $[10^x]$ (row 7, col. 1). Enter the exponential function by pressing this combination of keys and then enter the exponent 0.30103 followed by a right parenthesis. The TI-83® will display

$$10\wedge(.30103)$$

Press ENTER . The answer will appear in the display.

$$2.00000002$$

Thus, rounded to the nearest whole number,

$$f(0.30103) = 10^{0.30103} = 2.$$

Alternately, $f(0.30103) = 10^{0.30103}$ could be calculated as in Example 1.

Logarithmic Functions

Example 5: Find $\log(72.39)$ and round the answer to five decimal places.

Solution 5: The common logarithm function $\log x$ is pre-programmed into the TI-83® and is accessed by the key labeled ⟦ **LOG** ⟧ (row 7, column 1). Enter the common logarithm function by pressing this key and then enter the number 72.39 followed by a right parenthesis. The TI-83® will display

$$\boxed{\text{log}(\,72.39\,)}$$

Press ⟦ **ENTER** ⟧ . The answer will be displayed.

$$\boxed{1.859678577}$$

Thus, rounded to the five decimal places,
$$\log(72.39) = 1.85968.$$

Example 6: Find $\ln(72.39)$ and round the answer to five decimal places.

Solution 6: The natural logarithm function $\ln x$ is pre-programmed into the TI-83® and is accessed by the key labeled ⟦ **LN** ⟧ (row 8, column 1). Enter the natural logarithm function by pressing this key and then enter the number 72.39 followed by a right parenthesis. The TI-83® will display

$$\boxed{\text{ln}(\,72.39\,)}$$

Press ⟦ **ENTER** ⟧ . The answer will be displayed.

$$\boxed{4.282068168}$$

Thus, rounded to the five decimal places,
$$\ln(72.39) = 4.28207.$$

Notice that $\log(72.39)$ and $\ln(72.39)$ are quite different. Confusing the common logarithm (log) and the natural logarithm (ln) is a common mistake.

Example 7: Find $\ln(-2.631)$.

Solution 7: Since -2.631 is not a positive number, it is not in the domain of the logarithmic functions. Thus $\ln(-2.631)$ is not defined. When you try to evaluate $\ln(-2.631)$ using the method from Example 6, the TI-83® will display the error message **ERR:NONREAL ANS**.

PRACTICE PROBLEMS

In problems 1 - 25, round off all answers to five decimal places.

1. Let $f(x) = 2^x$. Find $f(8)$.

2. Let $f(x) = (5.4)^x$. Find $f\left(\dfrac{4}{5}\right)$.

3. Let $f(x) = (0.294)^x$. Find $f(-2.37)$.

4. Let $f(x) = \left(\dfrac{10}{3}\right)^x$. Find $f\left(-\dfrac{5}{8}\right)$.

5. Let $f(x) = e^x$. Find $f(6)$.

6. Find $10^{-0.345}$.

7. Find $e^{-\pi}$.

8. Find $10^{\sqrt{6}}$.

9. Find $e^{1.34}$.

10. Find $\left(2^{1/1.35}\right)\left(5^{\sqrt{10}}\right)$.

11. Find $4.23^{-1/8.71} + e^{0.0258}$.

12. Find $10^{1/0.7901} - e^{2.596}$.

13. Let $f(x) = \log(x)$. Find $f(5)$.

14. Let $f(x) = \ln(x)$. Find $f(2.349)$.

15. Let $f(x) = \log(x)$. Find $f\left(0.294^{2/5}\right)$.

16. Let $f(x) = \ln(x)$. Find $f\left(34^{\sqrt{2}}\right)$.

17. Find $\log\left(e^{1.79}\right)$.

18. Find $\ln\left(e^{\sqrt{5}}\right)$.

19. Find $\log\left(2.43^{-1/4.5}\right)$.

20. Find $\log(-5.79)$.

21. Calculate $e^{4.34} + \log 25.8$.

22. Calculate $\ln 58.7 - 2.41^{-7.93}$.

23. Calculate $10^{-0.345} + \log 8.13$.

24. Calculate $\dfrac{\ln 77.1 - 10^{1.94}}{\log 3}$.

25. Calculate $\dfrac{\left(e^{-1/0.315}\right)(\log 40.5)}{10^{-2.11}}$.

OBJECTIVE 1.4

(a) Given $b > 0$, $b \neq 1$, sketch the graph of $f(x) = b^x$.

(b) Given the graph of an exponential function $f(x) = b^x$, estimate b.

DISCUSSION

Functions can be specified in more than one way. We have used equations, graphs and calculators to specify functions. In this Discussion we examine the connection between equations for and graphs of exponential functions.

As a first example, we graph the exponential function with base 2, $f(x) = 2^x$. The first step is to make a table of values of the function for different values of x.

x	-4	-3	-2	-1	0	1	2	3	4
$f(x) = 2^x$	$\frac{1}{16}$	$\frac{1}{8}$	$\frac{1}{4}$	$\frac{1}{2}$	1	2	4	8	16

Table 1.1

Next, plot these points in a rectangular coordinate system as in Figure 1.32. Finally, draw a smooth curve through the points plotted as in Figure 1.33.

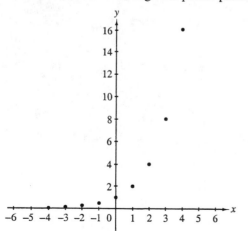

Figure 1.32 Points on the graph $f(x) = 2^x$

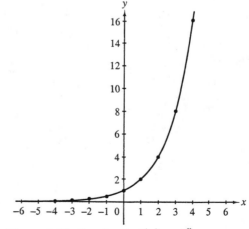

Figure 1.33 Graph of $f(x) = 2^x$

As a second example, we graph the exponential function with base $\frac{2}{3}$, $f(x) = \left(\frac{2}{3}\right)^x$. First, make a table of function values.

x	-4	-3	-2	-1	0	1	2	3	4
$f(x) = \left(\frac{2}{3}\right)^x$	$\frac{81}{16}$	$\frac{27}{8}$	$\frac{9}{4}$	$\frac{3}{2}$	1	$\frac{2}{3}$	$\frac{4}{9}$	$\frac{8}{27}$	$\frac{16}{81}$

Table 1.2

Next, plot these points in a rectangular coordinate system as in Figure 1.34. Finally, draw a smooth curve through these points as in Figure 1.35.

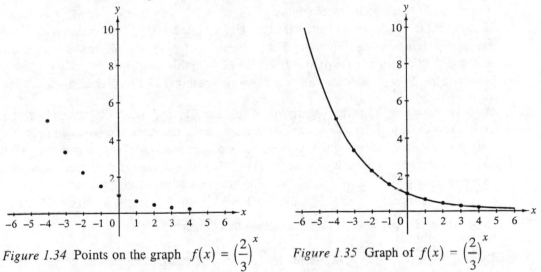

Figure 1.34 Points on the graph $f(x) = \left(\frac{2}{3}\right)^x$ *Figure 1.35* Graph of $f(x) = \left(\frac{2}{3}\right)^x$

Figures 1.33 and 1.35 show the general shape of the graphs of exponential functions. Note that both of these graphs have y-intercept 1, *i.e.*, the graph crosses the y-axis at $(0, 1)$. Since we always have $b^0 = 1$, the graph of every exponential function $f(x) = b^x$ has y-intercept 1.

The points $(1, 2)$ and $\left(-1, \frac{1}{2}\right)$ are on the graph of $f(x) = 2^x$ (see Figure 1.33). The points $\left(1, \frac{2}{3}\right)$ and $\left(-1, \frac{3}{2}\right)$ are on the graph of $f(x) = \left(\frac{2}{3}\right)^x$ (see Figure 1.35). The graph of $f(x) = b^x$ always includes the points $(1, b)$ and $\left(-1, \frac{1}{b}\right)$ because $f(1) = b^1 = b$ and $f(-1) = b^{-1} = \frac{1}{b}$.

Since a positive number b can be raised to any power, b^x is defined for every number x. Thus, the domain of an exponential function $f(x) = b^x$ is all real numbers. Of course, no graph can show the entire domain of an exponential function.

A positive number raised to a power is another positive number. When $b > 1$, b^x can be made arbitrarily large by choosing x to be a large positive number and b^x can be made arbitrarily small (but still positive) by choosing x to be a large negative number. Consequently, when $b > 1$ the range of $f(x) = b^x$ is all positive numbers (zero excluded). Similarly, when $0 < b < 1$ the range of $f(x) = b^x$ is also all positive numbers. In particular, the graph of every exponential function lies entirely above the horizontal axis and does not touch it. Of course, a graph cannot show the entire range of an exponential function.

When $b > 1$, the value of the function $f(x) = b^x$ becomes larger as x increases. Consequently, its graph rises from left to right as in Figure 1.33. In this situation we say that the function is **increasing**. When $0 < b < 1$, the value of $f(x) = b^x$ decreases as x increases and its graph falls from left to right as in Figure 1.35. In this situation we say that the function is **decreasing**. Every exponential function is either increasing ($b > 1$) or decreasing ($0 < b < 1$).

As x becomes very large in a negative direction, the graph of $f(x) = 2^x$ (see Figure 1.33) comes very close to the negative x-axis. In fact, we can find points as close to the negative x-axis as we please by choosing x to be negative and large enough. We say that the negative x-axis is a **horizontal asymptote** of the graph of $f(x) = 2^x$. The graph of every exponential function $f(x) = b^x$ with $b > 1$ has the negative x-axis as a horizontal asymptote. Similarly, the graph of every exponential function $f(x) = b^x$ with $0 < b < 1$ has the positive x-axis as a horizontal asymptote. Figure 1.35 shows this property for $f(x) = \left(\dfrac{2}{3}\right)^x$.

By using these properties of exponential functions, we can sketch an accurate graph of a given exponential function after plotting only a few points. Conversely, using these properties we can recognize the graphs of exponential functions and also determine the equation for an exponential function from its graph. Both of these processes are illustrated by the Examples.

CALCULATOR COMMENTARY

The graph of $f(x) = 2^x$ shown in Figure 1.33 can be generated on the TI-83®. In the coordinate system in Figure 1.33, x values lie between -6 and 6 and y values lie between -2 and 16. Tick marks on the horizontal axis are one unit apart and those on the vertical axis are two units apart. To establish a coordinate system with this range of values for x and y and tick marks spaced in this way, press $\boxed{\text{WINDOW}}$ and enter the following settings.

```
WINDOW
Xmin = -6
Xmax = 6
Xscl = 1
Ymin = -2
Ymax = 16
Yscl = 2
Xres = 1
```

TI Tip

If the **WINDOW** menu on your TI-83® doesn't look like this, your machine is probably not set to Function mode. Press MODE (row 2, column. 2), scroll to **Func** (fourth line), and press ENTER . Press 2nd , [QUIT] to return to the home screen.

To generate the graph of $y = 2^x$, enter **Y1 = 2 ^ X** on the **Y=** screen. Delete all other expressions from the **Y=** screen by scrolling to each one and pressing CLEAR . Press GRAPH to generate the graph.

Notice that the graph on the calculator screen appears to increase less rapidly than the graph in Figure 1.33. This is because on the calculator screen the units of distance are not the same on the two axes. The coordinate system on the TI-83® screen is unavoidably only two-thirds as high as it is wide while the coordinate system in Figures 1.33 is much higher than it is wide. The units on the graph in Figure 1.33 are the same length on both axes. On the calculator screen, one unit of distance on the horizontal axis is longer than one unit on the vertical axis. As a result, angles and diagonal distances are distorted and the graph of $f(x) = 2^x$ on the calculator does not look exactly like Figure 1.33. We can avoid this phenomena by choosing **Xmin**, **Xmax**, **Ymin**, and **Ymax** so that

Ymax − Ymin = 2/3 [Xmax − Xmin] = 2/3 [6 − (-6)] = 9.

Press WINDOW and set **Ymin = -1** and **Ymax = 8** so **Ymax − Ymin = 9**.   Again press GRAPH and obtain a graph more like (a portion of) the one in Figure 1.33.

To explore these ideas further, use these techniques to generate the graph in Figure 1.35.

Because of characteristics of the TI-83® screen, **WINDOW** settings where **Xmax − Xmin = 9.4** and **Ymax − Ymin = 6.2** work especially well. With these settings, units of distance on the two axes are almost the same so distortion is minimized. In addition, the coordinates of the discrete points displayed on the screen are at even tenths of a unit. We will refer to range settings where **Xmax − Xmin = 9.4** and **Ymax − Ymin = 6.2** as a **decimal viewing window**. Pressing ZOOM and choosing **4: ZDECIMAL** causes the graph to be immediately regenerated in the decimal viewing window $-4.7 \le x \le 4.7$, $-3.1 \le y \le 3.1$.

The graph of an exponential function can be recognized by the "signature" properties described in the Discussion and listed in the Summary below. Once a graph has been identified as an exponential function $y = b^x$, the base can be found from the points $\left(-1, \dfrac{1}{b}\right)$ and $(1, b)$ both of which must lie on the graph. Choose various positive numbers b different from 1 and graph $y = b^x$ in a decimal viewing window on your TI-83®. Use the cursor move keys or TRACE (row 1, column 4) to locate the points on the graph with x coordinates -1 and 1 and verify that these points are $(1, b)$ and $\left(-1, \dfrac{1}{b}\right)$.

TI Tip

Pressing TRACE (row 1, column 4) causes a special cursor (sometimes called the "spider") to appear on the graph. The coordinates of the location of the spider are displayed at the bottom of the screen. Pressing the left and right arrows moves the spider along the graph. Press GRAPH to cancel **TRACE**. Press 2nd , [QUIT] to return to the home screen. Read the TI-83® *Guidebook* for more information about tracing a graph.

SUMMARY

The graph of $f(x) = b^x$ has the following properties.

1. y-intercept is 1.
2. $(1, b)$ and $\left(-1, \dfrac{1}{b}\right)$ are on the graph.
3. Domain is all numbers. Range is all positive numbers.
4. Increasing when $b > 1$. Decreasing when $0 < b < 1$.
5. Negative x-axis is an asymptote when $b > 1$. Positive x-axis is an asymptote when $0 < b < 1$.

EXAMPLES

Example 1: Sketch the graph of $f(x) = \left(\dfrac{1}{2}\right)^x$.

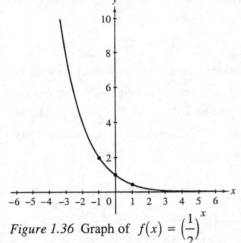

Figure 1.36 Graph of $f(x) = \left(\dfrac{1}{2}\right)^x$

Solution 1:

Use the properties of the graph of an exponential function from the Summary and the fact that the base of this exponential function is $b = \dfrac{1}{2}$ to sketch the graph (see Figure 1.36).

From the first property, the y-intercept of the graph is 1. Plot the point $(0, 1)$.

From the second property, the points $\left(1, \dfrac{1}{2}\right)$ and $(-1, 2)$ are on the graph. Plot these points.

The domain of the function is all real numbers and its range is all positive real numbers. Thus, its graph lies entirely above the horizontal axis and extends right, left and upward without bound. Because $0 < b < 1$, the function is decreasing and has the positive x-axis is an asymptote.

Through the three points plotted, draw a smooth curve that lies entirely above the x-axis, has the positive x-axis as an asymptote, and bends continually upward as it decreases from left to right. Of course, you can't show the function's entire domain (all of the x-axis) or entire range (the positive half of the y-axis) in your graph. This curve, shown in Figure 1.36, is the graph of the function.

Compare this graph with the graph of $f(x) = \left(\dfrac{2}{3}\right)^x$ in Figure 1.35.

Example 2: Sketch the graph of $f(x) = 3^x$.

Solution 2:

Use the properties of the graph of an exponential function from the Summary and the fact that the base of this exponential function is $b = 3$ to sketch the graph.

From the first property, the y-intercept of the graph is 1. Plot the point $(0, 1)$.

From the second property, the points $(1, 3)$ and $\left(-1, \dfrac{1}{3}\right)$ are on the graph. Plot these points.

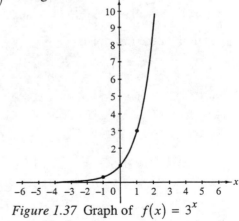

Figure 1.37 Graph of $f(x) = 3^x$

The domain of the function is all real numbers and its range is all positive real numbers. Thus, the graph lies entirely above the horizontal axis and extends right, left and upward without bound. Because $1 < b$, the function is increasing and has the negative x-axis as an asymptote.

Through the three points plotted, draw a smooth curve that lies entirely above the x-axis, has the negative x-axis as an asymptote, and bends continually upward as it increases from left to right. Of course, you can't show the function's entire domain (all of the x-axis) or entire range (the positive half of the y-axis) in your graph. This curve, shown in Figure 1.37, is the graph of the function. Compare this graph with the graph of $f(x) = 2^x$ in Figure 1.33.

Example 3: The graph of an exponential function $f(x) = b^x$ is shown in Figure 1.38. What is the equation for this function?

Solution 3:

For every exponential function $f(x) = b^x$, $f(1) = b$ and $f(-1) = \dfrac{1}{b}$. Find b by finding $f(1)$ or $f(-1)$.

Since this function is increasing, it is easier to find $f(1)$. Use the techniques discussed in Objective 1.2 to find from the graph that $f(1) = \dfrac{5}{2}$. Therefore, $b = \dfrac{5}{2}$ and the equation for the function is

$$f(x) = \left(\frac{5}{2}\right)^x.$$

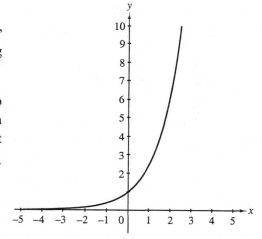

Figure 1.38 Graph of some exponential function

Example 4: The graph of an exponential function $f(x) = b^x$ is shown in Figure 1.39. What is the equation for this function?

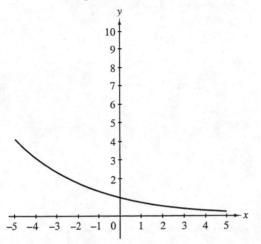

Figure 1.39 Graph of some exponential function

Solution 4:

For every exponential function $f(x) = b^x$, $f(1) = b$ and $f(-1) = \dfrac{1}{b}$. Find b by finding $f(1)$ or $f(-1)$.

Since this function is decreasing, it is easier to find $f(-1)$. Use the techniques discussed in Objective 1.2 to find from the graph that $f(-1) = \dfrac{4}{3}$. Therefore, $\dfrac{1}{b} = \dfrac{4}{3}$ and $b = \dfrac{3}{4}$. The equation for the function is

$$f(x) = \left(\frac{3}{4}\right)^x.$$

PRACTICE PROBLEMS

1. Use the coordinate system in Figure 1.40 to sketch the graph of $y = \left(\dfrac{3}{2}\right)^x$.

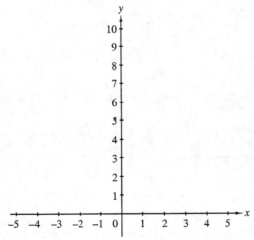

Figure 1.40

Follow these steps.

Step 1. Plot the *y*-intercept $(0, 1)$.

Step 2. Plot $\left(-1, \dfrac{2}{3}\right)$ and $\left(1, \dfrac{3}{2}\right)$.

Step 3. Draw a smooth curve with the properties of the graph of an exponential function with base $b > 1$ through these three points.

2. Use the coordinate system in Figure 1.41 to sketch the graph of $f(x) = \left(\dfrac{4}{3}\right)^x$.

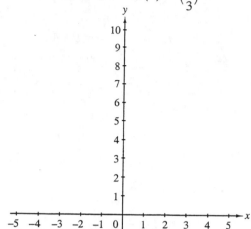

Figure 1.41

3. Use the coordinate system in Figure 1.42 to sketch the graph of $y = \left(\dfrac{1}{4}\right)^x$.

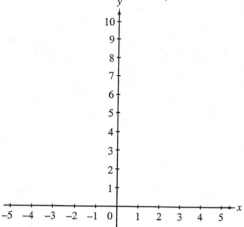

Figure 1.42

4. Use the coordinate system in Figure 1.43 to sketch the graph of $f(x) = \left(\dfrac{3}{5}\right)^x$.

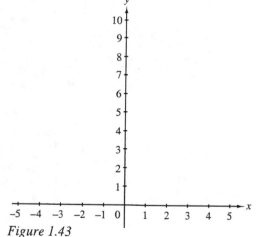

Figure 1.43

5. Graph the exponential functions in Practice Problems 1 - 4 on the TI-83®
    (*i*)   using the viewing window suggested by the coordinate system given in the problem and
    (*ii*) using a decimal viewing window.

6. The graph of an exponential function
$f(x) = b^x$ is shown in Figure 1.44.
What is the equation for this function?

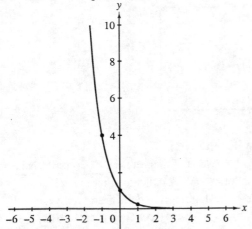

Figure 1.44

7. The graph of an exponential function $y = b^x$
is shown in Figure 1.45.
What is the equation for this function?

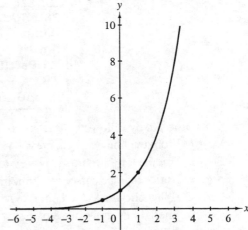

Figure 1.45

8. The graph of an exponential function $y = b^x$
is shown in Figure 1.46.
What is the equation for this function?

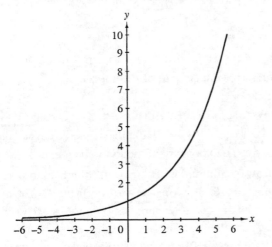

Figure 1.46

9. The graph of an exponential function
$f(x) = b^x$ is shown in Figure 1.47.
What is the equation for this function?

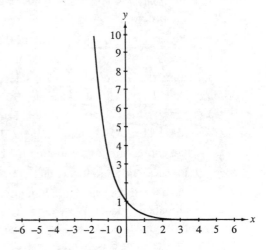

Figure 1.47

10. Use the following program for the TI-83® to practice finding the base of an exponential function from its graph. This program randomly chooses a number b between 0 and 5 and displays the graph of $y = b^x$.

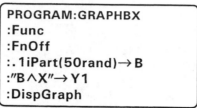

```
PROGRAM:GRAPHBX
:Func
:FnOff
:.1iPart(50rand)→B
:"B∧X"→Y1
:DispGraph
```

Enter this program by following these steps.

Step 1. From the home screen, press PRGM (row 4, column 3).

Step 2. Use the left or right arrow key to highlight **NEW** and then press 1 or ENTER .

Step 3. Notice that the cursor is a blinking reverse letter "**A**" to indicates that the calculator is in alphabetic mode. When a key is pressed, the letter printed in green above it will be entered. Enter the name of the program by typing **GRAPHBX**. Then press ENTER to move to the first line of the program.

Step 4. Press MODE (row 2, column 2), scroll to the fourth line so **Func** is highlighted, and press ENTER . Press ENTER a second time to move to the next line of the program.

Step 5. Press VARS (row 4, column 4), Use the left and right arrows to scroll to **Y-VARS**. Press 4 to choose **On/Off**. Press 2 to choose **FnOff** and turn off all expressions under the **Y** = screen so they will not be graphed. Then press ENTER to move to the next line of the program.

Step 6. Press • , 1 to enter 0.1.

Step 7. Press MATH (row 4, column 1). Use the left-right arrow keys to scroll to **NUM** (for numerical). Press 3 to select **iPart(** (for integer part of a number).

Step 8. Press 5 , 0 to enter **50** .

Step 9. Press MATH . Use the left-right arrow keys to scroll to **PRB** (for probability). Press 1 to select **rand** (random number). Press) . This right parenthesis marks the end of the expression for computing the base b for the exponential function to be graphed.

Step 10. Press STO▶ (row 9, column 1), ALPHA (row 3, column 1), (**B**) (row 4, column 2) to store the base of the exponential function in memory **B**. Pressing ALPHA shifts the TI-83® to alphabetic mode. We will indicate that a letter, space, or punctuation mark is accessed through the ALPHA key by enclosing it in parentheses. Thus, the sequence of keystrokes for the letter **B** is given as ALPHA , (**B**). Press ENTER to indicate the end of this line of the program.

Step 11. Press ALPHA , (") (row 9, column 5), ALPHA , (B) , ∧ , ALPHA , (X) , ALPHA , (").

Step 12. Press STO→ , then VARS . Use the left-right arrow keys to scroll to **Y-VARS**. Press 1 , 1 (press 1 twice!) to store the expression for b^x as **Y1**. Press ENTER to move to the next line of the program.

Step 13. Press PRGM (row 4, column 3). Use the arrow keys to scroll to **I/O** (for Input/Output). Press 4 to select **DispGraph** (for display graph) .

Step 14. Compare your calculator screen with the listing of the program given at the beginning of this problem. Use the arrow keys, DEL (delete) and 2nd , [INS] (insert) to make corrections as necessary. When the program is entered correctly, press 2nd , [QUIT] to return to the home screen.

Before executing **GRAPHBX**, set the **WINDOW** variables to **Xmin = -4.7, Xmax = 4.7, Xscl = 1, Ymin = -1, Ymax = 5.2, Yscl = 1** and **Xres = 1** to establish a decimal viewing window. Now execute **GRAPHBX**. Press PRGM . **EXEC** (execute) will be highlighted. Scroll to **GRAPHBX** and press ENTER . The calculator will return to the home screen and display

> **prgmGRAPHBX**

Press ENTER to begin execution of the program. The graph of an exponential function will be generated on the display immediately. Your task is to figure out the expression for the exponential function shown in the graph. Use TRACE (or the arrow keys, if you prefer) to locate the points on the graph with x-coordinate 1 or -1. Determine the base b of the exponential function shown in the graph from the y-coordinates of these points.

TI Tip

If you can't position the cursor exactly at the points with x-coordinates -1 and 1, you probably did not establish a decimal viewing window before executing the program.

Check the value you determined for the base of the exponential function in the graph by pressing ALPHA , (B) , ENTER to recall the number **B** from the calculator's memory. Press GRAPH to return to the graph of the function.

To investigate the graph of another exponential function, press PRGM and execute **GRAPHBX** again.

11. Use the following program for the TI-83® to practice finding the base of an exponential function from its graph. This program randomly chooses a number c between 0 and 1 and displays the graph of $y = c^x$.

```
PROGRAM:GRAPHCX
:Func
:FnOff
:.01iPart(100rand
) → C
:"C∧X"→ Y2
:DispGraph
```

Enter this program by adapting the steps given in Practice Problem 10.

Before executing **GRAPHCX**, set the **WINDOW** variables to **Xmin = -4.7, Xmax = 4.7, Xscl = 1, Ymin = -1, Ymax = 5.2, Yscl = 1** and **Xres = 1** to establish a decimal viewing rectangle. Adapt the steps given in Practice Problem 10 to execute the program **GRAPHCX**. The program will generate the graph of an exponential function. Your task is to use TRACE (or the arrow keys) to locate the points on the graph with x-coordinate 1 or -1 and determine the base c of this exponential function from the y-coordinates of these points.

Check your value for the base of the exponential function in the graph by pressing 2nd , [QUIT] to return to the home screen. Then press ALPHA , (**C**) , ENTER to recall the number **C**. Press GRAPH to return to the graph of the function.

To investigate the graph of another exponential function, press PRGM and execute **GRAPHCX** again.

OBJECTIVE 1.5

   (a) **Given two functions** f **and** g, **and given a number** a, **compute** $f\bigl(g(a)\bigr) = f \circ g(a)$ **or state that** $f \circ g(a)$ **is not defined.**

   (b) **Given two functions,** $y = f(x)$ **and** $y = g(x)$, **find an expression for their composition and simplify it.**

DISCUSSION

There are many ways to combine two functions to obtain a new function. Adding, subtracting, multiplying and dividing are the most familiar, but another method for combining functions is at the heart of the relation between exponential and logarithmic functions. It is called **composition of functions** and is denoted $f \circ g$ (read *f circle g*) or $f\bigl(g(x)\bigr)$ (read *f of g of x*).

To specify $f \circ g$ we must give the domain of $f \circ g$ and a procedure for determining exactly one number y from each number x in this domain. The procedure for $f \circ g$ is a two-step process. To determine $f \circ g(a)$ for some number a, first apply the procedure for g to the number a. Some number, let's call it b, will result. Second, apply the procedure for f to the number $b = g(a)$ to obtain a final number c. This final number, c, is $f \circ g(a)$.

The procedure for evaluating $f\bigl(g(x)\bigr)$ is easily illustrated with functions given by equations. Let $f(x) = x^2$ and $g(x) = 2x + 1$. To compute $f \circ g(3)$, first, apply the procedure for g to the number 3 and get

$$g(3) = 2(3) + 1 = 7.$$

(Seven is the number called b in the general discussion.) Second, apply the procedure for f to the number

$$f(7) = (7)^2 = 49.$$

We have, then,

$$f \circ g(3) = f\bigl(g(3)\bigr) = f(7) = (7)^2 = 49.$$

The domain of the composition $y = f \circ g(x)$ is the collection of all real numbers x to which the procedure for $f \circ g$ can be applied to yield another real number y. The composition procedure can be applied to a number a when the following two conditions are met.

Condition 1: The number a must be in the domain of g. Otherwise, the first step of the procedure for $f \circ g$ (computation of $g(a)$) cannot be carried out.

Condition 2: The number $b = g(a)$ must be in the domain of f. Otherwise, the second step of the procedure for $f \circ g$ (computation of $f(b)$) cannot be carried out.

Thus, the domain of $f \circ g$ consists of all numbers a in the domain of g such that $g(a)$ is in the domain of f.

The domain of $f \circ g$ is not necessarily all of the domain of g. To see this, consider the functions $f(x) = \sqrt{x}$ and $g(x) = x + 1$. The number $a = 3$ **is** in the domain of $f \circ g$. The first condition is met because $a = 3$ is in the domain of g. The second condition is met because $g(3) = 3 + 1 = 4$ is in the domain of f. Since both conditions are met, $a = 3$ is in the domain of $f \circ g$ and, incidentally,

$$f \circ g(3) = f(4) = \sqrt{4} = 2.$$

Now consider the number $a = -2$, which is **not** in the domain of $f \circ g$. The first condition is met because $a = -2$ is in the domain of g. The second condition is **not** met. On evaluating $g(-2)$ we obtain $g(-2) = -2 + 1 = -1$. This number is not in the domain of f because $\sqrt{-1}$ is not a real number. Therefore, the number $a = -2$ is not in the domain of the composition $f \circ g$, so the domain of $f \circ g$ is not all of the domain of g.

The order in which the procedures for f and g are applied to evaluate $f \circ g(a)$ is important. Applying the procedure for g and following that with the procedure for f is much different than applying the procedure for f and following that with the procedure for g. For example, above we computed $f \circ g(3)$ using the functions $f(x) = x^2$ and $g(x) = 2x + 1$. We found

$$f \circ g(3) = f\big(g(3)\big) = 49.$$

For comparison, let's now compute $g \circ f(3)$. First, compute $f(3)$ and get

$$f(3) = (3)^2 = 9.$$

(This time 9 is the number we have called b in the general discussion.) Second, compute $g(9) = 2(9) + 1 = 19$. We have, then,

$$g \circ f(3) = g\big(f(3)\big) = g(9) = 19.$$

The two outcomes are strikingly different. The notation gives explicit instructions, but it must be read carefully. To interpret $f \circ g(x)$ work from right to left. To interpret $f\big(g(x)\big)$ work from the inner-most parentheses outward.

When the functions f and g are given by equations, we can get an expression for their composition from the equations for f and g. To compute an expression for $f \circ g(x) = f(g(x))$, replace the variable x in the expression for $f(x)$ with the expression for $g(x)$ and then simplify the result. For instance, using the functions $f(x) = x^2$ and $g(x) = 2x + 1$ again, find an equation for $f(g(x))$ as follows:

$$f \circ g(x) = f(g(x)) = [g(x)]^2 = (2x + 1)^2 = 4x^2 + 4x + 1.$$

Following the same procedure to find an expression for $g \circ f(x)$, we have

$$g \circ f(x) = g(f(x)) = 2[f(x)] + 1 = 2[x^2] + 1 = 2x^2 + 1.$$

The fact that the expressions for $f \circ g(x)$ and $g \circ f(x)$ are strikingly different shows again that the order of composition is important and that $f \circ g$ and $g \circ f$ are not usually the same functions.

When the domain of a function given by an equation is not stated, it is understood to be all numbers that can be substituted into the equation to get a real number. Contrary to this understanding, the domain of a composition may or may not consist of all numbers that can be substituted into the simplified expression for the composition function.

The domain of the composition of $f(x) = \sqrt{x}$ and $g(x) = x + 1$ does consist of all numbers that can be substituted into the expression for $f \circ g$. In particular, the domain of

$$f \circ g(x) = f(g(x)) = \sqrt{g(x)} = \sqrt{x + 1}$$

is all numbers $x \geq -1$. Similarly, the domain of

$$g \circ f(x) = g(f(x)) = [f(x)] + 1 = \sqrt{x} + 1$$

is all numbers $x > 0$.

In contrast, the domain of the composition $F \circ G(x)$ of $F(x) = x^2 + 3$ with $G(x) = \sqrt{x}$ cannot be inferred from the simplified expression for $F \circ G$. A simplified expression for $F \circ G$ is obtained as follows:

$$F \circ G(x) = F(G(x)) = [G(x)]^2 + 3 = (\sqrt{x})^2 + 3 = x + 3.$$

Any real number can be substituted into this expression to obtain another real number. However, only those numbers a which satisfy the two conditions stated above are in the domain of $F \circ G$. The first condition is that a must be in the domain of G. The domain of G is the non-negative numbers. Therefore, the first condition is that $a \geq 0$. The second condition is that $G(a) = b$ must be in the domain of F. The domain of F is all real numbers, so every number a satisfies this condition. Thus, the domain of $F \circ G$ is the non-negative numbers and **not** all real numbers that can be substituted into the expression for $F \circ G$!

CALCULATOR COMMENTARY

To explore the compositions of the functions $f(x) = \sqrt{x}$ and $g(x) = x + 1$ from the discussion above on the TI-83®, enter $f(x) = \sqrt{x}$ as **Y1** and $g(x) = x + 1$ as **Y2** on the **Y =** screen. Evaluating $f \circ g(3) = f(g(3))$ requires evaluating $g(3)$ and then using the results of that evaluation as the input to evaluate f. To evaluate $g(3)$, enter **Y2(3)**. (Enter **Y2** by pressing $\boxed{\text{VARS}}$, highlighting **Y-VARS** and pressing $\boxed{1}$, $\boxed{2}$.) Press $\boxed{\text{ENTER}}$. The calculator will evaluate **Y2(3)**, store the result in the temporary memory called **ANS** (answer), and display

Next we must evaluate f at $g(3) = 4$. The value 4 was just calculated and is stored as **ANS**, so to evaluate f at $g(3)$, enter **Y1(ANS)**. (Press $\boxed{\text{2nd}}$, [**ANS**] ((row 10, column 4)) to enter **ANS**.) Press $\boxed{\text{ENTER}}$. The calculator will evaluate **Y1** at 4 and display

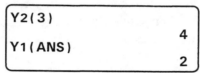

Thus, $f(g(3)) = 2$.

Since **Y1** $= f$ and **Y2** $= g$, the expression $f(g(3))$ could also be written **Y1(Y2(3))**. This notation suggests that $f(g(3))$ could have been evaluated without using **ANS** by simply entering **Y1(Y2(3))** and pressing $\boxed{\text{ENTER}}$. Indeed, this is the case. Try it!

The TI-83® does not do algebraic or symbolic manipulations and so is of little use for finding an expression for the composition of two functions.

SUMMARY

1. The composition of $y = f(x)$ with $y = g(x)$ is denoted $y = f \circ g(x)$ or $y = f(g(x))$. To evaluate $f \circ g(a)$, first, evaluate $g(a)$ to get a number b and, second, evaluate $f(b)$ to get $f \circ g(a) = f(g(a))$.

2. To obtain an expression for $f \circ g(x) = f(g(x))$ from equations for f and g, replace the variable x in the equation $y = f(x)$ with the expression for $g(x)$ and simplify the result.

3. The domain of $f \circ g$ is all numbers a in the domain of g such that $g(a)$ is in the domain of f. The domain of $f \circ g$ may or may not be all of the numbers that can be substituted into the simplified expression for $f \circ g$.

EXAMPLES

Example 1: Let $f(x) = 3x - 1$ and $g(x) = 2x + 2$.
Find $f \circ g(3)$ and $g \circ f(3)$
(a) by hand calculation and
(b) by using the TI-83®.

Solution 1: (a) Since $g(3) = 2(3) + 2 = 8$, we have
$$f \circ g(3) = f(g(3)) = f(8) = 3(8) - 1 = 23.$$

Since $f(3) = 3(3) - 1 = 8$, we have
$$g \circ f(3) = g(f(3)) = g(8) = 2(8) + 2 = 18 \cdot$$

Solution 1: (b) Enter $3x - 1$ as **Y1** and $2x + 2$ as **Y2** on the **Y=** screen. Press | **2nd** |, [**QUIT**] to return to the home screen. Enter **Y1(Y2(3))**. Press |**ENTER**| to find
$$\textbf{Y1(Y2(3))} = f(g(3)) = 23.$$
Enter **Y2(Y1(3))**. Press |**ENTER**| to find
$$\textbf{Y2(Y1(3))} = g(f(3)) = 18.$$

Example 2: Let $g(x) = \sqrt{x - 3}$ and $h(x) - x^2 + x - 3$.
Find $h \circ g(4)$ and $g \circ h(-2)$
(a) by hand calculation and
(b) by using the TI-83®.

Solution 2: (a) Since $g(4) = \sqrt{4 - 3} = \sqrt{1} = 1$, we have
$$h \circ g(4) = h(g(4)) = h(1) = (1)^2 + (1) - 3 = 1 + 1 - 3 = -1.$$

Since $h(-2) = (-2)^2 + (-2) - 3 = -1$ and the number $b = -1$ is not in the domain of g, $g \circ h(-2)$ is not defined.

Solution 2: (b) Enter $\sqrt{x - 3}$ as **Y1** and $x^2 + x - 3$ as **Y2** on the **Y=** screen. Return to the home screen by pressing | **2nd** |, [**QUIT**].

Since $g(x) = $ **Y1** and $h(x) = $ **Y2**, $h(g(4)) = $ **Y2(Y1(4))**. Enter **Y2(Y1(4))** and press |**ENTER**|. The result shows that
$$h(g(4)) = \textbf{Y2(Y1(4))} = -1.$$

Since $g(x) = $ **Y1** and $h(x) = $ **Y2**, $g(h(-2)) = $ **Y1(Y2(-2))**. Enter **Y1(Y2(-2))** and press |**ENTER**|. The resulting error message shows that -2 is not in the domain of the composition $g(h(x))$.

Example 3: Let $F(x) = x + 3$ and $G(x) = x^2 - x + 1$.

  (a) Find an expression for the composite function $F \circ G$.

  (b) Find an expression for the composite function $G \circ F$.

Solution 3: (a) $F \circ G(x) = F(G(x)) = G(x) + 3 = (x^2 - x + 1) + 3 = x^2 - x + 4$

Solution 3: (b) $G \circ F(x) = G(F(x)) = [F(x)]^2 - F(x) + 1$
$$= (x + 3)^2 - (x + 3) + 1 = x^2 + 5x + 7$$

Example 4: Let $H(x) = \sqrt[3]{x - 1}$ and $K(x) = x^3 + 1$.

  (a) Find an expression for $H \circ K(x)$.

  (b) Find an expression for $K \circ H(x)$.

Solution 4: (a) $H \circ K(x) = H(K(x)) = \sqrt[3]{K(x) - 1} = \sqrt[3]{(x^3 + 1) - 1} = \sqrt[3]{x^3} = x$

Solution 4: (b) $K \circ H(x) = K(H(x)) = [H(x)]^3 + 1 = [\sqrt[3]{x - 1}]^3 + 1 = (x - 1) + 1 = x$

Example 5: Let $f(x) = \dfrac{2x - 5}{x + 1}$ and $g(x) = 3x - 2$.

  Find $g \circ f(-4) + f \circ g(x)$.

Solution 5:

  Since $f(-4) = \dfrac{2(-4) - 5}{-4 + 1} = \dfrac{-13}{-3} = \dfrac{13}{3}$, we have

$$g \circ f(-4) = g(f(-4)) = g\left(\frac{13}{3}\right) = 3\left(\frac{13}{3}\right) - 2 = 11.$$

  An expression for the composition $f \circ g(x)$ is

$$f \circ g(x) = f(g(x)) = \frac{2g(x) - 5}{g(x) + 1} = \frac{2(3x - 2) - 5}{(3x - 2) + 1} = \frac{6x - 9}{3x - 1}.$$

  Therefore,

$$g \circ f(-4) + f(g(x)) = 11 + \frac{6x - 9}{3x - 1} = \frac{11(3x - 1) + (6x - 9)}{3x - 1} = \frac{39x - 20}{3x - 1}.$$

Example 6: Let $p(x) \dfrac{\sqrt[3]{x} - 5}{3}$ and $q(x) = 3x + 5$.

  Find $q \circ p(x) + p \circ q(1)$.

Solution 6: An expression for the composition $q \circ p(x)$ is

$$q \circ p(x) = q\big(p(x)\big) = 3p(x) + 5 = 3\left(\frac{\sqrt[3]{x} - 5}{3}\right) + 5 = \sqrt[3]{x} - 5 + 5 = \sqrt[3]{x}.$$

Since $q(1) = 3(1) + 5 = 8$, we have

$$p \circ q(1) = p\big(q(1)\big) = p(8) = \frac{\sqrt[3]{8} - 5}{3} = \frac{2 - 5}{3} = -1.$$

Therefore,

$$q \circ p(x) + p \circ q(1) = \sqrt[3]{x} - 1.$$

PRACTICE PROBLEMS

In problems 1 - 5, evaluate the given functions by hand calculation and by using a TI-83® calculator.

1. Let $f(x) = 3x + 4$ and $g(x) = 2x - 7$.

   (a) Find $f\big(g(2)\big)$. (b) Find $g\big(f(\frac{-1}{3})\big)$.

2. Let $F(x) = \sqrt{x - 2}$ and $G(x) = x^2 - 11$.

   (a) Find $F \circ G(2)$. (b) Find $G \circ F(6)$.

3. Let $h(x) = \dfrac{x}{x - 3}$ and $k(x) = \dfrac{3x}{x - 1}$.

   (a) Find $h \circ k(4)$. (b) Find $k \circ h(-2)$.

4. Let $G(x) = \sqrt[3]{x + 1}$ and $H(x) = x^2 - 1$.

   (a) Find $H\big(G(-2)\big)$. (b) Find $G\big(H(-8)\big)$.

5. Let $f(x) = x^2$ and $k(x) = \sqrt{x - 10}$.

   (a) Find $k \circ f(4)$. (b) Find $f \circ k(4)$.

6. Let $f(x) = \dfrac{2}{3}x + 1$ and $g(x) = 9x^2 - 12x + 6$.

   (a) Find an expression for $g \circ f(x)$. (b) Find an expression for $f \circ g(x)$.

7. Let $T(x) = \dfrac{(2x - 1)}{3x}$ and $S(x) = 2x^2 + 1$.

  (a) Find an expression for the composition of S with T.

  (b) Find an expression for the composition of T with S.

8. Let $h(x) = 3\sqrt{\dfrac{4x - 1}{3x - 7}}$ and $k(x) = \dfrac{7x^3 - 1}{3x^3 - 4}$.

  (a) Find an expression for $h \circ k(x)$.   **(b)** Find an expression for $k \circ h(x)$.

9. Let $G(x) = \dfrac{2x^5 + 3}{6x^5}$ and $H(x) = 5\sqrt{\dfrac{6x}{2x + 3}}$.

  (a) Find an expression for $G(H(x))$.   **(b)** Find an expression for $H(G(x))$.

10. Let $k(x) = \dfrac{3}{2x + 7}$ and $g(x) = \dfrac{2x + 7}{3}$.

  (a) Find an expression for $g(k(x))$.   **(b)** Find an expression for $k(g(x))$.

11. Let $f(x) = \dfrac{3x + 4}{-2x}$ and $g(x) = \dfrac{5x}{-x - 3}$.   Find $f \circ g(2) + g \circ f(x)$.

12. Let $h(x) = \dfrac{x^3 + 8}{x^3}$ and $t(x) = 3\sqrt{\dfrac{5x + 4}{3x - 7}}$.   Find $h(t(x)) - t\left(h\left(-3\sqrt{\dfrac{40}{9}}\right)\right)$.

13. Let $f(x) = \dfrac{7x + 4}{3x - 5}$ and $h(x) = \dfrac{5x + 4}{3x - 7}$.   Find $h \circ f(4) + f(h(x))$.

14. Let $t(x) = 5\sqrt{\dfrac{2x}{3x - 4}}$ and $r(x) = \dfrac{3x^5 - 2}{12x^5}$.   Find $r(t(2)) - t(r(x))$.

15. Let $k(x) = \dfrac{2x^2 + 1}{x^2 - 3}$ and $h(x) = \sqrt{x - 2}$.   Find $h \circ k(1) + k(h(x))$.

UNIT 1
Sample Examination

1. Let $h(x) = \dfrac{-x + 8}{\sqrt{2x - 5}}$. What is $h\left(\dfrac{9}{2}\right) - h(3)$?

    A) $-\dfrac{33}{8}$ B) $-\dfrac{13}{4}$ C) $-\dfrac{5}{4}$ D) $\dfrac{27}{4}$ E) undefined

2. Which of the following statements correctly describe(s) the function $y = f(x)$ given by the graph in Figure 1.48? There is at least one correct response. Choose all correct responses.

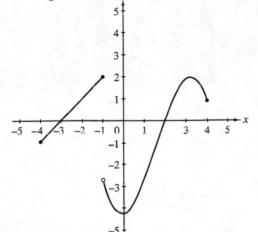

    A) The graph is not the graph of a function.

    B) The domain of f is the interval from -4 to 4.

    C) The range of f is the interval from -1 to 2.

    D) The largest number for which $f(a) = 0$ is $a - 2$.

    E) $f(-1) = 2$

Figure 1.48

3. Let $F(x) = 7^x$ and $G(x) = \log x$. Rounded to three decimal places, what is $F(1.35) - G(952)$?

    A) 0.879   B) 5.194   C) 6.973   D) 10.853   E) 19.409

4. The graph of a function of the form $f(x) = b^x$ is shown in Figure 1.49. What is the equation for this function?

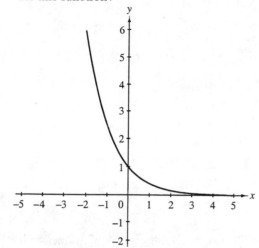

A) $y = \left(\dfrac{1}{2}\right)^x$

B) $y = \left(\dfrac{1}{3}\right)^x$

C) $y = \left(\dfrac{2}{5}\right)^x$

D) $y = 2^x$

E) $y = \left(\dfrac{5}{2}\right)^x$

Figure 1.49

5. Let $g(x) = \dfrac{x-2}{2}$ and $k(x) = 6x^2 - 7x - 3$. What is $k \circ g(x) - g \circ k(2)$?

A) $\dfrac{3x^2 - 19x + 15}{2}$

B) $\dfrac{3x^2 - 19x - 25}{2}$

C) $\dfrac{6x^2 - 7x + 1}{2}$

D) $\dfrac{6x^2 - 7x - 5}{2}$

E) undefined

INVERSE FUNCTIONS

OBJECTIVE 2.1

(a) Given the graph of a function, determine whether it has an inverse function.

(b) Given the graph of a function f that has an inverse function g and given a number b, find $g(b)$ or state that $g(b)$ is not defined.

(c) Given the graph of a function, sketch the graph of the inverse function or state that the function does not have an inverse function.

OBJECTIVE 2.2

Given a function $y = f(x)$ which has an inverse function, find the inverse function by solving the equation $x = f(y)$ for y.

OBJECTIVE 2.3

(a) Given a number $b > 0$, $b \neq 1$, sketch the graph of the logarithmic function base b, $f(x) = \log_b x$.

(b) Given the graph of a logarithmic function $f(x) = \log_b x$, estimate b.

OBJECTIVE 2.4

Given two functions $y = f(x)$ and $y = g(x)$, determine whether f and g are inverse functions by computing their compositions.

UNIT 2
INVERSE FUNCTIONS

OVERVIEW

In Unit 1 we learned that a function is a procedure for obtaining numbers from other numbers. When the procedure for a function can be reversed and the reverse procedure specifies another function, the resulting pair of functions are inverses of each other. In Unit 2 we will study the general notion of inverses for functions specified by graphs or algebraic expressions. We will define the logarithmic functions as inverses of exponential functions and obtain the graphs of logarithmic functions from the graphs of their companion exponential functions.

INVERSE FUNCTIONS

OBJECTIVE 2.1

    (a) Given the graph of a function, determine whether it has an inverse function.

    (b) Given the graph of a function f that has an inverse function g and given a number b, find $g(b)$ or state that $g(b)$ is not defined.

    (c) Given the graph of a function, sketch the graph of the inverse function or state that the function does not have an inverse function.

DISCUSSION

Many procedures, computational, mechanical or operational, can be reversed. In some cases the procedure which specifies a function can be reversed to obtain another function, the **inverse function**. Think about the function $f(x) = 2x + 3$. The procedure for determining a number y from a number x is *multiply the number x times 2 and then add 3 to the result.* The procedure for f can be reversed. The reverse procedure is *subtract 3 and divide the result by 2.* This reverse procedure specifies a function g, which is called the inverse function for f. We can translate the verbal description of g into an algebraic expression and write

$$g(x) = \frac{x - 3}{2}.$$

Many, but not all, functions f are specified by a procedure that can be reversed to obtain a new function g. When this is possible, we say that f **has an inverse function** and that g **is the inverse function for** f. If f is a function that has an inverse function g, then to specify g we must give two things:

    • the domain D of g, and

    • a procedure for determining exactly one number from each number in the domain.

Often, only the procedure for evaluating a function is given and the domain D must be inferred from the procedure. In fact, we can infer the domain of the inverse function g from the vague description, *the reverse of the procedure for f.* To what numbers would it make sense to apply *the reverse of the procedure for f*? The numbers in the range of f. These are the numbers which could result from applying the procedure for f in the first place. Thus, the domain of g is the range of f.

To describe the procedure for g precisely, consider a number b in the domain of g. Then, as we just observed, b is in the range of f, so there is a number a such that $f(a) = b$. This number a is $g(b)$ and we set $g(b) = a$. Briefly described, the procedure for finding $g(b)$ is to find the number a such that $f(a) = b$.

Now we recognize the property that a function f must have in order for it to have an inverse function g. For each number b in the range of f, there must be **exactly one** number a, such that $f(a) = b$. A function that has this property is called a **one-to-one** function. Every one-to-one function f has an inverse function g and $g(b) = a$ when and only when $f(a) = b$.

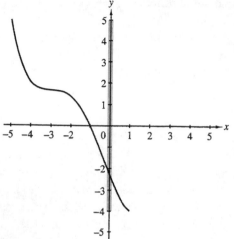

The inverse for a function can be described in terms of the graph of the function. Let $y = f(x)$ be the function given by the graph in Figure 2.1. Let g denote the inverse function for f. The domain of g is the range of f. By projecting the graph of f onto the y-axis we see that the range of f, and therefore the domain of g, is the shaded portion of the y-axis. The procedure for evaluating the function f from its graph is described in Objective 1.2. The procedure for evaluating g from the graph of f is the reverse of that procedure.

Figure 2.1 Graph of $y = f(x)$ The domain of inverse function g is shaded on the y-axis.

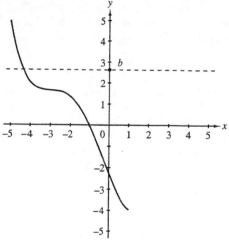

Figure 2.2 Step 1 for finding $g(b)$

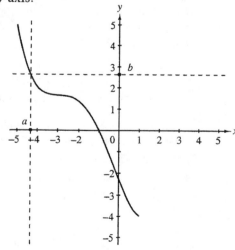

Figure 2.3 Steps 2 and 3 for finding $g(b)$

The procedure for finding $g(b)$ for a given number b in the domain of g from the graph of f is as follows.

Step 1. Locate b on the y-axis and draw a horizontal line through this point as in Figure 2.2.

Step 2. Locate the point where the line drawn in Step 1 intersects the graph and draw a vertical line through it as in Figure 2.3.

Step 3. Locate the point where the vertical line drawn in Step 2 crosses the x-axis. The x-coordinate of this point is $a = g(b)$ as shown in Figure 2.3.

Notice that when b is not in the domain of g this procedure cannot be carried out, so $g(b)$ is not defined. Compare the procedure for finding $g(b)$ from the graph of f with the procedure for finding $f(a)$ from the graph of f. Verify that each procedure is the reverse of the other. Notice again that $g(b) = a$ when and only when $f(a) = b$.

One can determine whether a function f has an inverse function by examining the graph of f. In order for the inverse g to be a **function**, the procedure for g must produce **exactly one** number y from each number x in its domain. From the procedure for g we see that this occurs when for each number x in the domain of g there is **exactly one** number y such that $x = f(y)$.

We can identify the graph of a function that has this property by using the HORIZONTAL LINE TEST:
A function f has an inverse function if and only if every line perpendicular to the y-axis intersects the graph of f in no more than one point.

To apply the HORIZONTAL LINE TEST to a function f, imagine moving a line perpendicular to the y-axis from top to bottom down the graph of f. If at every position the line cuts the graph at no more than one point, then the function has an inverse function. If there is even one position where the line cuts the graph at two or more points, then the function does not have an inverse function. Notice that increasing functions and decreasing functions always pass the HORIZONTAL LINE TEST and therefore always have an inverse function.

Now suppose that F is a function that has an inverse function G. We know that $G(b) = a$ if and only if $F(a) = b$. Therefore, the point (b, a) is on the graph of G if and only if the point (a, b) is on the graph of F. The point (b, a) is called **the reflection of** (a, b) **through the diagonal line** $y = x$. In a rectangular coordinate system which has the same units of distance on the two coordinate axes, the points (b, a) and (a, b) are mirror image of each other through the line $y = x$. In such a coordinate system, imagine a two-sided mirror (which reflects on both sides) standing on edge perpendicular to the coordinate plane along the line $y = x$. The image of the point (a, b) in the mirror will coincide with (b, a) and the image of (b, a) will coincide with (a, b). When (a, b) and (b, a) are plotted in a coordinate system where the units of distance are not the same on the two axes, (a, b) and (b, a) are still called the reflections of each other, but they will not appear as mirror images in this way. Use the TI-83® to explore this idea further in Practice Problem 19 at the end of this section.

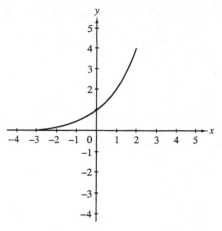

Figure 2.4 Graph of $y = F(x)$

We can use the relationship between points on the graph of a function F and on the graph of its inverse function G to obtain the graph of the inverse function from the graph of the function. Consider the specific function $y = F(x)$ graphed in Figure 2.4. The following table lists some points on the graph of f.

a	-3	-1	0	1	2
$b = F(a)$	0	$\frac{1}{2}$	1	2	4

Table 2.1

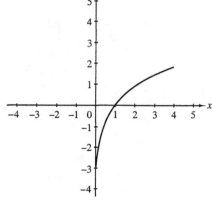

Use the fact that $G(b) = a$ if and only if $F(a) = b$ to make a table for G. Since $F(-3) = 0$, $G(0) = -3$. Since $F(-1) = \frac{1}{2}$, $G\left(\frac{1}{2}\right) = -1$. By continuing this process we get the values in Table 2.2. Plot these points and draw a smooth curve through them to get the graph of G in Figure 2.5.

b	0	$\frac{1}{2}$	1	2	4
$a = G(b)$	-3	-1	0	1	2

Table 2.2

Figure 2.5 Graph of $y = G(x)$

The graph of $y = F(x)$, the diagonal line $y = x$ and the graph of $y = G(x)$ are shown in Figure 2.6 in a coordinate system where the units of distance on the two axes are the same. Notice that the point $(0, -3)$ on the graph of G is the mirror image through the diagonal line $y = x$ of the point $(-3, 0)$ on the graph of F. Similarly, the point $(2, 1)$ on the graph of G is the mirror image of the point $(1, 2)$ on the graph of F. In fact, the graph of G is the mirror image through the diagonal line $y = x$ of the graph of F.

Figure 2.6 Graphs of F and G

The graph of a function and its inverse are always reflections of each other. In a coordinate system with the same units of distance on each axis, the graphs are mirror images through the line $y = x$.

We state this fact as the REFLECTION PRINCIPLE:

> If f and g are inverse functions, then the graphs of f and g are each the reflection of the other through the line $y = x$.

The REFLECTION PRINCIPLE suggests a way to sketch the graph of the inverse of a function from the graph of the function in a coordinate system with the same units of distance on the two axes. Just sketch the mirror image of the graph of f through the diagonal line $y = x$. Since the graph of the inverse function is the mirror image of the graph of the function, the two graphs will have the same geometric shapes.

The REFLECTION PRINCIPLE also shows that inverse functions come in pairs. The graph of g, the inverse function for f, is the reflection through the line $y = x$ of the graph of f. The graph of the inverse function for g is the reflection of the graph of g. Thus, the graph of the inverse of g is the **reflection of the reflection** of the graph of f. Two reflections return us to the graph of f. The graph of the inverse for g is exactly the graph of f. This means that if g is the inverse for f, then f is also the inverse for g. Because of this, we will often refer to **pairs of inverse functions.**

CALCULATOR COMMENTARY

When a function is given by a graph, we can apply the HORIZONTAL LINE TEST to see whether it has an inverse function. When a function is given by an expression or equation, there is no such easy test for determining whether the function has an inverse function. In this situation we can investigate the existence of an inverse function by graphing the function and then asking the question in geometric, rather than symbolic, terms.

To determine whether the graph of a function passes the HORIZONTAL LINE TEST, we must know something about the entire graph. Just as we can't always draw the entire graph of a function with pencil and paper, we can't always view the entire graph on the calculator screen. When the domain or the range of the function is unbounded we can examine parts of the graph but not the entire graph. In these cases we may be able infer properties of the function at the extremes of its domain and range by reasoning qualitatively without actually looking at those sections of the graph.

A portion of a graph that includes all the features of the graph that are important for a particular purpose is called a **complete graph** of a function. In using the calculator to investigate inverse functions, our problem is to choose, if possible, a viewing window (*i.e.*, a range of values for x and y) that shows a complete graph, *i.e.*, a portion of the graph that displays all the features relevant to the existence of an inverse function.

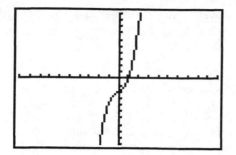

For example, consider the question of whether the function $f(x) = x^3 + x - 2$ has an inverse function. Figure 2CC.1 shows the graph of $f(x)$ in a standard viewing window. Within this window, every horizontal line intersects the graph at only one point. We must decide whether the same is true in every viewing window.

Figure 2CC.1

When x is large and positive, x^3 is much larger than any of the other terms in the expression. Furthermore, as x increases x^3 increases very rapidly. Thus, as x increases in a positive direction, the x^3 term dominates and the function continues to increase. When x is large and negative, x^3 is a large negative number. As x decreases through large negative values, x^3 decreases rapidly through even larger negative values. Thus, as x decreases in a negative direction, the x^3 term dominates and the function continues to decrease. You can use **ZOOM** to observe these behaviors graphically. First set the viewing window to

```
WINDOW
Xmin = -3
Xmax = 3
Xscl = 0
Ymin = -10
Ymax = 10
Yscl = 0
Xres = 1
```

Next, set the **ZOOM** factors to **XFact = 2**, **YFact = 8** by pressing $\boxed{\text{ZOOM}}$ (row 1, column 3), scrolling to **MEMORY**, pressing $\boxed{\ \ 4\ \ }$, and entering these values on the designated lines. Press $\boxed{\text{GRAPH}}$ to view the graph in this new window. Now press $\boxed{\text{ZOOM}}$ and select **Zoom Out** by pressing $\boxed{\ \ 3\ \ }$. Use the arrow keys to move the cursor to the y-intercept of the graph. Press $\boxed{\text{ENTER}}$. The graph will be generated in a new window centered at the y-intercept of the graph with the range of x-values doubled and the range of y-values multiplied by 8. Each time you press $\boxed{\text{ENTER}}$, the graph will be generated in a new window that is twice as wide and eight times as tall as the previous one. After pressing $\boxed{\text{ENTER}}$ five times, press $\boxed{\text{WINDOW}}$ to see the range of x and y values in the graph. Press $\boxed{\text{GRAPH}}$ to return to the graph. The successive graphs of f show that $f(x)$ increases as the cube of x. In each larger window the function satisfies the HORIZONTAL LINE TEST.

We can see that the graph of $f(x) = x^3 + x - 2$ satisfies the Horizontal Line Test in the standard window because of its shape. Since the function increases steadily to the right of this rectangle and decreases steadily to its left, the function passes the Horizontal Line Test in these regions, too. Thus, f passes the Horizontal Line Test and has an inverse function.

To evaluate the inverse function g of a function f at some number b from the graph of the function f, follow the procedure for finding all values a such that $f(a) = b$. If f has an inverse function, for each b in the domain of g (which is the range of f) there is exactly one number a such that $f(a) = b$. This number a is the value of g at b so $g(b) = a$. Techniques for using the TI–83® to find those numbers a such that $f(a) = b$ are given in the Calculator Commentary for Objective 1.2.

Suppose f is a function that has an inverse function g. In the discussion we saw that a point (a, b) is on the graph of f if and only if the point (b, a) is on the graph of g. In this connection, we noted that points (a, b) and (b, a) in a rectangular coordinate system are the reflections of each other through the line $y = x$. However, these two points will be mirror images and thus look like reflections only if the units of length on the horizontal and vertical axes are the same. On the TI-83® units of length on the two axes are equal in viewing windows that have

$$\text{Ymax} - \text{Ymin} = 2/3 (\text{Xmax} - \text{Xmin}).$$

Windows of these sizes are called **square viewing windows**. In square viewing windows, the graph of the inverse of a function is the mirror image through the line $y = x$ of the graph of the function. Practice Problem 19 illustrates the importance of having identical units on the two axes to study reflections.

We can use the TI-83® to obtain the graph of the inverse of a function given by an equation. The following program for the TI-83® will graph a function, the line $y = x$, and the reflection of the graph of the function through the line $y = x$ in a square viewing window. If the function has an inverse function, the reflected graph will be the graph of the inverse function. If the function does not have an inverse function, the reflected graph will not be the graph of a function.

Enter this program into your machine.

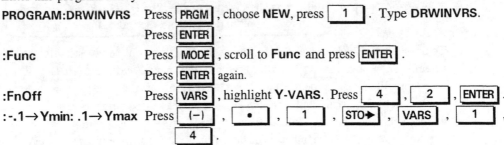

PROGRAM:DRWINVRS   Press ⌈PRGM⌉ , choose **NEW**, press ⌈ 1 ⌉ . Type **DRWINVRS**.
                                        Press ⌈ENTER⌉ .
:Func   Press ⌈MODE⌉ , scroll to **Func** and press ⌈ENTER⌉ .
                                        Press ⌈ENTER⌉ again.
:FnOff   Press ⌈VARS⌉ , highlight **Y-VARS**. Press ⌈ 4 ⌉ , ⌈ 2 ⌉ , ⌈ENTER⌉ .
:-.1→Ymin: .1→Ymax Press ⌈ (−) ⌉ , ⌈ • ⌉ , ⌈ 1 ⌉ , ⌈STO▸⌉ , ⌈VARS⌉ , ⌈ 1 ⌉ ,
                                        ⌈ 4 ⌉ .

Press |ALPHA| , [:]. Press | • | , | 1 | , |STO→| , |VARS| , | 1 | , | 5 | . Press |ENTER| .

: Disp *"Xmin ="* Press |PRGM| , scroll to I/O and press | 3 | . Press |ALPHA| , (*"*).

Press |VARS| , | 1 | , | 1 | . Press |2nd| , [TEST] , | 1 | .

Press |ALPHA| , (*"*) . Press |ENTER| .

:Input **Xmin** Press |PRGM| , scroll to I/O and press | 1 | .

Press |VARS| , | 1 | , | 1 | . Press |ENTER| .

: Disp *"Xmax ="* Press |PRGM| , choose I/O and press | 3 | . Press |ALPHA| , (*"*).

Press |VARS| , | 1 | , | 2 | . Press |2nd| , [TEST] , | 1 | .

Press |ALPHA| , (*"*) . Press |ENTER| .

:Input **Xmax** Press |PRGM| , scroll to I/O and press | 1 | .

Press |VARS| , | 1 | , | 2 | . Press |ENTER| .

FnOn 1 Press |VARS| , scroll to **Y-VARS**. Press | 4 | , | 1 | , | 1 | , |ENTER| .

:ZSquare Press |ZOOM| , | 5 | , |ENTER| .

:Pause Press |PRGM| , | 8 | , |ENTER| .

:DrawF **X** Press |2nd| , [**DRAW**] (row 4, column 3), | 6 | , |ALPHA| , (**X**), |ENTER| .

:DrawInvY1 Press |2nd| , [**DRAW**] , | 8 | , |VARS| , scroll to **Y-VARS**.

Press | 1 | , | 1 | , |ENTER| .

Finally, press | 2nd | , [QUIT] to leave the **PROGRAM** mode and return to the home screen.

TI Tip

If several people need the same program, it's not necessary for each of them to key the program into their TI-83®. TI-83s have a port and a cable for communicating with other TI-83s. After one person has keyed in the program and has it running reliably, use this communications **LINK** to transfer the program to other machines. The **LINK** is easy to use. Read the *TI-83® Guidebook* to learn how. (Look under LINK in the index.)

To use the program **DRWINVRS**, first enter the function you are investigating as **Y1** on the **Y =** screen. Then press |PRGM| , scroll to the program name, and press |ENTER| . The name of the program will appear in the display. Press |ENTER| to start the program. First the program will ask you to specify **Xmin** and **Xmax**. The program uses these numbers to define a square viewing window. For best results, choose **Xmin** ≤ 0 ≤ **Xmax** so the origin is included in the viewing window. Press |ENTER| to indicate you have finished entering a number and are ready to continue.

The machine will graph the function and then pause. When the busy indicator in the upper right corner of the screen has stopped moving, you may press ENTER to continue. The program will then add the line $y = x$ and the reflection of the graph of the function to the graph. When you have finished examining the graphs, press 2nd , [QUIT] to return to the home screen. You can run the program again with the same function by simply pressing ENTER .

SUMMARY

1. HORIZONTAL LINE TEST: A function f has an inverse function if and only if every line perpendicular to the y-axis intersects the graph of f in no more than one point.

2. Let f be a function which has an inverse function g. The domain of g is the range of f. To evaluate $g(b)$, find the number a such that $f(a) = b$.

3. REFLECTION PRINCIPLE: If f and g are inverse functions, then the graphs of f and g are each the reflection of the other through the line $y = x$.

EXAMPLES

Example 1: The graph of a function is shown in Figure 2.7. Determine whether this function has an inverse function.

Solution 1: Apply the Horizontal Line Test.

Imagine all possible lines perpendicular to the y-axis. The horizontal line at $y = 3$ (as well as others) intersects the graph in more than one point. Since there is a horizontal line that intersects the graph in more than one point, this function does not have an inverse function.

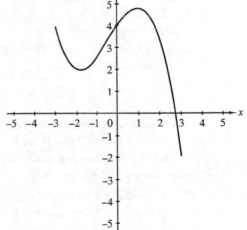

Figure 2.7

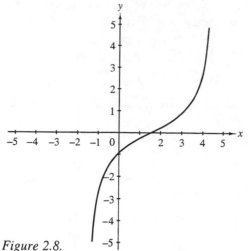

Figure 2.8.

Example 2: The graph of a function is shown in Figure 2.8. Determine whether this function has an inverse function.

Solution 2: Apply the Horizontal Line Test.

Imagine all possible lines perpendicular to the *y*-axis. Every one of them intersects the graph in no more than one point. Therefore, this function has an inverse function.

Example 3: Determine whether $f(x) = \dfrac{1}{300}x^3 + \dfrac{3}{20}x^2 + 2x$ has an inverse function.

Solution 3: Generate the graph of $f(x)$ in the standard viewing window on the TI-83®. (You can establish the standard viewing window from the **ZOOM** menu.) Within this window, every horizontal line intersects the graph at only one point.

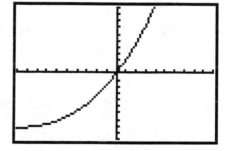

Figure 2CC.2

We must decide whether the same is true in every window. This time, instead of zooming, use the trace feature. Press TRACE . A flashing cursor will appear on the curve near the center of the window. Move it along the curve by pressing the left and right arrow keys. Move the cursor leftward along the curve. When the cursor reaches the edge of the window, the calculator will generate the next section of the graph. As you trace leftward, you will discover a small variation in the graph that makes it fail the HORIZONTAL LINE TEST. Thus, this function does not have an inverse function.

To see more clearly that this function fails the Horizontal Line Test, graph the function in the window **Xmin = -31, Xmax = 4, Ymin = -15, Ymax = 10**. The horizontal line at **y = -7.5** intersects the graph a three points!

Example 4: The graph of a function $y = f(x)$ is shown in Figure 2.9. This function has an inverse function $y = g(x)$.

(a) Find $g(-1)$ or state that -1 is not in the domain of g.

(b) Find $g(3)$ or state that 3 is not in the domain of g.

Solution 4:   *(a)*

Step 1. Locate -1 on the y-axis and draw a horizontal line through this point.

Step 2. Locate the point where this horizontal line intersects the graph and draw a vertical line through it.

Step 3. Locate the point where this vertical line crosses the x-axis. The x-coordinate of this point is -3. Therefore, $g(-1) = -3$.

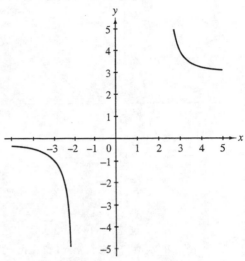

Solution 4:   *(b)*

Step 1. Locate 3 on the y-axis and draw a horizontal line through this point.

Step 2. This horizontal line does not intersect the graph of f. Therefore, 3 is not in the domain of g.

Figure 2.9 Graph of $y = f(x)$

Example 5: The function $f(x) = x^3 + x - 2$ has an inverse function g. Generate the graph of f using a graphics calculator and find $g(2)$ from the graph.

Solution 5: For convenience, specify a decimal viewing window on the TI-83® by setting $-4.7 \le x \le 4.7$ and $-3.1 \le y \le 3.1$. Enter $x^3 + x - 2$ as **Y1** on the **Y =** screen and generate the graph.

To find $g(2)$, use the cursor movement keys to position the cursor at $b = 2$ on the vertical axis. Use the left and right arrow keys to move the cursor horizontally until it coincides with a point on the graph. (Since f has an inverse function, there must be at most one such point.) Now use the up and down arrow keys to move the cursor vertically to the x-axis. The x-value associated with this point is 1.4. Thus, within the accuracy of the calculator's display, $g(2) = 1.4$.

Example 6: The graph of a function F is shown in Figure 2.10.
Sketch the graph of the inverse function G or state that F does not have an inverse function.

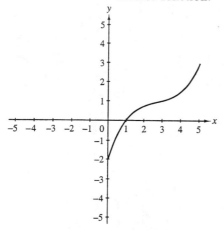

Figure 2.10   *Figure 2.11*

Solution 6: The Horizontal Line Test shows that F (see Figure 2.10) has an inverse function G. The graph of G (see Figure 2.11) is the reflection of the graph of F through the diagonal line $y = x$. Graph $y = x$. Plot a few points on the graph of G by reflecting points on the graph of F through the line $y = x$. Using these points as a guide, sketch the reflection of the graph of F through the line $y = x$ and obtain the graph of G, as shown in Figure 2.11.

Example 7: The graph of a function P is shown in Figure 2.12.
Sketch the graph of the inverse function Q or state that P does not have an inverse function.

Solution 7: The Horizontal Line Test shows that P has an inverse function Q. The graph of Q is the reflection of the graph of P through the diagonal line $y = x$. Graph $y = x$. Plot a few points on the graph of Q by reflecting points on the graph of P through the line $y = x$. Using these points as a guide, sketch the reflection of the graph of P through the line $y = x$ and obtain the graph of Q as shown in Figure 2.13.

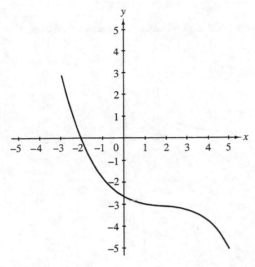

Figure 2.12

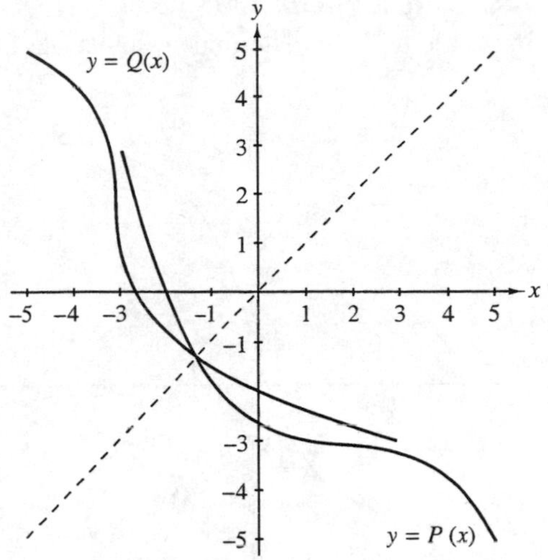

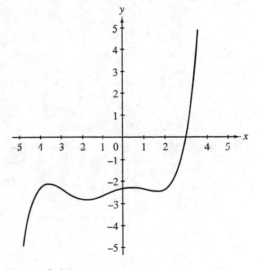

Figure 2.13

Example 8: The graph of a function *H* is shown in Figure 2.14. Sketch the graph of the inverse function *G* or state that *H* does not have an inverse function.

Solution 8: The Horizontal Line Test shows that *H* does not have an inverse function. The horizontal line at $y = -\dfrac{5}{2}$ (as well as others) intersects the graph of *H* at more than one point.

Figure 2.14

PRACTICE PROBLEMS

In problems 1 - 6, determine whether the function given by the graph has an inverse function.

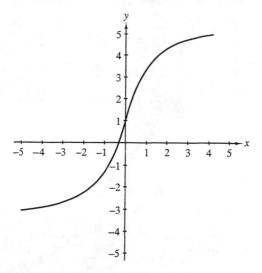

1. *Figure 2.15*

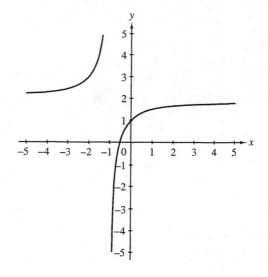

2. *Figure 2.16*

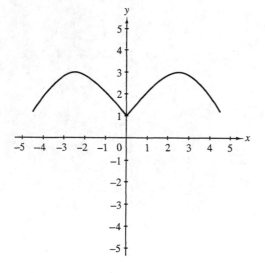

3. *Figure 2.17*

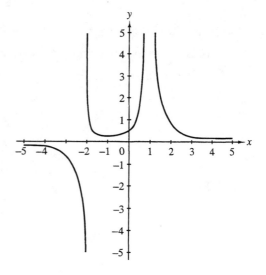

4. *Figure 2.18*

5. The function $y = f(x)$ shown by the graph in Figure 2.21 has an inverse function $y = g(x)$.

(a) Find $g(-2)$ or state that $g(-2)$ is not defined.
(b) Find $g(5)$ or state that 5 is not in the domain of g.

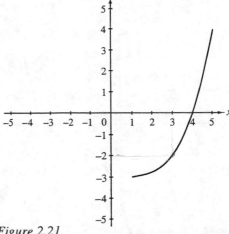

Figure 2.21

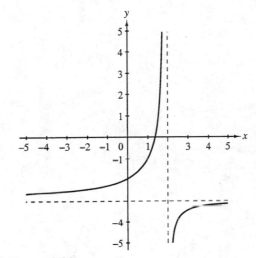

Figure 2.22

6. The function $y = p(x)$ shown by the graph in Figure 2.22 has an inverse function $y = q(x)$. (The dashed lines indicate asymptotes.)

(a) Find $q(-3)$ or state that $q(-3)$ is not defined.
(b) Find $q(1)$ or state that 1 is not in the domain of q

7. The function $y = S(t)$ shown by the graph in Figure 2.23 has an inverse function $y = R(t)$.

(a) Find $R(2)$ or state that $R(2)$ is not defined.
(b) Find $R(-4)$ or state that -4 is not in the domain of R.

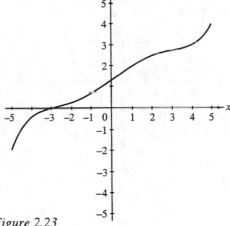

Figure 2.23

8. The function $y = g(x)$ shown by the graph in Figure 2.24 has an inverse function $y = f(x)$.

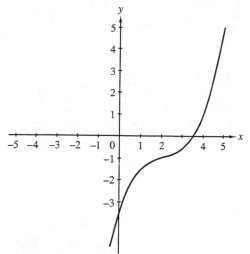

(a) Find $f(-1)$ or state that $f(-1)$ is not defined.

(b) Find $f(0)$ or state that 0 is not in the domain of f.

Figure 2.24

In problems 9 - 12, each figure shows the graph of a function.
For each function, sketch the graph of the inverse function or state that the function does not have an inverse function.

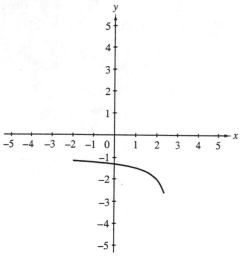

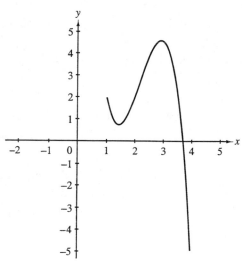

9. *Figure 2.25*

10. *Figure 2.26*

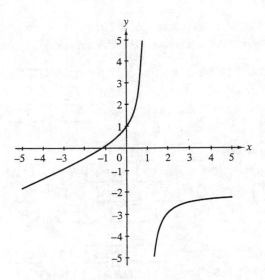

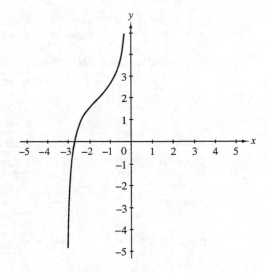

11. *Figure 2.27*   **12.** *Figure 2.29*

For each of the functions in problems 13 - 18:

  (a) Generate a complete graph of the function on the TI-83® and decide from the graph whether the function has an inverse function;

  (b) Execute the program **DRWINVRS** to obtain the reflection of the graph of the function; and

  (c) Decide whether the reflected graph is the graph of a function.

13. $f(x) = \dfrac{1}{2}x^3 - 4$

14. $f(x) = 0.5x - 2x^3$

15. $f(x) = \dfrac{x}{1 + x}$ (Beware the asymptote!)

16. $f(x) = 3x + x^2$

17. $f(x) = \left(1 - x^3\right)^{\frac{1}{3}}$

18. $f(x) = \dfrac{3}{x^2 + 2}$

19. (Optional) The following program for the TI-83® plots the point (A, B), the line $y = x$ and the point (B, A) for numbers A and B in the viewing window specified in advance.

PROGRAM:REFLCTN   Press [PRGM] , choose **NEW**, press [1] . Type **REFLCTN**. Press [ENTER] .

:FnOff   Press [VARS] and scroll to **Y-VARS**. Press [4] , [2] , [ENTER] .

:ClrDraw   Press [2nd] , [DRAW] , [1] , [ENTER] .

:Disp "A = "   Press [PRGM] , scroll to **I/O**, press [3] , [ALPHA] , ("), [ALPHA] , (A), [2nd] , [TEST] , [1] , [ALPHA] , (") , [ENTER] .

:Input A   Press [PRGM] , scroll to I/O, press [1] , [ALPHA] , (A) , [ENTER] .

:Disp "B = "   Press [PRGM] , scroll to I/O, press [3] , [ALPHA] , ("), [ALPHA] , (B), [2nd] , [TEST] , [1] , [ALPHA] , (") , [ENTER] .

:Input B   Press [PRGM] , scroll to   I/O, press [1] , [ALPHA] , (B), [ENTER] .

:Pt-On(A,B)   Press [2nd] , [DRAW], scroll to **POINTS**, press [1] , [ALPHA] , (A), [,] (row 6, column 2), [ALPHA] , (B), [ ] , [ENTER] .

:Pause   Press [PRGM] , [8] , [ENTER] .

:DrawF X   Press [2nd] , [DRAW] , [6] , [ALPHA] , (X), [ENTER] .

:Pause   Press [PRGM] , [8] , [ENTER] .

:Pt-On(B,A)   Press [2nd] , [DRAW] , scroll to   **POINTS**, press [1] , [ALPHA] , (B), [,] , [ALPHA] , (A), [ ] , [ENTER] .

Press [2nd] , [QUIT] to return to the home screen .

Step 1. Select a viewing window either by specifying values on the **WINDOW** menu or by choosing from the **ZOOM** menu. Write down two numbers **A** and **B** so the points **(A, B)** and **(B, A)** both lie within the viewing window. Predict where these points will lie in the TI-83® viewing window (coordinate system) you chose.

Step 2. Execute the program **REFLCTN** by pressing [PRGM] , scrolling to the program name, and pressing [ENTER] . When prompted, input **A** and **B** chosen in Step 1. Press [ENTER] after entering each one. The machine will plot **(A, B)**, then pause. Is the point **(A, B)** where you predicted?

Step 3. Press ENTER to continue. The machine will then plot the line $y = x$ and pause again. Is the line $y = x$ where you expected it to be? Where do you expect the point (**B, A**) to be?

Step 4. Press ENTER . The machine will plot the point (**B, A**). Is this point where you expected? Does it appear to be the mirror image of the point (**A, B**) in the line $y = x$? If not, why not?

Step 5. Press 2nd , [QUIT] to return to the home screen. Select another pair of numbers **A** and **B** and repeat Steps 2 - 4. Just press ENTER to repeat the program.

Step 6. Change the viewing window and repeat Steps 1 - 5. Under what conditions do the two points (**A, B**) and (**B, A**) appear to be mirror images in the line $y = x$?

AUTHOR'S NOTE

The first use of calculators in the classroom created concern among educators. Consequently, research was undertaken to determine the effect of their use on learning. Numerous studies have shown that the use of calculators does not harm the study of mathematics and actually improves achievment. The Calculator Information Center at Ohio State University reported that most students learn and master computation in the early years of studying mathematics, it's problem solving with which we all have difficulty. Calculators can improve problem solving by facilitating the application of computational skills.

The first pocket caluclator available in the consumer marketplace was sold for $249.00 in September, 1971. Annual retail sales of calculators are now in the range of a trillion dollars. With the introduction of versatile, sophisticated, scientific graphing and business calculators in the 1990s, annual sales of calculators in the early 21st century are expected to exceed this.

Recommended reading - IMP Support: *Texas Instruments TI-83®Graphing Calculator Guidebook.*

OBJECTIVE 2.2

Given a function $y = f(x)$ which has an inverse function, find the inverse function by solving the equation $x = f(y)$ for y.

DISCUSSION

Suppose that f is a function specified by an equation $y = f(x)$ and that f has an inverse function g. To find the value of g at a number x, we must find the number y for which $f(y) = x$. Then, $y = g(x)$. In Objective 2.1 we found $g(x)$ by solving the equation $x = f(y)$ graphically. Sometimes the equation $x = f(y)$ can be solved algebraically for y to get an explicit equation $y = g(x)$ for the inverse function.

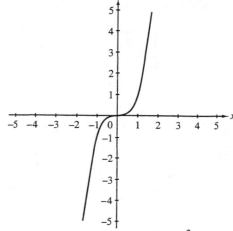

To make these ideas specific, consider the function $f(x) = x^3$. When we apply the Horizontal Line Test to the graph of $y = x^3$ in Figure 2.31 we see that f has an inverse function g.

To find $g(8)$, for example, we must find the number y for which $f(y) = 8$. Since $f(y) = y^3$, the equation to be solved is $y^3 = 8$. The solution to this equation is

$$y = \sqrt[3]{8} = 2, \quad \text{so,} \quad g(8) = 2.$$

Figure 2.31 Graph of $f(x) = x^3$

In the same way, $g(-5)$ is the number y for which $y^3 = -5$. The solution to this equation is

$$y = \sqrt[3]{-5} = -1.709975947$$

so

$$g(-5) = \sqrt[3]{-5} = -1.709975947.$$

For each number x, $g(x)$ is found by solving the equation $f(y) = x$ for y. Since, $f(y) = y^3$ the equation to be solved is $y^3 = x$ and the equation for y is $y = \sqrt[3]{x}$. Therefore, the inverse function is $g(x) = \sqrt[3]{x}$.

Suppose that a function f has an inverse function g. The algebraic process for finding g is best organized in three steps.

Step 1. Write an equation $y = f(x)$ for the function.

Step 2. Interchange x and y in the equation $y = f(x)$ to get $x = f(y)$.

Step 3. Solve $x = f(y)$ for y. The resulting equation $y = g(x)$ gives the inverse function.

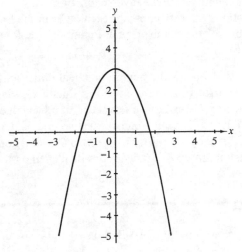

Figure 2.32 Graph of $f(x) = 3 - x^2$

This three step process cannot produce a function when the original function f does not have an inverse function. For instance, consider the function $f(x) = 3 - x^2$. The graph of f is shown in Figure 2.32. When we apply the Horizontal Line Test we see that $f(x) = 3 - x^2$ does not have an inverse function. Follow the process for finding an equation for the inverse function and see where difficulties arise.

Step 1. Write the equation $y = 3 - x^2$.

Step 2. Interchange x and y to get $x = 3 - y^2$.

Step 3. Solve for y.
$$y^2 = 3 - x$$
$$y = \pm\sqrt{3 - x}$$

Both the $+$ sign and the $-$ sign give a value for y. There are two y-values for each x-value. Hence, this equation does not specify a function! In particular, it does not give an inverse function for $f(x) = 3 - x^2$.

A practical difficulty can also arise. It is not always possible to solve the equation $x = f(y)$ for y. For instance, the function $f(x) = x^3 + x - 2$ has an inverse. This can be seen by applying the Horizontal Line Test to the graph of f shown in Figure 2.33. Solving the equation $x = y^3 + y - 2$ for y, however, is extremely difficult.

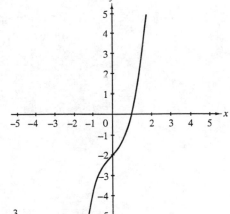

Figure 2.33 Graph of $f(x) = x^3 + x - 2$

CALCULATOR COMMENTARY

Most graphics calculators, and the TI-83® in particular, do not perform symbolic manipulations and cannot be used directly to solve an equation $x = f(y)$ for y. However, the machine's graphical capabilities can sometimes be used to check whether the function derived by solving $x = f(y)$ is actually the inverse function for f. (If it isn't, an error was made solving $f(y) = x$ for y!) Graph $f(x)$, the line $y = x$, and your candidate for the inverse function in a square viewing window. If the graphs of the two functions are reflections of each other in the line $y = x$, then the function you found is indeed the inverse of the original function. If not, the function you found is not the inverse function for f.

This graphical test for pairs of inverse functions is always valid but has practical limitations. To see whether the graphs of two functions are mirror images, one needs a square viewing window that shows a complete graph of each function. Often large intervals of x and y values are needed in such a viewing window. In such a large viewing window, the two graphs may not be represented accurately enough to tell whether they are mirror images. In this situation, you should have little confidence in any conclusion drawn from the graphs displayed on the calculator screen.

SUMMARY

Suppose that the function $y = f(x)$ has an inverse function. To find an equation for the inverse function $y = g(x)$, solve the equation $x = f(y)$ for y.

EXAMPLES

Example 1: Find an equation $y = g(x)$ for the inverse function for $f(x) = 2x^3 - 6$.

Solution 1: *Step 1.* Write an equation $y = f(x)$ for the function.
$$y = 2x^3 - 6$$

Step 2. Interchange x and y in the equation $y = f(x)$ to get
$$x = 2y^3 - 6.$$

Step 3. Solve for y.
$$2y^3 = x + 6 \implies y^3 = \frac{x + 6}{2}$$
$$y = \sqrt[3]{\frac{x + 6}{2}}$$

The inverse function is $g(x) = \sqrt[3]{\dfrac{x + 6}{2}}$.

Example 2: In Example 1, the inverse of $f(x) = 2x^3 - 6$ is found to be $g(x) = 3\sqrt{\dfrac{x + 6}{2}}$.
Verify graphically that these functions are indeed inverses.

Solution 2:   First, set your TI-83® to Function mode by selecting **Func** under the **MODE** menu.

Next, enter **Y1 = 2X³ - 6, Y2 = X** , and **Y3 =** $\sqrt[3]{}$ **((X + 6) / 2)** on the **Y=** screen.

Third, establish a **square viewing window**. Select the WINDOW menu and enter numerical values for **Xmin, Xmax, Ymin,** and **Ymax** so that

$$2(\text{Xmax} - \text{Xmin})/3 = \text{Ymax} - \text{Ymin}.$$

For example, you might choose

Xmin = -12, Xmax = 6, Ymin = -8 and **Ymax = 4.**

Finally, press GRAPH to generate the graphs.

Since the graphs of $f(x) = 2x^3 - 6$ and $g(x) = 3\sqrt{\dfrac{x + 6}{2}}$ are the reflections of each other through the line $y = x$, these functions are indeed inverse functions.

Example 3: Find an equation $y = G(x)$ for the inverse function for $F(x) = \dfrac{5x + 4}{2x - 7}$.

Solution 3:   *Step 1.*   Write an equation $y = F(x)$ for the function.

$$y = \frac{5x + 4}{2x - 7}$$

Step 2.   Interchange x and y in the equation to get

$$x = \frac{5y + 4}{2y - 7}.$$

Step 3.   Solve for y.

$$x(2y - 7) = 5y + 4$$
$$2xy - 7x = 5y + 4$$
$$2xy - 5y = 7x + 4$$
$$(2x - 5)y = 7x + 4$$
$$y = \frac{7x + 4}{2x - 5}$$

The inverse function is $G(x) = \dfrac{7x + 4}{2x - 5}$.

Example 4: Find an equation $y = P(x)$ for the inverse function for $R(x) = \dfrac{x}{\sqrt[3]{2x^3 + 1}}$.

Solution 4: *Step 1.* Write an equation $y = R(x)$ for the function.

$$y = \frac{x}{\sqrt[3]{2x^3 + 1}}$$

Step 2. Interchange x and y in the equation to get

$$x = \frac{y}{\sqrt[3]{2y^3 + 1}}.$$

Step 3. Solve for y.

$$x^3 = \frac{y^3}{2y^3 + 1}$$

$$x^3\left(2y^3 + 1\right) = y^3$$

$$2x^3 y^3 + x^3 = y^3$$

$$y^3 - 2x^3 y^3 = x^3$$

$$y^3\left(1 - 2x^3\right) = x^3$$

$$y^3 = \frac{x^3}{1 - 2x^3}$$

$$y = \sqrt[3]{\frac{x^3}{1 - 2x^3}} = \frac{x}{\sqrt[3]{1 - 2x^3}}$$

The inverse function is $P(x) = \dfrac{x}{\sqrt[3]{1 - 2x^3}}$.

PRACTICE PROBLEMS

In problems 1 - 5, find an equation for the inverse function. Verify that you have found the correct inverse function by examining the graphs of the function given and the function you computed in the specified viewing window on the TI-83®.

1. $S(x) = \dfrac{1}{2}x + 2$ Viewing window: $-5.7 \le x \le 5.7$ and $-3.8 \le y \le 3.8$.

2. $F(x) = (x - 2)^3$ Viewing window: $-9 \le x \le 9$ and $-6 \le y \le 6$.

3. $f(x) = \dfrac{x}{x + 1}$ Viewing window: $-6 \le x \le 6$ and $-4 \le y \le 4$. (Graph in **Dot** mode.)

4. $p(x) = \sqrt[3]{1 + x^3}$ Viewing window: $-4.7 \le x \le 4.7$ and $-3.1 \le y \le 3.1$

5. $R(x) = \dfrac{1}{1 - \sqrt[3]{x}}$ Viewing window: $-9.4 \le x \le 9.4$ and $-6.2 \le y \le 6.2$.

In problems 6 - 20, find an equation for the inverse function for each of the following functions.

6. $f(x) = 7x^3 - 4$

7. $h(x) = \dfrac{2x - 5}{7x - 4}$

8. $p(x) = \sqrt[3]{3x - 7}$

9. $r(x) = (2x + 3)^5$

10. $S(x) = \dfrac{2}{\sqrt[3]{1 - x}}$

11. $\iota(x) = \dfrac{1}{3}\sqrt[7]{x} - \dfrac{1}{3}$

12. $s(x) = \dfrac{7}{10x^5 - 3}$

13. $y = \dfrac{4\sqrt[3]{x}}{-5\sqrt[3]{x} + 3}$

14. $F(x) = \sqrt[7]{\dfrac{x - 4}{5}}$

15. $y = \left(\dfrac{2x - 1}{3x + 4}\right)^3$

16. $h(x) = \dfrac{2x}{\sqrt[3]{3 - x^3}}$

17. $g(x) = \dfrac{3x^7 + 4}{2x^7}$

18. $r(x) = 2x^5 - 15$

19. $y = (x - 5)^7 - 1$

20. $G(x) = -\dfrac{1}{12}x + \dfrac{7}{12}$

OBJECTIVE 2.3

    (a) Given a number $b > 0$, $b \neq 1$, sketch the graph of the logarithmic function base b,
        $f(x) = \log_b x$.
    (b) Given the graph of a logarithmic function $f(x) = \log_b x$, estimate b.

DISCUSSION

    In Unit 1 we defined an exponential function $f(x) = b^x$ for each positive number b different from 1. Figure 2.34 shows the graph of a typical exponential function with base $b < 1$. Figure 2.35 shows the graph of a typical exponential function with base $b > 1$. Every exponential function with base $b < 1$ is decreasing. Every exponential function with base $b > 1$ is increasing. By applying the Horizontal Line Test we see that every exponential function has an inverse function. The inverse of an exponential function is called a **logarithmic function.** For each positive number b different from 1, the **logarithmic function base b,** denoted $\log_b x$, is defined to be the inverse of the exponential function base b. The letters $\log_b$ are like the symbol f in the notation $f(x)$.

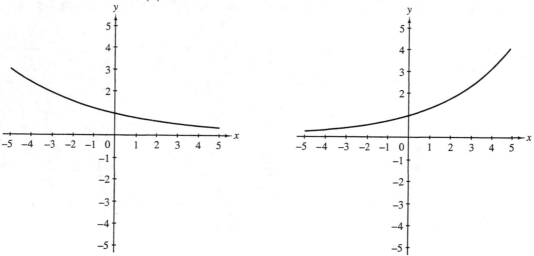

Figure 2.34 Graph of $f(x) = b^x$, $0 < b < 1$ *Figure 2.35* Graph of $f(x) = b^x$, $b > 1$

    According to the Reflection Principle the graph of a logarithmic function is the reflection through the line $y = x$ of the graph of the exponential function with the same base. The graphs of typical logarithmic functions are shown in Figures 2.36 and 2.37. These graphs are the reflection through the line $y = x$ of the graphs of the exponential functions in Figures 2.34 and 2.35.

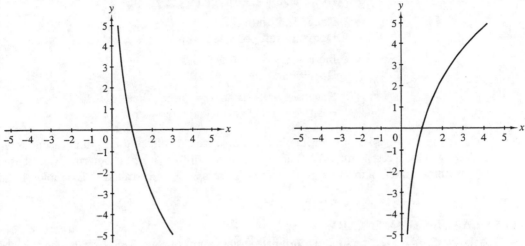

Figure 2.36 Graph of $f(x) = \log_b x$, $0 < b < 1$ *Figure 2.37* Graph of $f(x) = \log_b x$, $b > 1$

Implicit in the Reflection Principle is the idea that information about an exponential function $f(x) = b^x$ can be translated into information about its inverse function $g(x) = \log_b x$. From Objective 1.4, we know that the graph of any exponential function $f(x) = b^x$ has the following properties.

- y-intercept is 1.
- $(1, b)$ and $\left(-1, \dfrac{1}{b}\right)$ are on the graph.
- Domain is all numbers.
  Range is all positive numbers.
- Increasing when $b > 1$.
  Decreasing when $b < 1$.
- Negative x-axis is an asymptote when $b > 1$.
  Positive x-axis is an asymptote when $b < 1$.

The reflection process transforms these properties of the graphs of exponential functions into properties of the graphs of logarithmic functions. As Figures 2.36 and 2.37 show, reflecting a graph with y-intercept 1 through $y = x$ produces a graph with x-intercept 1. The reflection process interchanges the domain and the range. A graph which is increasing (decreasing) is reflected into another graph which is increasing (decreasing). Horizontal asymptotes are transformed into vertical asymptotes. Thus, the graph of a logarithmic function $g(x) = \log_b x$ inherits the following properties from its companion $f(x) = b^x$.

- x-intercept is 1.
- $(b, 1)$ and $\left(\dfrac{1}{b}, -1\right)$ are on the graph.
- Range is all numbers.
  Domain is all positive numbers.
- Increasing when $b > 1$.
  Decreasing when $b < 1$.
- Negative y-axis is an asymptote when $b > 1$.
  Positive y-axis is an asymptote when $b < 1$.

Using these properties of logarithmic functions, we can sketch their graphs accurately after plotting only three points. We can also use this information to determine the base of a logarithmic function from its graph. These processes are illustrated in Examples 1 and 2.

CALCULATOR COMMENTARY

The graph of $\log_b x$ in a square coordinate system (units of equal length on the coordinate axes) is the mirror image of the graph of $y = b^x$ through the line $y = x$. The program **DRWINVRS** given in the Calculator Commentary on Objective 2.1 is an ideal tool for exploring the relationship between the graphs of the inverse functions $y = b^x$ and $y = \log_b x$. Enter a *specific* exponential function as **Y1** and then execute **DRWINVRS**. For most exponential functions, the values **Xmin = -5** and **Xmax = 5** will work well as the minimum and maximum values for the independent variable. The machine will pause after generating the graph of $y = b^x$. Press ENTER to continue. The graphs of $y = x$ and $y = \log_b x$ will be generated. Because the program established a square viewing window, the graph of $y = \log_b x$ appears as a mirror image of the graph of $y = b^x$ through the line $y = x$.

Use the program **DRWINVRS** to explore how the base of a logarithmic function effects the shape of its graph. Graph some logarithmic functions with base smaller than 1 and some with base greater than 1. How can you recognize the graph of a logarithmic function with a very large base? With a very small base? Can you recognize the "signature" properties of a logarithmic function described in the Discussion in these graphs?

Once a graph has been identified as that of a logarithmic function $y = \log_b x$, the base b can be found from the first coordinate of the specific points $\left(\dfrac{1}{b}, -1\right)$ and $(b, 1)$ which both lie on the graph. In Practice Problem 11 you are invited to use the TI-83® to explore finding the equation for a logarithmic function from its graph.

SUMMARY

1. The **logarithm function base** b, $f(x) = \log_b x$, is the inverse of the exponential function base b, $g(x) = b^x$.

2. The graph of $y = \log_b x$ is the reflection of the graph of $y = b^x$ through the line $y = x$.

3. The graph of $y = \log_b x$ has these properties.

   - x-intercept is 1.

   - $(b, 1)$ and $\left(\dfrac{1}{b}, -1\right)$ are on the graph.

   - Range is all numbers.
     Domain is all positive numbers.

   - Increasing when $b > 1$.
     Decreasing when $b < 1$.

   - Negative y-axis is an asymptote when $b > 1$.
     Positive y-axis is an asymptote when $b < 1$.

EXAMPLES

Example 1: Sketch the graph of $y = \log_2 x$.

Solution 1: The graph of $y = \log_2 x$ is the reflection of the graph of $y = 2^x$ through the line $y = x$. Instead of reflecting the graph of $y = 2^x$, use the properties of the graphs of logarithmic functions from the Summary and the fact that the base of this logarithmic function is $b = 2$ to sketch the graph.

From the first property, the x-intercept of the graph is 1. Plot the point $(1, 0)$. From the second property, the points $(2, 1)$ and $\left(\dfrac{1}{2}, -1\right)$ are on the graph. Plot these points.

The domain of this function is all positive numbers and its range is all real numbers. Thus, its graph lies entirely to the right of the vertical axis and extends upward, downward and to the right without bound.

Because $1 < b$, the function is increasing and has the negative y-axis as an asymptote.

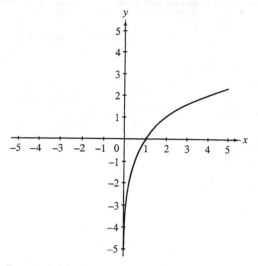

Figure 2.38 Graph of $y = \log_2 x$

Through the three points plotted, draw a smooth curve that lies entirely to the right of the y-axis, has the negative y-axis as an asymptote, and bends continually downward as it increases from left to right. Of course, you can't show the function's entire domain (the positive half of the x-axis) or entire range (all of the y-axis) in your graph. This curve, shown in Figure 2.38, is the graph of the function. Compare this graph with the graph of the exponential function in Figure 2.35.

Example 2: Sketch the graph of $y = \log_{2/3} x$.

Solution 2:

The graph of $y = \log_{2/3} x$ is the reflection of the graph of $y = \left(\frac{2}{3}\right)^x$ through the line $y = x$. Instead of reflecting the graph of $y = \left(\frac{2}{3}\right)^x$, use the properties of the graphs of logarithmic functions from the Summary and the fact that the base of this logarithmic function is $b = \frac{2}{3}$ to sketch the graph.

From the first property, the x-intercept of the graph is 1. Plot the point $(1, 0)$. From the second property, the points $\left(\frac{2}{3}, 1\right)$ and $\left(\frac{3}{2}, -1\right)$ are on the graph. Plot these points.

The domain of this function is all positive numbers and its range is all real numbers. Thus, its graph lies entirely to the right of the vertical axis and extends upward, downward and to the right without bound.

Because $0 < b < 1$, the function is decreasing and has the positive y-axis as an asymptote.

Through the three points plotted, draw a smooth curve that lies entirely to the right of the y-axis, has the positive y-axis as an asymptote, and bends continually upward as it decreases from left to right. Of course, you can't show the function's entire domain (the positive half of the x-axis) or entire range (all of the y-axis) in your graph. This curve, shown in Figure 2.39, is the graph of the function. Compare this graph with the graph of the exponential function in Figure 2.36.

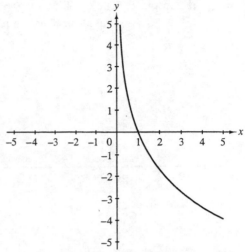

Figure 2.39 Graph of $y = \log_{2/3} x$

Example 3: The graph of a logarithmic function $f(x) = \log_b x$ is shown in Figure 2.40. What is the equation for this function?

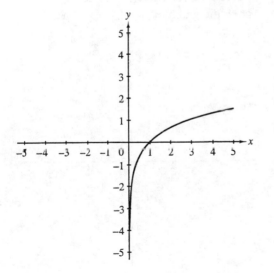

Figure 2.40

Solution 3:

This graph has the characteristic properties of a logarithmic function given in the Summary. The points $\left(\frac{1}{b}, -1\right)$ and $(b, 1)$ are always on the graph of $f(x) = \log_b x$. Since this function is increasing, it is easier to find $(b, 1)$. On the graph we see that this point is $(3, 1)$. Therefore, the base for this logarithmic function is $b = 3$ and the equation is

$$f(x) = \log_3 x.$$

Example 4: The graph of a logarithmic function $f(x) = \log_b x$ is shown in Figure 2.41. What is the equation for this function?

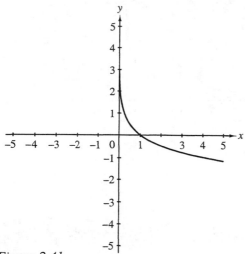

Figure 2.41

Solution 4:

This graph has the characteristic properties of a logarithmic function as described in the Summary .

The points $\left(\frac{1}{b}, -1\right)$ and $(b, 1)$ always lie on the graph of $f(x) = \log_b x$. Since this function is decreasing, it is easier to find $\left(\frac{1}{b}, -1\right)$. On the graph we see that this point is $(4, -1)$. Therefore, $\frac{1}{b} = 4$ and $b = \frac{1}{4}$. The base for this logarithmic function is $b = \frac{1}{4}$ and its equation is

$$f(x) = \log_{1/4} x.$$

PRACTICE PROBLEMS

1. Use the coordinate system in Figure 2.42 to sketch the graph of $y = \log_{1/2} x$.

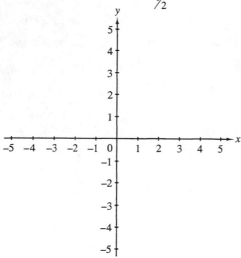

Figure 2.42

2. Use the coordinate system in Figure 2.43 to sketch the graph of $h(x) = \log_{3/2} x$.

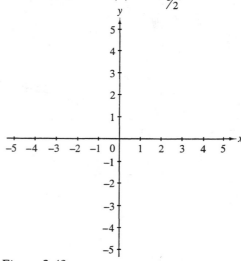

Figure 2.43

3. Use the coordinate system in Figure 2.44 to sketch the graph of $y = \log_4 x$.

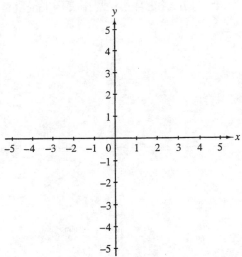

Figure 2.44

4. Use the coordinate system in Figure 2.45 to sketch the graph of $g(x) = \log_{1/3} x$.

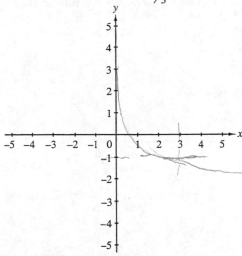

Figure 2.45

5. The graph of a logarithmic function is shown in Figure 2.46.
Find the equation for this function.

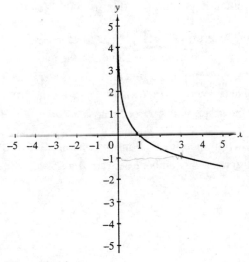

Figure 2.46

6. The graph of a logarithmic function is shown in Figure 2.47.
Find the equation for this function.

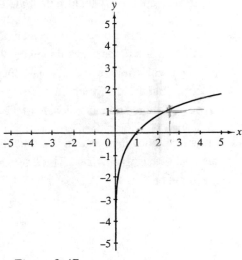

Figure 2.47

$$\frac{1}{b} = \frac{3}{1} \qquad b = 3$$

7. The graph of a logarithmic function is shown in Figure 2.48.
    Find the equation for this function.

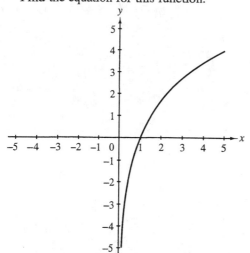

Figure 2.48

8. The graph of a logarithmic function is shown in Figure 2.49.
    Find the equation for this function.

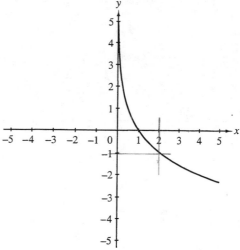

Figure 2.49

9. Enter **Y1 = logx** on the **Y=** screen of your TI-83®. Press ⟨**ZOOM**⟩, ⟨ **4** ⟩ to generate the graph of this function in the decimal viewing window. Verify that $b = 10$ is the base of the common logarithm function by finding the base for the common logarithm function from this graph.

10. Enter **Y1 = lnx** on the **Y=** screen of your TI-83®. Press ⟨**ZOOM**⟩, ⟨ **4** ⟩ to generate the graph of this function in the decimal viewing window. Find an approximate value for the number e by finding the base for the natural logarithm function from its graph. To find the base to several decimal places, examine the graph in successively smaller viewing windows by "zooming in" and "tracing" more and more closely to the point on the graph with y-coordinate 1.

11. Enter the following program into your TI-83®. (Step by step instructions for entering **GRPHLGBX** are given after this problem.) This program randomly chooses a number b between 0 and 5 and displays the graph of $y = \log_b x$.

```
PROGRAM:GRPHLGBX
:Func
:FnOff
:-3.9 → Xmin
:5.5 → Xmax
:1 → Xscl
:-3.1 → Ymin
:3.1 → Ymax
:1 → Yscl
:.1iPart ( 50rand ) → B
:" ln ( X ) / ln ( B ) " → Y1
:DispGraph
```

Execute **GRPHLGBX**. Press PRGM . **EXEC** (for execute) will be highlighted. Scroll to **GRPHLGBX** and press ENTER . The calculator will display

```
prgmGRPHLGBX
```

Press ENTER to begin execution of the program. The graph of a logarithmic function will be generated immediately. Your task is to figure out the base of the logarithmic function shown in the graph. Use TRACE to locate the points on the graph with y-coordinate 1 or -1. Determine the base b of the logarithmic function from the x-coordinate of one of these points.

Check the value you determined for the base of the logarithmic function in the graph by recalling the number **B** from the calculator's memory. (Press 2nd , [QUIT] , then ALPHA , (B) , ENTER to recall **B**.) Press GRAPH to return to the graph of the function.

To investigate the graph of another logarithmic function, press PRGM and execute **GRPHLGBX** again. If you have not recalled **B** , you can repeat the program by pressing 2nd , [QUIT] , ENTER .

Step by Step Instructions for Entering the Program GRPHLGBX.

Step 1. Press PRGM (row 4, column 3). Highlight **NEW**. Press 1 or ENTER .

Step 2. Notice that the cursor is a blinking reverse letter "**A**" indicating the calculator is in alphabetic mode. When a key is pressed, the letter printed above it in green will be entered. Enter the name of the program by typing **GRPHLGBX**. Then press ENTER .

Step 3. Press MODE (row 2, column 2). Scroll to the fourth line of the menu so **Func** is highlighted. Press ENTER . Press ENTER again to move to the next line of the program.

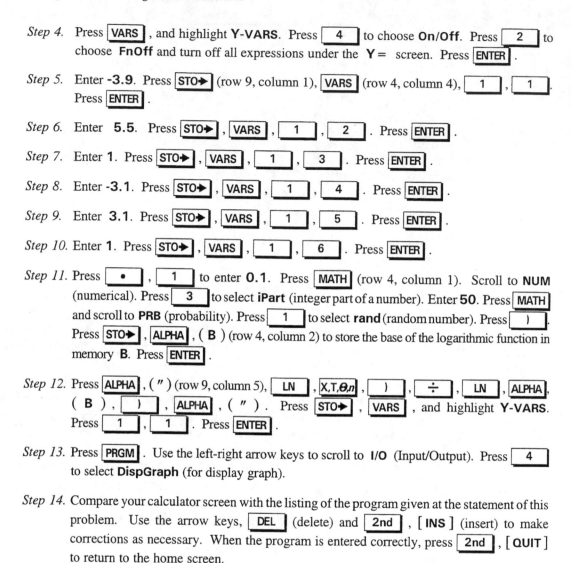

Step 4. Press [VARS], and highlight **Y-VARS**. Press [4] to choose **On/Off**. Press [2] to choose **FnOff** and turn off all expressions under the **Y=** screen. Press [ENTER].

Step 5. Enter **-3.9**. Press [STO▶] (row 9, column 1), [VARS] (row 4, column 4), [1], [1]. Press [ENTER].

Step 6. Enter **5.5**. Press [STO▶], [VARS], [1], [2]. Press [ENTER].

Step 7. Enter **1**. Press [STO▶], [VARS], [1], [3]. Press [ENTER].

Step 8. Enter **-3.1**. Press [STO▶], [VARS], [1], [4]. Press [ENTER].

Step 9. Enter **3.1**. Press [STO▶], [VARS], [1], [5]. Press [ENTER].

Step 10. Enter **1**. Press [STO▶], [VARS], [1], [6]. Press [ENTER].

Step 11. Press [.], [1] to enter **0.1**. Press [MATH] (row 4, column 1). Scroll to **NUM** (numerical). Press [3] to select **iPart** (integer part of a number). Enter **50**. Press [MATH] and scroll to **PRB** (probability). Press [1] to select **rand** (random number). Press [)]. Press [STO▶], [ALPHA], (**B**) (row 4, column 2) to store the base of the logarithmic function in memory **B**. Press [ENTER].

Step 12. Press [ALPHA], (") (row 9, column 5), [LN], [X,T,θ,n], [)], [÷], [LN], [ALPHA], (**B**), [)], [ALPHA], ("). Press [STO▶], [VARS], and highlight **Y-VARS**. Press [1], [1]. Press [ENTER].

Step 13. Press [PRGM]. Use the left-right arrow keys to scroll to **I/O** (Input/Output). Press [4] to select **DispGraph** (for display graph).

Step 14. Compare your calculator screen with the listing of the program given at the statement of this problem. Use the arrow keys, [DEL] (delete) and [2nd], [INS] (insert) to make corrections as necessary. When the program is entered correctly, press [2nd], [QUIT] to return to the home screen.

OBJECTIVE 2.4

Given two functions $y = f(x)$ and $y = g(x)$, determine whether f and g are inverse functions by computing their compositions.

DISCUSSION

Inverse functions occur in pairs. If g is the inverse function for f, then f is also the inverse function for g. A comparison of the graph of a function with the graph of its inverse will show why this is true.

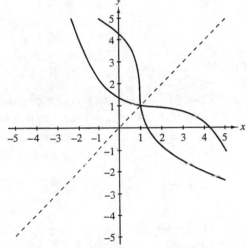

By the Reflection Principle the graph of g, the inverse function for f, is the reflection of the graph of f through the diagonal line $y = x$, as in Figure 2.50. The graph of the inverse for g, then, is the reflection of the graph of g through this line. Thus, the graph of the inverse for g is the **reflection of the reflection** of the graph of f.

Two reflections return us to the graph of f so the graph of the inverse function for g is exactly the graph of f. This means that if g is the inverse for f, then f is also the inverse for g.

Figure 2.50 Graph of f and the inverse of f

The Reflection Principle describes the geometric relationship between pairs of inverse functions. There is also an algebraic relationship between pairs of inverse functions. It is described in terms of composition of functions (see Objective 1.5). We can discover this algebraic relationship by analyzing the graphs of a pair of inverse functions.

Suppose that f is a function, as shown in the graph in Figure 2.51, which has an inverse function g. A typical number a in the domain of f is marked on the x-axis in the figure. According

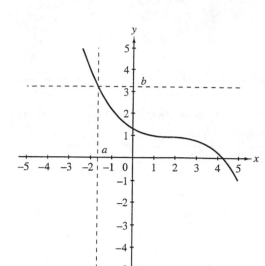

Figure 2.51 Evaluation of $g(f(a))$

to the procedure in Objective 1.2 for evaluating $f(a)$ graphically, $f(a) = b$ is the number indicated on the y-axis. Now, b is in the domain of g, which is just the range of f. By the procedure in Objective 2.1 for evaluating $g(b)$ graphically, $g(b) = a$. Since $b = f(a)$, we have $g(f(a)) = g(b) = a$.

This reasoning will apply to every number in the domain of f. We conclude that for every number x in the domain of f, $g(f(x)) = x$. Since it is also true that f is the inverse function for g, we also conclude that for every x in the domain of g,
$$f(g(x)) = x.$$

We now have established **Proposition 1:**

   If f and g are inverse functions, then

- for every x in the domain of f, $g \circ f(x) = g(f(x)) = x$, and
- for every x in the domain of g, $f \circ g(x) = f(g(x)) = x$.

Suppose that g and f are functions such that for every x in the domain of f,
$$g \circ f(x) = g(f(x)) = x.$$

Intuitively, this equation says that g reverses the procedure for f. In this situation one might reasonably expect that f and g must be inverse functions. Unfortunately, this is not the case as can be seen from the functions
$$f(x) = \sqrt{x} \quad \text{and} \quad g(x) = x^2.$$

For every x in the domain of f, that is, for every $x \geq 0$,
$$g \circ f(x) = g(f(x)) = g(\sqrt{x}) = (\sqrt{x})^2 = x.$$

However, the function $g(x) = x^2$ does not have an inverse function because its graph (which is a parabola) does not pass the Horizontal Line Test. Since g does not have an inverse, g and f cannot be a pair of inverse functions. To be certain that g and f are inverses, we must know not only that g reverses the procedure for f, but also that f reverses the procedure for g.

More precisely, we have **Proposition 2:**
> If two functions f and g have the properties that
> - for every x in the domain of g, $f(g(x)) = x$, and
> - for every x in the domain of f, $g(f(x)) = x$,
>
> then, f and g are inverse functions.

Propositions 1 and 2 give a complete algebraic description of the relationship between inverse functions. Using this relationship we can recognize pairs of inverse functions from equations for the functions without relying on their graphs.

We combine the statements of these two propositions into the COMPOSITION PRINCIPLE:
> Two functions f and g are inverses if and only if for every x in the domain
> of f, $g \circ f(x) = g(f(x)) = x$, and for every x in the domain of g,
> $f \circ g(x) = f(g(x)) = x$.

The equations $g \circ f(x) = x$ and $f \circ g(x) = x$ are called identities because when f and g are inverses, these equations are true for all values of x for which the compositions are defined.

The COMPOSITION PRINCIPLE is used to identify pairs of inverse functions which are given by equations. If $f \circ g(x) = x$ and $g \circ f(x) = x$, then, f and g are inverses. Otherwise, they are not.

CALCULATOR COMMENTARY

Since most advanced scientific calculators (and the TI-83® in particular) do not perform algebraic manipulations, they can't be used to manipulate algebraic symbols or simplify compositions as required in this objective. However, their graphing and programming capabilities can be used to investigate whether a pair of functions are inverses by numerical and graphical, rather than symbolic, means.

According to the Composition Principle functions f and g are inverses if and only if *for every number* x in the domain of g, $f \circ g(x) = x$ **and** *for every* x in the domain of f, $g \circ f(x) = x$. If we find even one number x in the relevant domain for which evaluation does not produce the number x, then f and g are not inverse functions. On the other hand, if for every x value that we examine, evaluation produces the number x back again, we can only tentatively conclude that f and g are inverse functions because there may be untested x values which will not produce x back again. However, if we find that for closely spaced values of x selected from across a large part of the domain of g, $f \circ g(x) = x$ and that for closely spaced values of x selected from across a large part of the domain of f, $g \circ f(x) = x$, we are willing, on experimental if not mathematical grounds, to believe that f and g are inverse functions.

Let's investigate whether the functions $f(x) = \dfrac{x}{\sqrt{1 + x^2}}$ and $g(x) = \dfrac{x}{\sqrt{1 - x^2}}$ are inverse functions numerically.

We would like to know whether it is true that

- for every number x in the domain of g, $f \circ g(x) = x$, and
- for every number x in the domain of f, $g \circ f(x) = x$.

The domain of g consists of the numbers x strictly between -1 and 1, so we can state the first question in another way. Is it true that for every number x with $-1 < x < 1$, $f \circ g(x) = x$? The domain of f is all real numbers, so the second question can be stated like this: Is it true that for every real number x, $g \circ f(x) = x$? If the answer to both questions is "Yes", then f and g are inverse functions. Otherwise, they are not inverse functions.

Suppose we evaluated $f \circ g(x)$ for a large number of values of x strictly between -1 and 1 and found that for every x that we examined $f \circ g(x) = x$. Suppose further, that we evaluated $g \circ f(x)$ for a large number of values of x and found that for every one of them and $g \circ f(x) = x$. Would we not then be fairly confident that f and g are inverses? This approach seems impractical because the prospect of evaluating these two compositions for a large number of x values is so onerous. But with the TI-83® this approach is practical!

To program the TI-83® to evaluate these compositions, on the **Y=** screen enter $f(x) = \dfrac{x}{\sqrt{1 + x^2}}$ as **Y1** and $g(x) = \dfrac{x}{\sqrt{1 - x^2}}$ as **Y2**. Then enter **Y3 = Y1(Y2(X))** by entering the right side exactly as it appears in print. (To enter **Y1** press VARS (row 4, column 4), scroll to **Y-VARS**, and press 1 , 1 . Enter **Y2** by pressing VARS (row 4, column 4), scroll to **Y-VARS**, and press 1 , 2 .) In the same way, enter **Y4 = Y2(Y1(X))**. Because **f(x)** is entered as **Y1** and **g(x)** is entered as **Y2**, **Y3** is the composition $f(g(x))$ and **Y4** is the composition $g(f(x))$.

To evaluate $f \circ g(.5)$, for example, after returning to the home screen just enter **Y3(.5)** by pressing VARS , scrolling to **Y-VARS**, pressing 1 , 3 , and then entering the number **.5** enclosed in parentheses so **Y3(.5)** is displayed. Finally, press ENTER . If you have done everything correctly, the calculator will display **0.5** as the result. To evaluate $f(g(x))$ for another value of x, press 2nd , [**ENTRY**] (row 10, column 5) to recall the entry **Y3(.5)** to the display. Edit this entry by using the left and right arrows to place the cursor over the decimal point, using the DEL key (row 2, column 3) to delete **.5**, and inserting another value for x. Then press ENTER to evaluate $f \circ g$ again. Repeat this procedure for values of x between -1 and 1 until you are confident that for every x in the domain of g the function value $f(g(x))$ is the same as the number x that was input. (What happens when you input a value for x that is not between -1 and 1? Why?)

The TI-83's **TABLE** feature automates the tedious process of repeatedly entering x-values and generates a table of function values for values of the independent variable chosen according to your directions. To generate a table, follow these steps. First, go to the **Y=** screen and turn off all the functions except those you want to have listed in the table. To turn on a function that is turned off, position the cursor over the equal sign and press enter. When the equal sign is in reverse type, the function is turned on. In this situation, only **Y3** and **Y4** should be turned on. Next, press ⎡ **2nd** ⎤, [**TblSet**] (row 1, column 2) to access the **TABLE SETUP** menu. Enter **TblStart = -1** and **ΔTbl = .05** to specify that the first entry of the table will be for **x = -1** and the x-values in successive entries will differ by **.05**. Now press ⎡ **2nd** ⎤, [**TABLE**] (row 1, column 5) to generate the table specified.

As the column headings indicate, in the table successive x-values are listed in the first column and corresponding values of the functions that are turned on on the **Y=** screen are listed in the following columns. In this case, in every row corresponding to an x-value between -1 and 1, the same number should appear in all three columns. For values of x greater than or equal to 1 or less than or equal to -1, the word **ERROR** appears in the **Y3** column because x is not in the domain of **Y3** $= f \circ g$. For all x-values, entries in the **X** and **Y4** columns are identical. For every number x in the table, if x is in the domain of g, $f \circ g(x) = x$. If x in the domain of f, then $g \circ f(x) = x$. This table provides compelling evidence that f and g are inverse functions. If you would like more compelling evidence, generate the table again with a smaller value for **ΔTbl**, for example **ΔTbl = .001**, so many more x-values are included.

Suppose that f and g are a pair of inverse functions. Then for every x in the domain of g, $f \circ g(x) = x$. Thus, for values of x in the domain of g, the equation $y = f \circ g(x)$ is the same as the equation $y = x$. This means that the graph of $f \circ g(x)$ coincides with the line $y = x$! Conversely, suppose that f and g are two functions and that the graph of $y = f \circ g(x)$ coincides with the graph of the line $y = x$. The only way this can happen is for $f \circ g(x)$ to be equal to x for every x in its domain. Thus, $f \circ g(x) = x$ for every x in its domain if and only if the graph of $y = f \circ g(x)$ coincides with the graph of the line $y = x$. Similarly, the graph of $g \circ f(x)$ coincides with the line $y = x$ if and only if for every x in the domain of f, $g \circ f(x) = x$. Thus, functions f and g are inverse functions if and only if the graphs of their compositions coincide with the graph of $y = x$.

Return to the functions discussed above. On the **Y =** screen, turn off all functions except **Y4** $= g \circ f(x)$. Graph $y = g \circ f(x)$ in the square viewing window **Xmin = -3, Xmax = 3, Ymin = -2, Ymax = 2**. As Figure 2CC.3 shows, the graph of $y = g \circ f(x)$ is the diagonal line $y = x$. Therefore, for all x in the domain of f, $g \circ f(x) = x$.

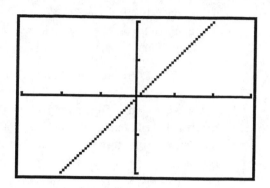

Figure 2CC.3

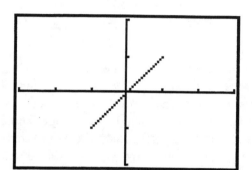

Figure 2CC.4

Now, turn off all functions except **Y3** $= f \circ g(x)$. Graph $y = f \circ g(x)$ in the same square viewing window. The graph of $y = f \circ g(x)$ is the portion of the diagonal line $y = x$ between the points $(-1, -1)$ and $(1, 1)$. Therefore, for all x between -1 and 1 (the x-values in the domain of g), $f \circ g(x) = x$. Thus, g and f are inverse functions.

SUMMARY

1. Inverse functions come in pairs. If f is the inverse for g, then g is the inverse for f.

2. COMPOSITION PRINCIPLE: Two functions f and g are inverses if and only if for every x in the domain of f, $g \circ f(x) = g(f(x)) = x$, and for every x in the domain of g, $f \circ g(x) = f(g(x)) = x$. These equations are called identities because when f and g are inverses, they are true for all values of x for which the compositions are defined.

EXAMPLES

Example 1: Determine whether $f(x) = \dfrac{1}{x - 3}$ and $g(x) = \dfrac{3x + 1}{x}$ are inverse functions by computing their compositions.

Solution 1: According to the Composition Principle, f and g are inverse functions if and only if $f\big(g(x)\big) = x$ and $g\big(f(x)\big) = x$.

Step 1. Determine whether $f\big(g(x)\big) = x$.

$$f\big(g(x)\big) = \frac{1}{g(x) - 3} = \frac{1}{\dfrac{3x + 1}{x} - 3} = \frac{x}{(3x + 1) - 3x} = \frac{x}{1} = x$$

Step 2. Determine whether $g\big(f(x)\big) = x$.

$$g\big(f(x)\big) = \frac{3f(x) + 1}{f(x)} = \frac{3\left(\dfrac{1}{x - 3}\right) + 1}{\left(\dfrac{1}{x - 3}\right)} = \frac{3 + (x - 3)}{1} = \frac{x}{1} = x$$

Since $f\big(g(x)\big) = x$ and $g\big(f(x)\big) = x$, f and g are inverse functions.

Example 2: Determine whether $P(x) = \dfrac{x - 2}{x - 3}$ and $Q(x) = \dfrac{2x - 3}{x - 1}$ are inverse functions by computing their compositions.

Solution 2: According to the Composition Principle, P and Q are inverse functions if and only if $P\big(Q(x)\big) = x$ and $Q\big(P(x)\big) = x$.

Step 1. Determine whether $P\big(Q(x)\big) = x$.

$$P\big(Q(x)\big) = \frac{Q(x) - 2}{Q(x) - 3} = \frac{\left(\dfrac{2x - 3}{x - 1}\right) - 2}{\left(\dfrac{2x - 3}{x - 1}\right) - 3} = \frac{(2x - 3) - 2(x - 1)}{(2x - 3) - 3(x - 1)}$$

$$= \frac{2x - 3 - 2x + 2}{2x - 3 - 3x + 3} = \frac{-1}{-x} = \frac{1}{x} \neq x$$

Since $P\big(Q(x)\big) \neq x$, P and Q are not inverse functions.

Example 3: Determine whether $h(x) = \dfrac{x}{\sqrt{1 + x^2}}$ and $k(x) = \dfrac{x}{\sqrt{1 - x^2}}$ are inverse functions by computing their compositions.

Solution 3: According to the Composition Principle, h and k are inverse functions if and only if $h(k(x)) = x$ and $k(h(x)) = x$.

Step 1. Determine whether $h(k(x)) = x$.

$$h(k(x)) = \frac{k(x)}{\sqrt{1 + (k(x))^2}} = \frac{\dfrac{x}{\sqrt{1-x^2}}}{\sqrt{1 + \left(\dfrac{x}{\sqrt{1-x^2}}\right)^2}} = \frac{\dfrac{x}{\sqrt{1-x^2}}}{\sqrt{1 + \dfrac{x^2}{1-x^2}}}$$

$$= \frac{\dfrac{x}{\sqrt{1-x^2}}}{\sqrt{\dfrac{1}{1-x^2}}} = \frac{\dfrac{x}{\sqrt{1-x^2}}}{\dfrac{1}{\sqrt{1-x^2}}} = \frac{x}{\sqrt{1-x^2}} \cdot \frac{\sqrt{1-x^2}}{1} = x$$

Step 2. Determine whether $k(h(x)) = x$.

$$k(h(x)) = \frac{h(x)}{\sqrt{1 - (h(x))^2}} = \frac{\dfrac{x}{\sqrt{1+x^2}}}{\sqrt{1 - \left(\dfrac{x}{\sqrt{1+x^2}}\right)^2}} = \frac{\dfrac{x}{\sqrt{1+x^2}}}{\sqrt{1 - \dfrac{x^2}{1+x^2}}}$$

$$= \frac{\dfrac{x}{\sqrt{1+x^2}}}{\sqrt{\dfrac{1}{1+x^2}}} = \frac{\dfrac{x}{\sqrt{1+x^2}}}{\dfrac{1}{\sqrt{1+x^2}}} = \frac{x}{\sqrt{1+x^2}} \cdot \frac{\sqrt{1+x^2}}{1} = x$$

Since $h(k(x)) = x$ and $k(h(x)) = x$, h and k are inverse functions.

PRACTICE PROBLEMS

Determine whether the following pairs of functions are inverses by computing their compositions. For several problems, substantiate your conclusion by either generating a table of values for the composite functions or graphing the composite functions.

1. $f(x) = -2x + 1$ and $g(x) = \dfrac{1}{2}x + \dfrac{1}{2}$

2. $h(x) = \dfrac{-8}{x + 4}$ and $k(x) = \dfrac{-4x - 8}{x}$

3. $F(x) = \dfrac{-3x + 5}{4x}$ and $G(x) = \dfrac{4x}{-3x + 5}$

4. $s(x) = \dfrac{3x}{\left(16 - x^2\right)^{1/2}}$ and $t(x) = \dfrac{4x}{\left(9 + x^2\right)^{1/2}}$

5. $p(x) = 2x^7 + 15$ and $q(x) = \sqrt[7]{\dfrac{1}{2}x - \dfrac{15}{2}}$

6. $g(x) = \sqrt{x - 2}$ and $h(x) = x^2 + 2$

7. $r(x) = \sqrt[5]{\dfrac{-8x}{11x + 1}}$ and $s(x) = \dfrac{-x^5}{11x^5 + 8}$

8. $f(x) = \left(1 - x^{3/2}\right)^{2/3}$ and $h(x) = \left(1 - x^{3/2}\right)^{2/3}$

9. $g(x) = \dfrac{x}{x + 1}$ and $p(x) = \dfrac{x}{x - 1}$

10. $k(x) = \dfrac{2x}{\left(25 + x^2\right)^{1/2}}$ and $h(x) = \dfrac{5x}{\left(4 - x^2\right)^{1/2}}$

11. $q(x) = 3x + 8$ and $t(x) = \dfrac{1}{3x + 8}$

12. $f(x) = \left(1 - x^3\right)^{1/3}$ and $g(x) = \left(1 - x^3\right)^{1/3}$

13. $R(x) = \dfrac{6x^7}{-2x^7 + 7}$ and $S(x) = \sqrt[7]{\dfrac{-7x}{-2x - 6}}$

14. $h(x) = \dfrac{1}{x}$ and $t(x) = x$

15. $p(x) = \dfrac{-11x + 7}{-3x + 5}$ and $q(x) = \dfrac{-5x + 7}{-3x + 11}$

16. Three ways to investigate whether a given pair of functions are inverses are described in the Discussion and Calculator Commentary for this Objective. The algebraic method involves simplifying the compositions. The numerical approach involves constructing tables of values for the composite functions. The graphical approach involves graphing the composite functions. Do you prefer one of these methods over the others? If so, which one? Why do you prefer it?

UNIT 2

SAMPLE EXAMINATION

1. The graph of function $y = f(x)$ is shown in Figure 2.52 (a).
    Let g denote the inverse function of f, if f has an inverse. Which of the following statements
    are true? There is at least one correct response. Choose all correct responses.

    A) The function f does not have an inverse function.   **B)** $g(-1) = 0$
    C) When $a = 5$, $g(a)$ is not defined.   **D)** Figure 2.52 (b) shows the graph of g.
    E) None of A), B), C), or D) is true.

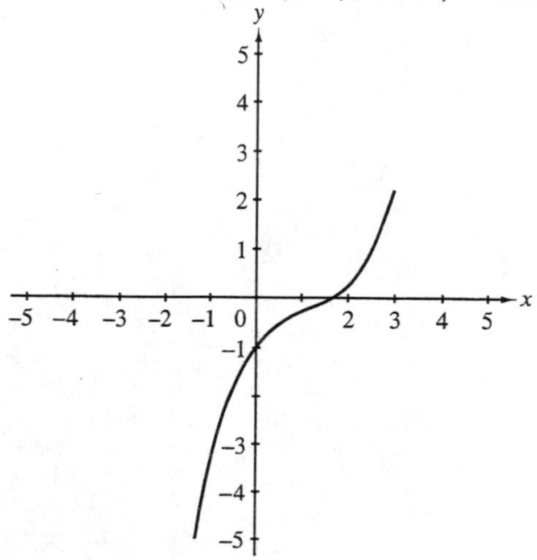

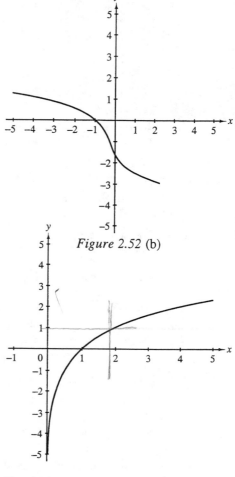

Figure 2.52 (a) Graph of $y = f(x)$

Figure 2.52 (b)

2. The graph of a function of the form $y = \log_b x$
    is shown in Figure 2.53. What is the equation for
    this function?

    A) $y = \log_2 x$ **D)** $y = \log_{1/4} x$

    B) $y = \log_3 x$ **E)** $y = \log_{5/2} x$

    C) $y = \log_{1/2} x$

Figure 2.53

3. Which one of the following is an equation for the inverse function for $r(x) = \dfrac{2}{6\sqrt[3]{x} + 7}$?

A) $y = \dfrac{6\sqrt[3]{x} + 7}{2}$ **B)** $y = \left(\dfrac{x - 14}{12}\right)^3$ **C)** $y = \left(\dfrac{2x - 7}{6}\right)^3$

D) $y = \dfrac{-7\sqrt[3]{x}}{6\sqrt[3]{x} - 2}$ **E)** $y = \left(\dfrac{-7x + 2}{6x}\right)^3$

4. Which one of the Figures 2.54 (a) - 2.54 (e) shows the graph of $y = \log_{3/4} x$?

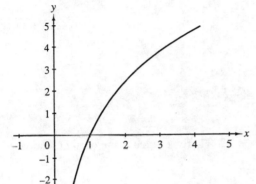

A) *Figure 2.54* (a)

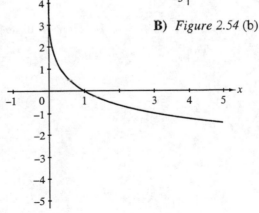

B) *Figure* 2.54 (b)

C) *Figure* 2.54 (c)

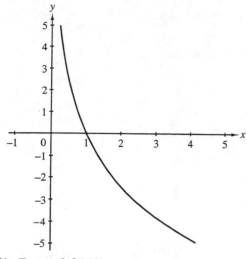

D) *Figure 2.54* (d)

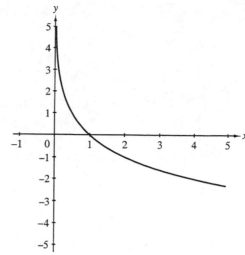

E) *Figure 2.54* (e)

5. Which of the following pairs of functions are inverses? There is at least one correct response. Choose all correct responses.

A) $u(x) = \dfrac{x + 3}{2x - 1}$ and $v(x) = \dfrac{x + 3}{2x - 1}$

B) $p(x) = \dfrac{1}{5x^7 + 6}$ and $q(x) = \sqrt[7]{\dfrac{x - 6}{5}}$

C) $h(x) = x^3 + 4$ and $k(x) = \sqrt[3]{x} - 4$

D) None of these

UNIT 3

MANIPULATION OF LOGARITHMIC FUNCTIONS

OBJECTIVE 3.1

(a) Given an exponential equation $b^a = c$, write a logarithmic equation with the same meaning.

(b) Given a logarithmic equation $\log_b c = a$, write an exponential equation with the same meaning.

(c) Given a point on the graph of either a logarithmic or an exponential function, write a logarithmic equation and an exponential equation each of which expresses the relation between the coordinates of the point.

OBJECTIVE 3.2

Given numbers a, b and c, where $a > 0$, $b > 0$ and $b \neq 1$, find numerical values of x so that,

(a) $\log_x a = c$,

(b) $\log_b x = c$ and

(c) $\log_b a = x$.

OBJECTIVE 3.3

State the Product Property, the Quotient Property and the Power Property for Logarithms.

OBJECTIVE 3.4

(a) Given a sum of multiples of logarithms of algebraic expressions, rewrite the sum as a single logarithm of an algebraic expression.

(b) Given a logarithm of an algebraic expression involving products, quotients, powers and roots, write the expression as a sum of multiples of logarithms of algebraic expressions.

UNIT 3
MANIPULATION OF LOGARITHMIC FUNCTIONS

OVERVIEW

Logarithmic functions are the inverses of exponential functions. In Unit 3 we will learn to use this relationship to transform logarithmic equations into exponential equations and vice versa. The ability to transform between logarithmic and exponential equations will be used to derive properties of logarithmic functions which are equivalent to the Laws of Exponents. Finally, these properties of logarithms will be used to write expressions involving logarithms in different forms to suit different purposes.

MANIPULATION OF LOGARITHMIC FUNCTIONS

OBJECTIVE 3.1

(a) **Given an exponential equation $b^a = c$, write a logarithmic equation with the same meaning.**

(b) **Given a logarithmic equation $\log_b c = a$, write an exponential equation with the same meaning.**

(c) **Given a point on the graph of either a logarithmic or an exponential function, write a logarithmic equation and an exponential equation each of which expresses the relation between the coordinates of the point.**

DISCUSSION

Let f and g be a pair of inverse functions and suppose $f(a) = c$. Then, according to the Discussion of inverse functions in Objectives 2.1 and 2.2, $g(c) = a$. Similarly, if $g(c) = a$, then it is also true that $f(a) = c$. The equations $f(a) = c$ and $g(c) = a$ are two ways of expressing the same relationship between a and c. The difference between these two equations is the point of view. In the equation $f(a) = c$ we think of beginning with a and applying the procedure for the function f to obtain c. In the equation $g(c) = a$ we think of beginning with c and applying the procedure for g (which is the reverse of the procedure for f) to obtain a. For specific numbers a and c, the equations $f(a) = c$ and $g(c) = a$ are either both true or both false. In this sense the two equations have the same meaning.

To illustrate this relationship, consider the exponential function $f(x) = e^x$ and the natural logarithm function $g(x) = \ln x$. These functions are a pair of inverse functions. Let $a = 1.6094379124$ and $c = 5$. Now, use your calculator to verify that (within round off) $f(1.6094379124) = e^{1.6094379124} = 5$, so $f(a) = c$. Since $g(x) = \ln x$ is the inverse function for f, it must also be true that $g(c) = a$. Use your calculator to verify that (again within round off) $g(5) = 1.6094379124$. The equations $e^{1.6094379124} = 5$ and $\ln 5 = 1.6094379124$ express the same relationship among the numbers 5, 1.6094379124 and e. Use your calculator to experiment with other numbers. For all numbers a and c, the equations $e^a = c$ and $\ln c = a$ are either both true or both false. They are just different ways of expressing the same relationship among the three numbers.

Let $f(x) = b^x$ and $g(x) = \log_b x$ where $b > 0$, $b \neq 1$. Since f and g are a pair of inverse functions, the equations $f(a) = c$ and $g(c) = a$ have the same meaning. Using the expressions for f and g we can rewrite these equations and conclude that $b^a = c$ and $\log_b c = a$ have the same meaning.

This connection between logarithmic equations and exponential equations can also be understood in terms of the graphs of the functions. Suppose (a, c) satisfies the exponential equation $y = b^x$ so $c = b^a$. Then the point with coordinates (a, c) lies on the graph of the exponential function $f(x) = b^x$. Since the graph of the logarithmic function $g(x) = \log_b x$ is the reflection of the graph of $f(x) = b^x$, the reflection of the point (a, c) lies on the graph of $g(x) = \log_b x$. The reflection of the point (a, c) is the point (c, a), so the point (c, a) lies on the graph of $g(x) = \log_b x$. This means that (c, a) satisfies the equation $a = \log_b c$. Thus, if $c = b^a$, then $a = \log_b c$. By reasoning in the same way about a point whose coordinates (c, a) satisfy the logarithmic equation $g(x) = \log_b x$, one concludes that if $a = \log_b c$, then $c = b^a$. Again we see that the equations $c = b^a$ and $a = \log_b c$ convey the same information about the relationship among the numbers a, b and c.

In this development it has been assumed, though not stated explicitly, that a, b and c are numbers. We concluded that the equation $b^a = c$ and $\log_b c = a$ have the same meaning whenever a, b and c are numbers for which the two expressions are defined. These two equations also have the same meaning when a, b and c are variables, algebraic expressions or functions which take on values for which the exponential and the logarithm are defined.

CALCULATOR COMMENTARY

The two statements

- (a, c) lies on the graph of $f(x) = b^x$ and
- (c, a) lies on the graph of $g(x) = \log_b x$

and the two equations

- $b^a = c$ and
- $\log_b c = a$

all express the same relationship among a, b, and c.

We can use the program **DRWINVRS** (see Calculator Commentary on Objective 2.1) to visualize the connections among these statements and equations. Use **DRWINVRS** to graph the exponential function $f(x) = 3.2^x$ and its inverse function $g(x) = \log_{3.2} x$ on the same screen. When the program prompts you for a range of values for the independent variable, choose **Xmin = -4.7** and **Xmax = 4.7**. The program will generate the graphs of $y = 3.2^x$, $y = x$ and $y = \log_{3.2} x$ as shown in Figure 3CC.1.

Use the arrow keys to position the cursor at the point $(0.5, 1.8)$. This point lies on the graph of the exponential function so $(3.2)^{0.5} = 1.8$ (rounded to one decimal place). Now move the cursor to the point $(1.8, 0.5)$. This point is on the graph of the logarithmic function so (rounded to one decimal place) $\log_{3.2}(1.8) = 0.5$. Examine other pairs of points on these curves and observe that a point with coordinates (p, q) lies on one of the curves if and only if its reflection (q, p) lies on the other. Since a point lies on the graph of a function if and only if its coordinates satisfy the equation for the function, this means that $p = 3.2^q$ if and only if $\log_{3.2} p = q$.

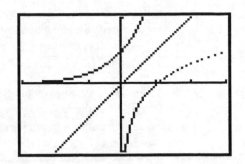

Figure 3CC.1

Now choose another exponential function and repeat the investigation of paired points on a new pair of graphs. Recall that the base of an exponential function must be greater than 0 and different from 1. Convince yourself that regardless of the base b involved, a point with coordinates (p, q) lies on one of the curves if and only if its reflection, (q, p) lies on the other. This fact about the graphs can be restated in terms of their equations. Regardless of the base b, $p = b^q$ if and only if $\log_b p = q$.

When you choose **Xmin = -4.7** and **Xmax = 4.7** the program **DRWINVRS** produces a decimal viewing window. In this window the change in the value of x and the value of y between adjacent screen pixels is 0.1. In a decimal viewing window problems of round off that result from the limitations of the screen are reduced. If you choose some other range of values for the independent variable, you probably will not be able to move the cursor exactly to the points you want on the graphs of the functions.

SUMMARY

1. Let f and g be a pair of inverse functions. The equations $f(a) = c$ and $g(c) = a$ express the same relationship between a and c.

2. Since $f(x) = e^x$ and $g(x) = \ln x$ are inverse functions, the equations $e^a = c$ and $\ln c = a$ express the same relationship among a, b, and c.

3. Since $f(x) = b^x$ and $g(x) = \log_b x$ (where $b > 0$, $b \neq 1$) are inverse functions, the equations $b^a = c$ and $\log_b c = a$ express the same relationship among a, b and c.

4. • If (c, d) is a point on the graph of a logarithmic function $y = \log_b x$, then its coordinates (c, d) satisfy the equation $d = \log_b c$. Because the exponential equation $c = b^d$ expresses the same relationship among the numbers b, c, and d as the logarithmic equation, the coordinates (c, d) also satisfy the equation $c = b^d$.

• If (c, d) is a point on the graph of a exponential function $y = b^x$, then its coordinates (c, d) satisfy the equation $d = b^c$. Because the logarithmic equation $c = \log_b d$ expresses the same relationship among the numbers b, c, and d as the exponential equation, the coordinates (c, d) also satisfy the equation $c = \log_b d$.

EXAMPLES

Example 1: Write a logarithmic equation which has the same meaning as the exponential equation $7^w = z$.

Solution 1:

Step 1. The exponential has base 7. The logarithmic equation will involve the logarithm base 7, $\log_7$.

Step 2. The variable z does not appear in the exponential 7^w. The function $\log_7$ will apply to z in the logarithmic equation.

Step 3. The variable w appears as the power in the exponential equation. It will appear alone in the logarithmic equation.

The logarithmic equation is $w = \log_7 z$.

Example 2: Write a logarithmic equation which has the same meaning as the exponential equation $(A + B)^{uv} = \sqrt{G}$.

Solution 2:

Step 1. The exponential has base $(A + B)$. The logarithmic equation will involve the logarithmic function base $(A + B)$, $\log_{(A + B)}$.

Step 2. The expression $\sqrt{G}$ does not appear in the exponential $(A + B)^{uv}$. The function $\log_{(A + B)}$ will apply to $\sqrt{G}$ in the logarithmic equation.

Step 3. The expression uv appears as the power in the exponential equation. It will appear alone in the logarithmic equation.

The logarithmic equation is $uv = \log_{(A + B)} \sqrt{G}$.

Note that the process in Examples 1 and 2 can only be applied to an exponential equation written in the form

$$(\text{Base})^{\text{Power}} = \text{Result}.$$

Example 3: Write an exponential equation that has the same meaning as the logarithmic equation $\log_R 13 = s$.

Solution 3:

Step 1. The logarithmic function has base R. The exponential equation will involve an exponential function base R.

Step 2. The logarithmic function $\log_R$ does not apply to variable s. The variable s will be the power of R in the exponential equation.

Step 3. The logarithmic function applies to the number 13 in the logarithmic equation. The number 13 will appear alone in the exponential equation.

The exponential equation is $R^s = 13$.

Example 4: Write an exponential equation that has the same meaning as the logarithmic equation $\log_{\left(1 + x^2\right)} w = 3y$.

Solution 4:

Step 1. The logarithmic function has base $\left(1 + x^2\right)$. The exponential equation will involve an exponential function base $\left(1 + x^2\right)$.

Step 2. The logarithmic function $\log_{\left(1 + x^2\right)}$ does not apply to the expression $3y$. The expression $3y$ will be the power of $\left(1 + x^2\right)$ in the exponential equation.

Step 3. The logarithmic function applies to the variable w in the logarithmic equations. The variable w will appear alone in the exponential equation.

The exponential equation is $w = \left(1 + x^2\right)^{3y}$.

Note that the process in Examples 3 and 4 can only be applied to a logarithmic equation written in the form

$$\log_{\text{Base}}(\text{Result}) = \text{Power}.$$

Example 5: The point with coordinates $(2, p)$ lies on the graph of the logarithmic function $g(x) = \log_5 x$. Write a logarithmic equation and an exponential equation each of which expresses the relation between the coordinates of the point.

Solution 5: Since the point lies on the graph of $g(x) = \log_5 x$, its coordinates $(2, p)$ satisfy the equation $p = \log_5 2$. Since the exponential equation $5^p = 2$ expresses the same relationship among the numbers 2, p, and 5 as the logarithmic equation, the coordinates $(2, p)$ also satisfy the equation $5^p = 2$.

PRACTICE PROBLEMS

In problems 1 - 12, write a logarithmic equation with the same meaning as the given exponential equation.

1. $b^{0.5} = c$

2. $3^a = c$

3. $b^a = 7$

4. $x^a = 5$

5. $s^{4.2} = 11.3$

6. $\left(\dfrac{1}{2}\right)^{0.517} = K$

7. $w^z = y$

8. $b^{(p + q)} = c$

9. $(x + y)^k = B$

10. $\left(\dfrac{u}{v}\right)^s = t$

11. $x^{(1 + kt)} = S + R$

12. $R^{p/q} = s - t$

In problems 13 - 24, write an exponential equation with the same meaning as the given logarithmic equation.

13. $\log_3 c = a$

14. $\log_b c = 2.319$

15. $\log_b 12 = a$

16. $\log_R T = S$

17. $\log_5 q = 1.573$

18. $\log_x 64 = 3$

19. $\log 238 = W$

20. $\ln r = 0.7513$

21. $\log_b P = s + r$

22. $\log_{(uv)} Q = z$

23. $\log_p\left(4 + x^2\right) = y$

24. $\log_{(a + b)} B = \dfrac{n}{k}$

25. The point $(1.5361, 2.900094678)$ lies on the graph of the exponential function with base 2. Which of the following equations correctly expresses the relationship between the numbers 1.5361 and 2.900094678 (within the limitations of the calculator)?

(a) $\log_2(1.5361) = 2.900094678$

(b) $\log_2(2.900094678) = 1.5361$

(c) $\log_2(1.5361) = \log_2(2.900094678)$

(d) $2^{1.5361} = 2.900094678$

(e) $2^{2.900094678} = 1.5361$

(f) $2^{1.5361} = 2^{2.900094678}$

(g) None of these

To the extent possible, check your answers graphically and numerically. Some ingenuity may be required to find a suitable viewing window.

26. The point $(7.9433, 0.9000009652)$ lies on the graph of the common logarithm function .   Which of the following equations correctly expresses the relationship between the numbers 7.9433 and 0.9000009652 (within the limitations of the calculator)?

(a) $\log_{10}(7.9433) = 0.9000009652$

(e) $10^{0.9000009652} = 7.9433$

(b) $\log_{10}(0.9000009652) = 7.9433$

(f) $10^{7.9433} = 10^{0.9000009652}$

(c) $\log_{10}(7.9433) = \log_{10}(0.9000009652)$

(g) None of these

(d) $10^{7.9433} = 0.9000009652$

To the extent possible, check your answers graphically and numerically.   Some ingenuity may be required to find a suitable viewing window.

In problems 27 - 32, determine whether the given equations have the same meaning.

27. $x^3 = y$ and $\log_3 x = y$

30. $\ln p = 4.1$ and $e^p = 4.1$

28. $\log_5(kP) = 1 + t$ and $5^{(1 + t)} = kP$

31. $K^4 = x^2 + 4$ and $\log_4\left(x^2 + 4\right) = K$

29. $(1 + r)^n = B$ and $\log_B(1 + r) = n$

32. $\log \dfrac{r}{R} = d$ and $(d)^{r/R} = 10$

OBJECTIVE 3.2

Given numbers a, b **and** c, **where** $a > 0$, $b > 0$ **and** $b \neq 1$, **find numerical values of** x **so that, (a)** $\log_x a = c$,
(b) $\log_b x = c$ **and**
(c) $\log_b a = x$.

DISCUSSION

Many problems require finding the numerical value of a quantity x from a logarithmic equation. The basic logarithmic equations are $\log_x a = c$, $\log_b x = c$ and $\log_b a = x$ where a, b and c are given numbers. The numerical value of x is found by rewriting the logarithmic equation as an exponential equation and, when possible, computing x from the exponential equation. The first two equations can be solved by this procedure for all numbers a, b and c where $a > 0$, $b > 0$ and $b \neq 1$. For these equations, a calculator is usually needed to find the numerical value of x. The third equation can be solved by this direct approach when the numbers a and b are each an integer power of the same base. Otherwise, the methods which will be discussed in Unit 4 are needed to solve the third equation.

SUMMARY

To find the numerical value of x from a basic logarithmic equation $\log_x a = c$, $\log_b x = c$ or $\log_b a = x$, rewrite the logarithmic equation as an exponential equation. Then compute x by inspection or by using a calculator.

EXAMPLES

Example 1: Find the numerical value of x so that $\log_5 x = 3$.

Solution 1:   *Step 1.* Write the exponential equation with the same meaning.

$$5^3 = x$$

Step 2. Compute x.

$$x = 5^3 = 5 \cdot 5 \cdot 5 = 125$$

Example 2: Find the numerical value of x so that $\log_{7.23} x = 0.93$. Round off the answer to two decimal places.

Solution 2: *Step 1.* Write the exponential equation with the same meaning.
$$(7.23)^{0.93} = x$$

Step 2. Compute x using a calculator.
$$x = (7.23)^{0.93} = 6.295041775$$

Step 3. Round to two decimal places and get
$$x = 6.30.$$

Example 3: Find the numerical value of x so that $\log_x 81 = 4$.

Solution 3: *Step 1.* Write the exponential equation with the same meaning.
$$x^4 = 81$$

Step 2. Solve for x by raising both sides of the equation to the power $\left(\dfrac{1}{4}\right)$.
$$x = 81^{\left(1/4\right)} = 3$$

Example 4: Find the numerical value of x so that $\log_x 16.731 = -1.869$. Round off the answer to three decimal places.

Solution 4: *Step 1.* Write the exponential equation with the same meaning.
$$x^{-1.869} = 16.731$$

Step 2. Solve for x by raising both sides of the equation to the power $\dfrac{1}{-1.869}$.
$$x - (16.731)^{\left(1/-1.869\right)}$$

Step 3. Compute x using a calculator.
$$x = (16.731)^{\left(1/-1.869\right)} = (16.731)^{(-0.5350454798)} = 0.2214930684$$

Step 4. Round to three decimal places and get
$$x = 0.221.$$

Example 5: Find the numerical value of x so that $\log_2 16 = x$.

Solution 5: *Step 1.* Write the exponential equation with the same meaning.
$$2^x = 16$$
Step 2. Solve for x by recognizing (by trial and error if necessary) that
$$2^4 = 2 \cdot 2 \cdot 2 \cdot 2 = 16.$$
Therefore,
$$x = 4.$$

Example 6: Find the numerical value of x so that $\log_9 27 = x$.

Solution 6: *Step 1.* Write the exponential equation with the same meaning.
$$9^x = 27$$

Step 2. Write both members of the equation as a power of the same base. We have
$$9^x = \left(3^2\right)^x = 3^{2x} \quad \text{and} \quad 27 = 3^3.$$
Now, write the exponential equation as
$$3^{2x} = 3^3.$$
Step 3. Equate the exponents and solve for x.
Thus,
$$2x = 3 \quad \text{and} \quad x = \frac{3}{2} = 1.5.$$

Note that methods from Unit 4 are needed to solve the equation $\log_b a = x$ when Step 2 of Example 6 cannot be accomplished by inspection.

PRACTICE PROBLEMS

Find the numerical value of x from each equation. Express answers as exact fractions when possible. Otherwise, round off to five decimal places or as directed.

1. $\log_7 x = 4$

2. $\log_x 125 = 3$

3. $\log_2 32 = x$

4. $\log_{16} x = 4$

5. $\log_x 12 = \frac{1}{2}$

6. $\log_8 128 = x$

7. $\log_{11} x = \frac{2}{3}$

8. $\log_x 11 = \frac{2}{3}$

9. $\log_4 (0.5) = x$

10. $\log_{1/5} 125 = x$

11. $\log_{0.30103} x = -0.71492$

12. $\log_x (7.1828) = 2.8445$

(Round to 4 decimal places.)

OBJECTIVE 3.3
State the Product Property, the Quotient Property and the Power Property for Logarithms.

DISCUSSION

The properties of exponentials for multiplication, division and powers are familiar:

$$b^x \cdot b^y = b^{(x + y)},$$

$$\frac{b^x}{b^y} = b^{(x - y)} \quad \text{and}$$

$$\left(b^x\right)^y = b^{xy}.$$

These equations are called **identities** because they are true for every positive base b and all exponents x and y. Since exponential and logarithmic functions are inverses, these exponential identities can be rewritten as logarithmic identities. The logarithmic identities express the corresponding properties of logarithmic functions for multiplication, division and powers.

In Unit 2 we found that when f and g are a pair of inverse functions, for every x in the domain of g, $f \circ g(x) = x$. The functions $f(x) = b^x$ and $g(x) = \log_b x$ are inverse functions, so for every $x > 0$, $b^{(\log_b x)} = x$. Objective 3.1 showed that an exponential equation $b^a = c$ can be rewritten as the logarithmic equation $\log_b c = a$. These two facts can be used to obtain the logarithmic identities from the exponential identities.

For any positive numbers x and y, $b^{(\log_b x)} = x$ and $b^{(\log_b y)} = y$. As a result, from the Product Property for Exponentials, for any positive numbers x and y

$$xy = b^{(\log_b x)} \cdot b^{(\log_b y)} = b^{(\log_b x + \log_b y)}.$$

On rewriting the exponential equation $xy = b^{(\log_b x + \log_b y)}$ as a logarithmic equation, we conclude that for all positive numbers x and y

$$\log_b x + \log_b y = \log_b xy.$$

This identity expresses the **Product Property for Logarithms**. It asserts that for every base b and for every pair of positive numbers x and y the numbers computed from the expressions $\log_b x + \log_b y$ and $\log_b xy$ will be identical. This claim can be confirmed experimentally for log and ln by using a calculator. Let

$$x = 27.357 \quad \text{and} \quad y = 93.289.$$

Use your calculator to compute that

$$\log(xy) = \log(27.357)(93.289)$$
$$= \log(2552.107173)$$
$$= 3.406898908.$$

Now compute that

$$\log(x) + \log(y) = \log(27.357) + \log(93.289)$$
$$= 1.437068470 + 1.969830438$$
$$= 3.406898908.$$

Observe that for these numbers x and y, $\log(x) + \log(y)$ and $\log(xy)$ are identical. Repeat this calculation with ln. Experiment with positive numbers x and y which you choose.

From the Quotient Property for Exponentials, for all positive numbers x and y

$$\frac{x}{y} = \frac{b^{(\log_b x)}}{b^{(\log_b y)}} = b^{(\log_b x - \log_b y)}.$$

By rewriting the exponential equation $\dfrac{x}{y} = b^{(\log_b x - \log_b y)}$ as a logarithmic equation, we conclude that for all positive numbers x and y

$$\log_b\left(\frac{x}{y}\right) = \log_b x - \log_b y.$$

This identity is called the **Quotient Property for Logarithms**. It asserts that for every base b and for every pair of positive numbers x and y the numbers computed from the expressions $\log_b x - \log_b y$ and $\log_b\left(\dfrac{x}{y}\right)$ will be identical. This claim can be confirmed experimentally for log and ln. Choose positive numerical values for x and y, as was done above, and evaluate these two expressions with your calculator. Verify that you do get the same results from the two expressions!

From the Power Property for Exponentials we know that, for every positive number x and every power p,

$$x^p = \left[b^{\left(\log_b x \right)} \right]^p = b^{\left(p \log_b x \right)}.$$

Rewrite the exponential equation $x^p = b^{\left(p \log_b x \right)}$ as a logarithmic equation to obtain the **Power Property for Logarithms:** For all real numbers p, for all positive numbers x,

$$\log_b x^p = p \log_b x.$$

Choose any values for p and any positive values for x and confirm this identity by experimenting with your calculator.

The Product, Quotient and Power Properties for Logarithms are derived assuming that x and y are positive numbers. These identities are also true when x and y are replaced by algebraic expressions or functions that take on positive values.

CALCULATOR COMMENTARY

The product, quotient, and power properties for logarithmic functions are called identities because these equations hold for all numbers x and y for which all of the functions involved are defined. That is to say, these equations are identities because for *all* positive numbers x and y,

$$\log_b xy = \log_b x + \log_b y$$

$$\log_b \frac{x}{y} = \log_b x - \log_b y \quad \text{and}$$

$$\log_b x^p = p \log_b x.$$

The following program for the TI-83® automates numerical confirmation of the Product Property for the natural logarithm. When executed, this program invites the user to enter numerical values for x and y. If any of the expressions involved are undefined, an error message is displayed. If all expressions are defined, the calculator displays both $\ln xy$ and $\ln x + \ln y$.

```
PROGRAM:LOGIDNTY
:Disp "X = "
:Input X
:Disp "Y = "
:Input Y
:Disp "In(XY) = "
:Disp In(XY)
:Pause
:Disp "In(X) + In(Y) = "
:Disp In(X) + In(Y)
:Disp "PRESS ENTER TO"
:Disp "REPEAT"
```

Enter this program into your calculator. To execute **LOGIDNTY**, press PRGM . **EXEC** (execute) will be highlighted. Press the number of the program **LOGIDNTY**. The calculator will return to the home screen and display **PrgmLOGIDNTY**. Press ENTER . Enter numerical values of your choice for x and y in response to calculator prompts. The calculator will display $\ln(xy) =$ and the calculated value and then pause. Press ENTER to continue. The calculator will display $\ln x + \ln y =$ and the calculated value. Press ENTER to repeat the program with new selection of x and y. Press any other key to proceed with some other calculation.

Enter many different values for x and y into this program and confirm experimentally that when all of the functions are defined, the results of the two evaluations are always the same so Product Property is, indeed, an identity.

SUMMARY

Logarithmic functions satisfy the identities

(a) $\log_b AB = \log_b A + \log_b B$ **(Product Property)**,

(b) $\log_b\left(\dfrac{A}{B}\right) = \log_b A - \log_b B$ **(Quotient Property)** and

(c) $\log_b A^p = p \log_b A$ **(Power Property)**,

where A and B may be positive numbers, variables, algebraic expressions or functions that take on positive values.

PRACTICE PROBLEMS

In problems 1 - 6, complete each identity.

1. $\log_b xy = $ _____

2. $p \log_b x = $ _____

3. $\log_b x - \log_b y = $ _____

4. $\log_b\left(x^p\right) = $ _____

5. $\log_b\left(\dfrac{x}{y}\right) = $ _____

6. $\log_b x + \log_b y = $ _____

In problems 7 - 24, identify those equations which state an identity for the common or natural logarithm functions.

7. $\log(xy) = (\log x)(\log y)$

8. $\ln\left(x^p\right) = (\ln x)^p$

9. $\ln\left(\dfrac{x}{y}\right) = \dfrac{\ln x}{\ln y}$

10. $\ln(xy) = x \ln y$

11. $\log\left(x^p\right) = \log p + \log x$

12. $\log\left(\dfrac{x}{y}\right) = \log y - \log x$

13. $\ln(xy) = \ln x + \ln y$

14. $\log\left(x^p\right) = x \log p$

15. $\log\left(\dfrac{x}{y}\right) = \log x - \log y$

16. $\log x + \log y = \log(x + y)$

17. $p \log x = \log\left(x^p\right)$

18. $\ln x - \ln y = \ln(x - y)$

19. $\ln x + \ln y - \ln\left(\dfrac{x}{y}\right)$

20. $p \log x = \log\left(p^x\right)$

21. $\log x - \log y = \log\left(\dfrac{x}{y}\right)$

22. $\log x + \log y = \log(xy)$

23. $p \ln x = \ln(px)$

24. $\ln x - \ln y = \ln\left(\dfrac{x}{y}\right)$

25. Enter negative values for x and y in the program **LOGINDTY**. At what point in the program does an error message appear? Why does it occur at that point? What does this say about the meaning of the word "*identity*" in the statement "the Product Property is an identity"?

26. Modify the program **LOGINDTY** to confirm the Product Property for the common logarithm numerically. Are there values of the variables for which the expression on one side of the equality is defined but the expression on the other is not?

27. Modify the program **LOGINDTY** to confirm the Quotient Property for the natural logarithm and for the common logarithm numerically. Are there values of the variables for which the expression on one side of the equality is defined but the expression on the other is not?

28. Modify the program **LOGINDTY** to confirm the Power Property for the natural logarithm and for the common logarithm numerically. Are there values of the variables for which the expression on one side of the equality is defined but the expression on the other is not?

AUTHOR'S NOTE

The Product, Quotient and Power Properties for Logarithms can be used to simplify many numerical calculations by converting multiplications to additions, divisions to subtractions, and powers to multiplications. Thus, complicated arithmetic processes are replaced by simpler ones. Because of this, after John Napier invented logarithms in the early 17th century, logarithms were widely used to perform complicated calculations arising in astronomy and navigation. Now calculators and computers have replaced tables of logarithms and hand computations. The properties of logarithms studied in this Objective are no longer needed for calculating, but they are important for solving equations and manipulating expressions involving logarithms.

Recommended reading - Mathematics History: *The Construction of the Wonderful Canon of Logarithms* by John Napier (1550-1617), Baron of Merchiston.

OBJECTIVE 3.4

(a) **Given a sum of multiples of logarithms of algebraic expressions, rewrite the sum as a single logarithm of an algebraic expression.**

(b) **Given a logarithm of an algebraic expression involving products, quotients, powers and roots, write the expression as a sum of multiples of logarithms of algebraic expressions.**

DISCUSSION

The Discussion of Objective 3.3 demonstrated that logarithmic functions satisfy identities involving multiplication, division and powers. These identities are

$$\log_b AB = \log_b A + \log_b B \quad \textbf{(Product Property)},$$

$$\log_b\left(\frac{A}{B}\right) = \log_b A - \log_b B \quad \textbf{(Quotient Property)} \quad \text{and}$$

$$\log_b A^p = p \log_b A \quad\quad\quad \textbf{(Power Property)},$$

where A and B can be numbers, variables, expressions or functions that take on values for which the logarithmic functions are defined.

In the Examples we will use these identities to write expressions involving logarithmic functions in different forms to suit different purposes. These forms are all equal, even though they will look quite different.

The appearance of a logarithmic expression can also be changed by evaluating the logarithms of numbers which may occur. It is customary to do this when the numerical value of the logarithm can be expressed exactly as a whole number or a fraction. Three equations from previous discussions are helpful:

$$\log_b 1 = 0,$$
$$\log_b b = 1$$

and for every number p,

$$\log_b\left(b^p\right) = p \log_b b = p \cdot 1 = p.$$

CALCULATOR COMMENTARY

An equation that results from (correctly) manipulating an expression involving logarithmic functions into a different form is an *identity*. When numerical values for which all of the functions involved are defined are assigned to the independent variables, evaluating the expressions on the left side of the equal sign will produce the same numerical result as evaluating the expression on the right side.

Since the TI-83® does not perform algebraic manipulations, it can't be used to rewrite expressions involving logarithmic functions. However, one can check the results of manipulating an expression into another form by using the calculator to numerically test whether the result of the manipulations is an identity. If numerical testing shows that the equation is not an identity, an error was made in the manipulations.

To verify numerically that an equation is an identity, under the **Y=** menu, enter the expression from the left side of the equality as **Y1** and the expression from the right side as **Y2**. Use alphabetic variables (memories) from the calculator keyboard to enter the independent variables that appear in the expressions into **Y1** and **Y2**. If the equation derived is an identity, then for *every possible* selection of numbers entered for the variables, evaluation of **Y1** and of **Y2** will produce the same result, provided all of the expressions involved are defined. To test whether this is true, store numerical values for all of the variables that appear in the equation (and, hence, in **Y1** and **Y2**) in the memory locations denoted by the variable names. Then direct the calculator to evaluate the two expressions for the values assigned the variables. To evaluate the expression from left side of the equation, select **Y1** by pressing ⃞VARS⃞ , using the left-right arrow keys to highlight **Y-VARS** , and then pressing ⃞ 1 ⃞ , ⃞ 1 ⃞ . The display will show **Y1**. Press ⃞ENTER⃞. The calculator will take the values of the variables from the various memories, use them to perform the calculations specified in memory **Y1**, and display the result. To evaluate the expression from the right side of the equation, select **Y2** by pressing ⃞VARS⃞ , highlighting **Y-VARS** , and pressing ⃞ 1 ⃞ , ⃞ 2 ⃞ . Then press ⃞ENTER⃞. The calculator will evaluate the right side of the equation and display the result. If the equation is an identity, the results of these two evaluations will be identical.

If for even one set of values for the variables the two evaluations can both be carried out and they produce different results, then the equation is not an identity. One can never demonstrate with absolute certainty that an equation is an identity by testing the equation numerically. However, if the two evaluations produce the same numerical result (or one or both are not defined) for *many* different values for the variables, then one can be confident, though not certain, that the equation is an identity.

Because numerical verification of an identity requires evaluating the expressions for many different values of the variables and it can be difficult to remember all the values of the variables used, you may find it helpful to record the results of the evaluations in a pencil and paper table. Numerical checking procedures such as this are valuable because few of us can perform algebraic manipulations flawlessly.

SUMMARY

The logarithmic identities,

$$\log_b AB = \log_b A + \log_b B$$

$$\log_b\left(\frac{A}{B}\right) = \log_b A - \log_b B$$

and

$$\log_b A^p = p \log_b A,$$

are used to write expressions involving logarithms in different forms to suit different purposes.

EXAMPLES

Example 1: Write the expression $3 \log x + \dfrac{1}{2} \log y - 2 \log z$ as a single logarithm.

Solution 1:

Step 1. Use the identity $p \log A = \log A^p$ to write each term as the logarithm of a power.

$$3 \log x + \frac{1}{2} \log y - 2 \log z = \log x^3 + \log y^{1/2} - \log z^2$$

Step 2. Use the identities $\log A + \log B = \log AB$ and $\log A - \log B = \log\left(\dfrac{A}{B}\right)$ to combine these terms into a single logarithm.

$$\log x^3 + \log y^{1/2} - \log z^2 = \left[\log x^3 + \log y^{1/2}\right] - \log z^2$$

$$= \log x^3 y^{1/2} - \log z^2 = \log \frac{x^3 y^{1/2}}{z^2}$$

We conclude that

$$3 \log x + \frac{1}{2} \log y - 2 \log z = \log \frac{x^3 y^{1/2}}{z^2}.$$

To use the TI-83® to verify numerically that the expression $3\log x + \frac{1}{2}\log y - 2\log z$ has been rewritten correctly as a single logarithm, enter **3 log (X) + .5 log (Y) − 2 log (Z)** as **Y1** and **log ((X³Y∧.5) / Z²)** as **Y2**. Next, choose numerical values for x, y, and z and store these numbers in memory locations **X**, **Y**, and **Z**. (To store a number in a memory location, enter the number, press $\boxed{\text{STO→}}$, (row 9, column 1), $\boxed{\text{ALPHA}}$ (row 3, column 1) the key with the letter designating the memory location printed in green above it and, finally, $\boxed{\text{ENTER}}$.) Evaluate **Y1** for these values of x, y, and z by pressing $\boxed{\text{VARS}}$ (row 4, column 4), scrolling to **Y-VARS** , and pressing $\boxed{\ \ 1\ \ }$, $\boxed{\ \ 1\ \ }$, $\boxed{\text{ENTER}}$. Evaluate **Y2** for these values of x, y, and z by pressing $\boxed{\text{VARS}}$, scrolling to **Y-VARS** , and pressing $\boxed{\ \ 1\ \ }$, $\boxed{\ \ 2\ \ }$, $\boxed{\text{ENTER}}$.

If the original expression was rewritten correctly so the equation

$$3\log x + \frac{1}{2}\log y - 2\log z = \log\frac{x^3 y^{1/2}}{z^2}$$

is an identity, these two evaluations will produce the same result whenever x, y, and z are values for which both of the expressions are defined (in this case, for all positive x, y, and z). If there is even one set of values of x, y, and z for which **Y1** and **Y2** can both be evaluated (no error messages) and the results are different, then the equation is not an identity — indicating that the original expression was not rewritten correctly!

Example 2:   Write the expression $\log_5 3(x + 4) - 4\log_5(x - 2) + 2\log_5\left(x^2 - 4\right)$ as a single logarithm and simplify.

Solution 2:

Step 1. Use the identity $p\log_5 A = \log_5 A^p$ to write each term as the logarithm of a power.

$$\log_5 3(x + 4) - 4\log_5(x - 2) + 2\log_5\left(x^2 - 4\right)$$

$$= \log_5 3(x + 4) - \log_5(x - 2)^4 + \log_5\left(x^2 - 4\right)^2$$

Step 2. Use the identities $\log_5 A - \log_5 B = \log_5\left(\frac{A}{B}\right)$ and $\log_5 A + \log_5 B = \log_5 AB$ to combine these terms into a single logarithm.

$$\log_5 3(x + 4) - \log_5(x - 2)^4 + \log_5\left(x^2 - 4\right)^2$$

$$= \left[\log_5 3(x + 4) - \log_5(x - 2)^4\right] + \log_5\left(x^2 - 4\right)^2$$

$$= \log_5 \frac{3(x + 4)}{(x - 2)^4} + \log_5 \left(x^2 - 4\right)^2$$

$$= \log_5 \frac{3(x + 4)\left(x^2 - 4\right)^2}{(x - 2)^4}$$

Step 3. Simplify by factoring and dividing out common factors.

$$\log_5 \frac{3(x + 4)\left(x^2 - 4\right)^2}{(x - 2)^4} = \log_5 \frac{3(x + 4)\left[(x + 2)(x - 2)\right]^2}{(x - 2)^4}$$

$$= \log_5 \frac{3(x + 4)(x + 2)^2(x - 2)^2}{(x - 2)^4}$$

$$= \log_5 \frac{3(x + 4)(x + 2)^2}{(x - 2)^2}$$

We conclude that

$$\log_5 3(x + 4) - 4 \log_5(x - 2) + 2 \log_5\left(x^2 - 4\right) = \log_5 \frac{3(x + 4)(x + 2)^2}{(x - 2)^2}.$$

Example 3: Write the expression $\frac{1}{4} \ln(x - 1) - \frac{3}{4} \ln\left(x^2 + 2x - 3\right) - 2 \ln(x + 3)$ as a single logarithm and simplify.

Solution 3:

Step 1. Use the identity $p \ln A = \ln A^p$ to write each term as the logarithm of a power.

$$\frac{1}{4} \ln(x - 1) - \frac{3}{4} \ln\left(x^2 + 2x - 3\right) - 2 \ln(x + 3)$$

$$= \ln(x - 1)^{1/4} - \ln\left(x^2 + 2x - 3\right)^{3/4} - \ln(x + 3)^2$$

Step 2. Use the identity $\ln A - \ln B = \ln\left(\frac{A}{B}\right)$ to combine these terms into a single logarithm.

$$\ln(x - 1)^{1/4} - \ln\left(x^2 + 2x - 3\right)^{3/4} - \ln(x + 3)^2$$

$$= \left[\ln(x-1)^{\frac{1}{4}} - \ln\left(x^2 + 2x - 3\right)^{\frac{3}{4}} \right] - \ln(x+3)^2$$

$$= \ln \frac{(x-1)^{\frac{1}{4}}}{\left(x^2 + 2x - 3\right)^{\frac{3}{4}}} - \ln(x+3)^2$$

$$= \ln \frac{(x-1)^{\frac{1}{4}}}{\left(x^2 + 2x - 3\right)^{\frac{3}{4}}(x+3)^2}$$

Step 3. Simplify by factoring and dividing out common factors.

$$\ln \frac{(x-1)^{\frac{1}{4}}}{\left(x^2 + 2x - 3\right)^{\frac{3}{4}}(x+3)^2} = \ln \frac{(x-1)^{\frac{1}{4}}}{\left[(x-1)(x+3)\right]^{\frac{3}{4}}(x+3)^2}$$

$$= \ln \frac{(x-1)^{\frac{1}{4}}}{(x-1)^{\frac{3}{4}}(x+3)^{\frac{3}{4}}(x+3)^2}$$

$$= \ln(x-1)^{-\frac{1}{2}}(x+3)^{-1\frac{1}{4}}$$

We conclude that

$$\frac{1}{4}\ln(x-1) - \frac{3}{4}\ln\left(x^2 + 2x - 3\right) - 2\ln(x+3) = \ln(x-1)^{-\frac{1}{2}}(x+3)^{-1\frac{1}{4}}.$$

Example 4: Write the expression $\log_3 \dfrac{xy^2}{z^3}$ in terms of logarithms of x, y and z.

Solution 4:

Step 1. Use the identity $\log_3\left(\dfrac{A}{B}\right) = \log_3 A - \log_3 B$ to write the expression as a difference of logarithms.

$$\log_3 \frac{xy^2}{z^3} = \log_3 xy^2 - \log_3 z^3$$

Step 2. Use the identity $\log_3 AB = \log_3 A + \log_3 B$ to write $\log_3 xy^2$ as a sum of logarithms.

$$\log_3 xy^2 - \log_3 z^3 = \log_3 x + \log_3 y^2 - \log_3 z^3$$

Step 3. Use the identity $\log_3 A^p = p \log_3 A$ to write $\log_3 y^2$ and $\log_3 z^3$ as multiples of simple logarithms.

$$\log_3 x + \log_3 y^2 - \log_3 z^3 = \log_3 x + 2 \log_3 y - 3 \log_3 z$$

We conclude that

$$\log_3 \frac{xy^2}{z^3} = \log_3 x + 2 \log_3 y - 3 \log_3 z.$$

Example 5: Write the expression $\ln \left(\dfrac{\sqrt[3]{rs^2}}{5(t^2 + 4)} \right)^{1/2}$ in expanded form as a sum of multiples of logarithms.

Solution 5:

Step 1. Use the identity $\ln A^p = p \ln A$ to write

$$\ln \left(\frac{\sqrt[3]{rs^2}}{5(t^2 + 4)} \right)^{1/2} = \frac{1}{2} \ln \frac{\sqrt[3]{rs^2}}{5(t^2 + 4)}.$$

Step 2. Use the identity $\ln \left(\dfrac{A}{B} \right) = \ln A - \ln B$ to write

$$\frac{1}{2} \ln \frac{\sqrt[3]{rs^2}}{5(t^2 + 4)} = \frac{1}{2} \left[\ln \sqrt[3]{rs^2} - \ln 5(t^2 + 4) \right].$$

Step 3. Express the cube root in terms of fractional exponents and use the identity $\ln A^p = p \ln A$ to write

$$\frac{1}{2} \left[\ln \sqrt[3]{rs^2} - \ln 5(t^2 + 4) \right] = \frac{1}{2} \left[\ln \left(rs^2 \right)^{1/3} - \ln 5(t^2 + 4) \right]$$

$$= \frac{1}{2} \left[\frac{1}{3} \ln rs^2 - \ln 5(t^2 + 4) \right]$$

$$= \frac{1}{6} \ln rs^2 - \frac{1}{2} \ln 5(t^2 + 4).$$

Step 4. Use the identity $\ln AB = \ln A + \ln B$ to write

$$\frac{1}{6}\ln rs^2 - \frac{1}{2}\ln 5\left(t^2 + 4\right) = \frac{1}{6}\left[\ln r + \ln s^2\right] - \frac{1}{2}\left[\ln 5 + \ln\left(t^2 + 4\right)\right]$$

$$= \frac{1}{6}\ln r + \frac{1}{6}\ln s^2 - \frac{1}{2}\ln 5 - \frac{1}{2}\ln\left(t^2 + 4\right).$$

Step 5. Use the identity $\ln A^P = p \ln A$ to rewrite this expression as

$$\frac{1}{6}\ln r + \frac{1}{3}\ln s - \frac{1}{2}\ln 5 - \frac{1}{2}\ln\left(t^2 + 4\right).$$

We conclude that

$$\ln\left(\frac{\sqrt[3]{rs^2}}{5\left(t^2 + 4\right)}\right)^{1/2} = \frac{1}{6}\ln r + \frac{1}{3}\ln s - \frac{1}{2}\ln 5 - \frac{1}{2}\ln\left(t^2 + 4\right).$$

Note that the same conclusion is reached by writing $\left(\dfrac{\sqrt[3]{rs^2}}{5\left(t^2 + 4\right)}\right)^{1/2}$ in the exponential form

$$5^{-1/2}\, r^{1/6}\, s^{1/3}\left(t^2 + 4\right)^{-1/2}$$ before using the logarithmic identities.

Example 6: Write the expression $\log_6 \sqrt[4]{\dfrac{x^{2/5}\left(x^2 + x + 2\right)}{6(x + 1)^3}}$ in expanded form as a sum of multiple logarithms.

Solution 6:

Step 1. Use the identity $\log_6 A^P = p \log_6 A$ to obtain

$$\log_6 \sqrt[4]{\frac{x^{2/5}\left(x^2 + x + 2\right)}{6(x + 1)^3}} = \log_6\left[\frac{x^{2/5}\left(x^2 + x + 2\right)}{6(x + 1)^3}\right]^{1/4}$$

$$= \frac{1}{4}\log_6 \frac{x^{2/5}\left(x^2 + x + 2\right)}{6(x + 1)^3}.$$

Step 2.　Use the identities $\log_6\left(\dfrac{A}{B}\right) = \log_6 A - \log_6 B$ and $\log_6 AB = \log_6 A + \log_6 B$ to write

$$\frac{1}{4}\log_6 \frac{x^{2/5}\left(x^2 + x + 2\right)}{6(x + 1)^3} = \frac{1}{4}\left[\log_6 x^{2/5}\left(x^2 + x + 2\right) - \log_6 6(x + 1)^3\right]$$

$$= \frac{1}{4}\left[\log_6 x^{2/5} + \log_6\left(x^2 + x + 2\right) - \log_6 6 - \log_6 (x + 1)^3\right].$$

Step 3.　Use the identity $\log_6 A^p = p \log_6 A$ and the fact that $\log_6 6 = 1$ to write

$$\frac{1}{4}\left[\log_6 x^{2/5} + \log_6\left(x^2 + x + 2\right) - \log_6 6 - \log_6 (x + 1)^3\right]$$

$$= \frac{1}{4}\left[\frac{2}{5}\log_6 x + \log_6\left(x^2 + x + 2\right) - 1 - 3\log_6 (x + 1)\right]$$

$$= \frac{1}{10}\log_6 x + \frac{1}{4}\log_6\left(x^2 + x + 2\right) - \frac{1}{4} - \frac{3}{4}\log_6 (x + 1).$$

We conclude that

$$\log_6 \sqrt[4]{\frac{x^{2/5}\left(x^2 + x + 2\right)}{6(x + 1)^3}} = \frac{1}{10}\log_6 x + \frac{1}{4}\log_6\left(x^2 + x + 2\right) - \frac{1}{4} - \frac{3}{4}\log_6 (x + 1).$$

Note that the same conclusion is reached by writing $\sqrt[4]{\dfrac{x^{2/5}\left(x^2 + x + 2\right)}{6(x + 1)^3}}$ in the exponential form $6^{-1/4}\, x^{1/10}\left(x^2 + x + 2\right)^{1/4}(x + 1)^{-3/4}$ before using the logarithmic identities.

PRACTICE PROBLEMS

In problems 1 and 2, use the numerical checking procedure described in Calculator Commentary in this Objective to decide whether you believe the given equation is an identity.

1. $\frac{1}{4}\ln(x-1) - \frac{3}{4}\ln(x^2 + 2x - 3) - 2\ln(x + 3) = \ln\left((x-1)^{\frac{1}{4}}(x^2 + 2x - 3)^{\frac{3}{4}}(x + 3)^{-2}\right)$

2. $\log\left(\frac{x^3 y^{\frac{1}{2}}}{z^2}\right) = 3\log x + \frac{1}{2}\log y - 2\log z$

In problems 3 - 12, write the given expression as a single logarithm and simplify where possible. Check some of your results by using the TI-83® to verify numerically that the equation you derived is an identity. (If the problem involves a logarithmic function with base other than e or 10, you can still test numerically by changing all the logarithmic functions involved to either common or natural logarithms.)

3. $5\log x - \frac{2}{3}\log y - \log z$

4. $\frac{3}{5}\log_2 u + \frac{1}{4}\log_2 v - 3\log_2(2w)$

5. $\ln(t-1) - 2\ln\left(t^2 - 3t + 2\right) + \ln 3\left(t^2 + 2\right)$

6. $3\log_7 5(2s + 1) - 5\log_7 s - 2\log_7\left(2s^2 - s - 1\right)$

7. $3\log(s + r) - \frac{2}{3}\log s + \frac{3}{2}\log(r + 1)$

8. $\log_5 15(z - w) + \log_5 2(z + w) - \log_5 6\left(z^2 - w^2\right)$

9. $\frac{2}{3}\ln\left(x^2 - 10x + 25\right) - \frac{1}{3}\ln(x - 5) + 2\ln(x + 1)$

10. $4\log_3(x - 2) - \frac{1}{2}\log_3\left(x^2 - x - 2\right) + \frac{3}{2}\log_3(x + 1)$

11. $3 \log\left(x^2 + 8xy + 12y^2\right) - 4 \log\left(x + 6y\right) - \dfrac{2}{3} \log\left(x + 2y\right)$

12. $\dfrac{1}{2} \log_5\left(w + 1\right) - 2 \log_5 w + 2 \log_5\left(w^2 + w\right)$

In problems 13 - 22, write the given expression in expanded form as a sum and/or difference of multiples of logarithms. Check some of your results by using the TI-83® to verify numerically that the equation you derived is an identity. (If the problem involves a logarithmic function with base other than e or 10, you can still test numerically by changing all the logarithmic functions involved to either common or natural logarithms.)

13. $\log \dfrac{x^{5/3} y^{-3}}{z^4}$

14. $\log_8 \dfrac{64 \sqrt[3]{u^5 v^2}}{w^{-2}}$

15. $\log_4 \dfrac{2r^{-3/8} s^{1/5}}{\sqrt{rst}}$

16. $\ln \sqrt[3]{\dfrac{x^{1/3}\left(2x^2 + x + 5\right)}{(x + 5)^2}}$

17. $\log \left[\dfrac{10 s^{4/3}}{r^3 t^{-2/5}} \right]^6$

18. $\log_3 \dfrac{(a + b)^3 c^{2/3}}{\sqrt[3]{3a^{-2/3}(a + b)}}$

19. $\log \left[\dfrac{2x^{3/4}}{y^{-2} z^{1/3}} \right]^{-3/2}$

20. $\log_6 \sqrt[3]{\dfrac{3z^{-2/3}}{x^{-2/3} y^2}}$

21. $\ln \left[\dfrac{s^{-4/5} t^{1/3}}{e^2 r^2} \right]^5$

22. $\log_2 \left[\dfrac{8 \sqrt[3]{t^5}}{\sqrt[4]{r^3} s^{-5}} \right]^{3/10}$

UNIT 3
SAMPLE EXAMINATION

1. The equation $\log_z w = 6$ has the same meaning as

A) $z^6 = w$ B) $z^w = 6$ C) $w^6 = z$ D) $6^w = z$ E) $6^z = w$

2. If $\log_x 4.21 = 0.63$, then rounded to two decimal places, $x =$

A) 0.14   B) 0.90   C) 2.47   D) 6.68   E) 9.79

3. Which of the following are properties of logarithms? There is at least one correct response. Choose
   all correct responses.

A) $\log_a x + \log_a y = \log_a(x + y)$

D) $\log_a xy = \log_a x + \log_a y$

B) $\log_a \dfrac{x}{y} = \log_a(x - y)$

E) $\log_a x - \log_a y = \dfrac{\log_a x}{\log_a y}$

C) $\log_a x^p = p \log_a x$

4. In expanded form, using multiples of logarithms but **no** exponents or radicals, $\log\left(\sqrt[3]{\dfrac{100(2y + 7)^5}{x^{-3/4} z^6}}\right) =$

A) $\dfrac{\frac{2}{3} + \frac{5}{3}\log(2y + 7)}{-\frac{1}{4}\log x + 2\log z}$

D) $\dfrac{2}{3} + \dfrac{1}{4}\log x + \dfrac{5}{3}\log(2y + 7) - 2\log z$

B) $\dfrac{\frac{5}{2}(\log x)\log(2y + 7)}{6\log z}$

E) $2 + \dfrac{1}{4}\log x + 5\log(2y + 7) - 6\log z$

C) $\dfrac{2}{3} - \dfrac{1}{4}\log x + \dfrac{5}{3}\log(2y + 7) - 2\log z$

5. Expressed as a single logarithm and simplified,

$$\frac{4}{3}\log_4(2r - 3s) + 2\log_4 3(r - 2s) - \frac{1}{3}\log_4\left(2r^2 + rs - 6s^2\right) =$$

A) $\log_4 \dfrac{9(2r - 3s)(r - 2s)^2}{(r + 2s)^{1/3}}$

D) $\log_4 \dfrac{3(2r - 3s)(r - 2s)^2}{(r + 2s)^{1/3}}$

B) $\log_4 \dfrac{9(2r - 3s)^{4/3}(r - 2s)^{5/3}}{(2r + 3s)^{1/3}}$

E) $\log_4 \dfrac{3(2r - 3s)(r - 2s)}{(r + 2s)^{1/3}}$

C) $\log_4 3(2r - 3s)(r - 2s)^{5/3}$

$x^{0.63} = 4.21$

$9.79^{0.63} = 4.21$

UNIT 4

EXPONENTIAL AND LOGARITHMIC EQUATIONS

OBJECTIVE 4.1

Simplify expressions involving the composition of exponential and logarithmic functions with the same base.

OBJECTIVE 4.2

Solve logarithmic equations algebraically.

OBJECTIVE 4.3

Solve exponential equations algebraically.

OBJECTIVE 4.4

Given an applied problem described by a given exponential or logarithmic equation, solve the problem.

UNIT 4
EXPONENTIAL AND LOGARITHMIC EQUATIONS

OVERVIEW

Exponential and logarithmic functions are used to give mathematical descriptions of phenomena which occur in the social, management, biological and physical sciences. These descriptions are called mathematical models. One must evaluate logarithmic and exponential functions and solve equations involving them in order to obtain information about the phenomena described by these models. In this Unit we will study the methods for solving logarithmic and exponential equations and then use these methods to analyze several mathematical models.

EXPONENTIAL AND LOGARITHMIC EQUATIONS

OBJECTIVE 4.1

Simplify expressions involving the composition of logarithmic and exponential functions with the same base.

DISCUSSION

We saw in Objective 2.4 that if $y = f(x)$ and $y = g(x)$ are inverse functions, then for every x in the domain of f, $g \circ f(x) = g(f(x)) = x$ and for every x in the domain of g, $f \circ g(x) = f(g(x)) = x$. Let $f(x) = b^x$ and $g(x) = \log_b x$, $b > 0$, $b \neq 1$. Since these functions are inverses, for every positive number x,

$$f(g(x)) = b^{(\log_b x)} = x$$

and for every number x,

$$g(f(x)) = \log_b(b^x) = x.$$

Every pair of exponential and logarithmic functions with the same base satisfies these two **Composition Identities**.

The Composition Identities can be verified numerically for the pair of inverse functions

$$f(x) = 10^x \text{ and } g(x) = \log x$$

and the pair of inverse functions

$$F(x) = e^x \text{ and } G(x) = \ln x.$$

Let $x = 12.317$. Use your calculator to compute

$$f(g(12.317)) = f(\log 12.317) = f(1.090504941) = 10^{1.090504941} = 12.317$$

and

$$F(G(12.317)) = F(\ln 12.317) = F(2.510980422) = e^{2.510980422} = 12.317.$$

Now let $x = -0.60591$. Use your calculator to compute

$$g(f(-0.60591)) = g(10^{-0.60591}) = g(0.2477935514)$$
$$= \log(0.2477935514) = -0.60591,$$

and

$$G(F(-0.60591)) = G(e^{-0.60591}) = G(0.5455777249)$$
$$= \ln(0.5455777249) = -0.60591.$$

Repeat these calculations and verify the Composition Identities using several numbers x that you have chosen.

The Composition Identities were derived assuming that x is a number. However, these identities also hold when x is replaced by any variable, algebraic expression or function that takes on values for which the compositions are defined.

Complex expressions involving the composition of exponential and logarithmic functions with the same base can be simplified by using the Composition Identities. To simplify an expression involving a number b raised to a power which is a sum and/or difference of multiples of logarithms base b, follow these steps.

Step 1. Use the Product, Quotient and Power Properties for Logarithms to write the exponent of b as a single logarithm. The exponential will have the form $b^{(\log_b A)}$.

Step 2. Use a Composition Identity to rewrite $b^{(\log_b A)}$ as A.

Step 3. If possible, simplify further by combining and dividing out like factors.

This process is illustrated in Examples 1 - 3.

To simplify an expression involving a logarithm base b of a product and/or quotient of powers of b, follow these steps.

Step 1. Use the Laws of Exponents to combine the exponentials so the logarithm base b applies to a single term which is b raised to some power A. The expression will now have the form $\log_b\left(b^A\right)$.

Step 2. Use a Composition Identity to rewrite $\log_b\left(b^A\right)$ as A.

Step 3 If possible, simplify further by combining and dividing out like factors.

This process is illustrated in Examples 4 - 6.

CALCULATOR COMMENTARY

An equation that results from (correctly) simplifying an expression is an *identity*. When numerical values for which all of the functions involved are defined are assigned to the independent variables, evaluating the expression in its original form and evaluating the expression in its simplified form will produce the same result.

As discussed in the Calculator Commentary for Objective 3.4, the TI-83® can be used to carry out these evaluations and test numerically whether an equation is an identity. If for some set of values for the variables the two evaluations can both be carried out and they produce different results, then the equation is not an identity. If there are no values of the variables for which the two evaluations can both be carried out that produce different results, then the equation is an identity.

It is impossible to evaluate expressions for an infinite number of values for the variables, so ordinarily one cannot demonstrate with absolute certainty that an equation is an identity by numerical testing. However, if the two evaluations produce the same numerical result (or one or both are not defined) for *a very large number of* different values for the variables selected from across the domains of the functions, then we are likely to be confident that the equation is an identity. Even with patience and prodigious calculator skills, one can test only a relatively small number of the possible values for the independent variables. This difficulty can be minimized, though not completely avoided, by using the graphs of the two expressions involved.

The graph of an expression is a geometric representation of its values. Two expressions have the same values if and only if they have the same graphs. Consequently, an equation is an identity if and only if the graphs of the expressions on the two sides of the equality coincide whenever both expressions are defined.

The expression

$$(x + 1)\, e^{\left[\ln\left(x^3 - 1\right) - \ln(x + 1)\right]}$$

simplifies to

$$x^3 - 1$$

(see problem 5 from the Practice Problems for this Objective). That is to say, the equation

$$(x + 1)\, e^{\left[\ln\left(x^3 - 1\right) - \ln(x + 1)\right]} = x^3 - 1$$

is an identity. Let's verify this claim graphically.

For the logarithmic functions in the expression on the left to be defined, both $x^3 - 1$ and $x + 1$ must be positive, so the domain of the function on the left consists of all numbers x greater than 1. At the same time, the domain of the expression on the right is all real numbers. When we say that this equation is an identity, we mean that for every $x > 1$ (*i. e.* for every number in the domain of *both* expressions), the two expressions have the same numerical values.

We can verify that for a very large number of values $x > 1$ these expressions do have the same values by using the TI-83® to see that their graphs coincide in the half of the coordinate plane where $x > 1$. This is the part of the plane to the right of the vertical line $x = 1$. Under the **Y =** menu, enter the expression on the left side of the equation as **Y1** and the expression on the right side as **Y2**. Under the WINDOW menu, set the calculator so the expressions are graphed one after the other by selecting **Sequential** on the ⌈MODE⌉ menu.

> Xmin = -1.5
> Xmax = 3.5
> Ymin = -5
> Ymax = 20

Press ⌈GRAPH⌉ and watch the graphs of the two functions evolve. Because the graphs coincide wherever both expressions are defined and because the graphs are generated quickly, it is difficult to see any differences between the two graphs on the calculator screen. This problem can be alleviated by graphing **Y1** and **Y2** in different styles. Change the style in which **Y2** is graphed by following these steps:

Step 1.   Press ⌈ Y= ⌉ to display the **Y** = editor.

Step 2.   Press the down arrow key to move the cursor to **Y2**.

Step 3.   Press the left arrow key twice to move the cursor left, past the = sign, to the style icon in the first column of the screen.

Step 4.   Press ⌈ENTER⌉ repeatedly until the icon −**O** for the "path" style appears.

Now press ⌈GRAPH⌉. First, **Y1** should be graphed as a solid line. Then **Y2** should be graphed as a circular cursor traces the leading edge of the graph as it is drawn.

TI Tip

> While the TI-83® is generating a graph, a moving vertical bar, called the busy indicator, is displayed in the upper right- hand corner of the screen. If you press ⌈ENTER⌉ while a graph is being plotted and the busy indicator is moving, the TI-83® will pause and only resume graphing after you press ⌈ENTER⌉ again.

The graphs show that the expressions $(x + 1) e^{\left[\ln\left(x^3 - 1\right) - \ln(x + 1)\right]}$ and $x^3 - 1$ have the same values for a very large number of values of the variable x for which both expressions are defined. Even though this experimental evidence does not prove that

$$(x + 1) e^{\left[\ln\left(x^3 - 1\right) - \ln(x + 1)\right]} = x^3 - 1$$

is an identity, most of us are now willing to believe that it is.

Even though we can't generate a graph of an expression involving several variables on the calculator, we can test equations involving several variables graphically for an identity by testing one variable at a time. Choose one of the variables in the expression to use as the "test" variable. Replace this variable by x on both sides of the equation. (If x is already the name of some other variable, change the name of that variable to some letter that does not appear in the equation.) The variable **Y** is reserved for special purposes and cannot be a variable in an expression to be graphed. If y is used as a variable in the equation, replace it by some other letter not already in use.

Enter these revised expressions from the left and right sides of the equation as **Y1** and **Y2**, using the ALPHA key to enter the variables as alphabetic characters. Choose the "path" style for the graph of **Y2**. Now store numerical values for all of the variables *other than* x in the memory locations bearing the names of the respective variables. Next, establish a viewing window by setting **Xmin**, **Xmax**, **Ymin**, and **Ymax** on the **WINDOW** screen. (If in doubt, use the standard viewing window.) Press GRAPH and compare the graphs.

Repeat this procedure several times with different viewing windows and different numerical values assigned to the variables *other than* x. If for some choice of numerical values for which both expressions are defined the graphs obtained do not coincide, the equation is not an identity. If the graphs coincide for every choice of numerical values and every viewing window, the equation is probably an identity. (What would you have to do to be sure it is an identity? Is it possible to do that?)

SUMMARY

1. **Composition Identities.** Let $f(x) = b^x$ and $g(x) = \log_b x$, $b > 0$, $b \neq 1$.
   For every positive number x,
   $$f(g(x)) = b^{(\log_b x)} = x.$$
   For every number x,
   $$g(f(x)) = \log_b(b^x) = x.$$

2. The Composition Identities hold when x is replaced by any variable, expression or function that takes on values for which the composition is defined.

3. To simplify b raised to a power which is a sum of multiples of logarithms base b, write the exponent as a single simplified logarithm. Then use a Composition Identity to eliminate the exponential and the logarithm.

4. To simplify the logarithm base b of a product and/or quotient of powers of b, combine the exponentials into a single simplified power of b. Then use a Composition Identity to eliminate the logarithm and the exponential.

EXAMPLES

Example 1: Simplify $5^{\log_5\left(3t^2+7\right)}$.

Solution 1: The Composition Identity $5^{\log_5 x} = x$ holds when x is replaced by $\left(3t^2+7\right)$. Therefore,

$$5^{\log_5\left(3t^2+7\right)} = 3t^2 + 7.$$

Example 2: Simplify $7^{\left[\log_7(s-r) + \log_7(s+r)\right]}$.

Solution 2: Using the Properties of Logarithms, write the exponent as a single logarithm. The expression becomes

$$7^{\left[\log_7(s-r) + \log_7(s+r)\right]} = 7^{\log_7(s-r)(s+r)}.$$

Use a Composition Identity to simplify further and get

$$7^{\left[\log_7(s-r) + \log_7(s+r)\right]} = 7^{\log_7(s-r)(s+r)} = (s-r)(s+r).$$

Example 3: Simplify $(x + 2y)e^{\left[\ln(x-2y) - \frac{1}{2}\ln\left(x^2-4y^2\right)\right]}$.

Solution 3: *Step 1.* Use the Properties of Logarithms to write the exponent as a single logarithm.

The expression becomes

$$(x+2y)e^{\left[\ln(x-2y) - \frac{1}{2}\ln\left(x^2-4y^2\right)\right]} = (x+2y)e^{\left[\ln\frac{x-2y}{\left(x^2-4y^2\right)^{1/2}}\right]}.$$

Step 2. By a Composition Identity,

$$(x+2y)e^{\left[\ln\frac{x-2y}{\left(x^2-4y^2\right)^{1/2}}\right]} = (x+2y) \cdot \frac{(x-2y)}{\left(x^2-4y^2\right)^{1/2}}.$$

Step 3. Simplify by factoring and dividing out common factors.

$$\frac{(x+2y)(x-2y)}{\left(x^2-4y^2\right)^{1/2}} = \frac{(x+2y)(x-2y)}{(x+2y)^{1/2}(x-2y)^{1/2}} = (x+2y)^{1/2}(x-2y)^{1/2}$$

The expression simplifies to $(x-2y)^{1/2}(x+2y)^{1/2}$.

Example 4: Verify graphically that the equation

$$(x + 2y)e^{\left[\ln (x - 2y) - \frac{1}{2}\ln \left(x^2 - 4y^2\right)\right]} = (x - 2y)^{\frac{1}{2}}(x + 2y)^{\frac{1}{2}}$$

derived in Example 3 is an identity.

Solution 4: The variable y cannot be used in any expression entered under the **Y=** menu. Replace y in the expression involved with some other letter (w, for example). Then enter

Y1 = (X + 2W)e∧(ln(X−2W) − 1/2 ln(X2 − 4W2))

and

Y2 = (X − 2W)∧(1/2)(X + 2W)∧(1/2)

under the **Y=** menu. Use the procedure described in the calculator commentary to choose the "path" style for the graph of **Y2**.

Store some numerical value (1, for example,) for w in memory **W**. Establish an appropriate viewing window—either by choosing **Standard** under the **ZOOM** menu or by specifying values for **Xmin**, **Xmax**, **Ymin**, and **Ymax** on the **WINDOW** screen. Now compare the graphs of the two expressions. Change the viewing window, compare the graphs again. Repeat this procedure several times with different numerical values assigned to the variable w and different viewing windows. For every choice of w and every viewing window the graphs will coincide, so we are willing to believe that this equation is an identity.

Example 5: Simplify $\log_{13} 13^{\left(\frac{1}{2z^2 + 1}\right)}$.

Solution 5: The Composition Identity $\log_{13}\left(13^x\right) = x$ holds when x is replaced by $\dfrac{1}{2z^2 + 1}$.

Therefore,

$$\log_{13} 13^{\left(\frac{1}{2z^2 + 1}\right)} = \frac{1}{2z^2 + 1}.$$

Example 6: Simplify $(3t - 1)\log\left[10^{(3t + 1)}10^{(t - 1)}\right]$.

Solution 6: *Step 1.* Multiply the exponential terms and obtain

$$(3t - 1)\log\left[10^{(3t + 1)}10^{(t - 1)}\right] = (3t - 1)\log\left[10^{3t + 1 + t - 1}\right]$$

$$= (3t - 1)\log\left(10^{4t}\right).$$

Step 2. By a Composition Identity,

$$(3t - 1) \log \left(10^{4t}\right) = (3t - 1)(4t).$$

The expression simplifies to $4t(3t - 1)$.

Example 7: Simplify $(a + b) \log_2 \sqrt{\dfrac{2^{(a + b)^2}}{2^{4ab}}}$.

Solution 7:   *Step 1.*   Write the exponentials as a single term which is 2 raised to some power.

$$\sqrt{\frac{2^{(a + b)^2}}{2^{4ab}}} = \left[2^{(a + b)^2 - 4ab}\right]^{1/2} = \left[2^{a^2 - 2ab + b^2}\right]^{1/2}$$

$$= \left[2^{(a - b)^2}\right]^{1/2} = 2^{1/2(a - b)^2}$$

Step 2. By a Composition Identity,

$$(a + b) \log_2 \left[2^{1/2(a - b)^2}\right] = (a + b)\frac{1}{2}(a - b)^2.$$

The expression simplifies to $\dfrac{1}{2}(a + b)(a - b)^2$.

PRACTICE PROBLEMS
In problems 1 - 6, simplify the given expression by following the steps used in Examples 1 - 3. For several of these problems, verify graphically that the equation you obtained by simplifying the given expression is an identity.

1. $e^{\ln (2t + 5)}$

2. $3^{3 \log_3 [x(x + 1)]}$

3. $10^{\left[2 \log (t + 3) - \log \left(t^2 + t - 6\right)\right]}$

4. $(x - y)7^{\left[\log_7 \left(x^2 - y^2\right) - 3/2 \log_7 (x + y)\right]}$

5. $(t + 1)e^{\left[\ln \left(t^3 - 1\right) - \ln (t + 1)\right]}$

6. $2^{\left[3/2 \log_2 \left(y^2 + y - 6\right) + \log_2 \left(y^2 - 4y + 4\right) - \log_2 \left(y^3 - 4y^2 + 4y\right)\right]}$

In problems 7 - 12, simplify the given expression by following the steps used in Examples 5 - 7. For several of these problems, verify graphically that the equation you obtained by simplifying the given expression is an identity.

7. $\log_{15} 15^{\left(\frac{1}{y^2+1}\right)}$

10. $\log \sqrt[3]{\dfrac{10^{\left(a^2+b^2\right)}}{10^{2ab}}}$

8. $\ln\left[e^{(5y-1)} \cdot e^{(y+3)}\right]$

11. $(x+y)\log_6 \sqrt[7]{\dfrac{6^{\left(x^2+4y^2\right)}}{6^{-4xy}}}$

9. $\log_5 \dfrac{5^{(z+1)} \cdot 5^{(z-1)}}{5^{2z}}$

12. $(b-c)\log_4\left[4^{3a/(b+c)} \cdot 4^{1/(b-c)}\right]$

In problems 13 - 24, simplify the given expression.

13. $\dfrac{1}{x+2y}\log_3 3^{\left(x^2-4y^2\right)}$

16. $(t-s)^{-1}\log\left[10^{\left(5st+t^2\right)} \cdot 10^{\left(s^2-3st\right)}\right]$

14. $(t+3)5^{\left[\log_5\left(t^2-5t+6\right)-\log_5\left(t^2-9\right)\right]}$

17. $\left(x^2+xy+y^2\right)5^{\left[\log_5\left(x^3+y^3\right)-\log_5(x+y)\right]}$

15. $e^{\left[\frac{1}{2}\ln(2a-b)-\frac{3}{2}\ln\left(4a^2-4ab+b^2\right)^{-1}\right]}$

18. $\ln\sqrt[5]{\dfrac{e^{10y}}{e^{25x^2}}}$

19. $(a + b)^{1/2} \log_7 \left[7^{(2a - 3b)} \cdot 7^{(4b - a)} \right]$

20. $(t - u) 10^{\left[\log(t^2 - u^2) + \frac{1}{3} \log(t^2 + 2ut + u^2) - \frac{5}{3} \log(t - u) \right]}$

21. $\dfrac{1}{x - y} \log_4 \sqrt[3]{\dfrac{4^{3x^2} \cdot 4^{3xy}}{4^{6y^2}}}$

22. $\log \left[10^{\left(5st + t^2 \right)} \cdot 10^{\left(s^2 - 3st \right)} \right] + 4^{\log_4 5st}$

23. $2^{\left[\ln e^{\left(\log_2 (7x + 3) - \log_2 (2x - 1) \right)} \right]}$

24. $(3 + y) \log \left[5^{\log_5 \left(10^{(2y + 3)} \cdot 10^{(2y - 3)} \right)} \right]$

AUTHOR'S NOTE

"'...First you have the natural numbers. The ones that are whole and positive. The numbers of a small child. But human consciousness expands. The child discovers a sense of longing, and do you know what the mathematical expression is for longing?'...'The negative numbers. The formalization of the feeling that you are missing something...and the child discovers the in between spaces...[And that] leads to fractions. Whole numbers plus fractions produce rational numbers. And human consciousness doesn't stop there. It wants to go beyond reason. It add an operation as absurd as the extraction of roots. And produces irrational numbers...It's a form of madness. Because the irrational numbers are infinite. They can't be written down. They force human consciousness out beyond the limits. And by adding irrational numbers to rational numbers, you get real numbers...It doesn't stop. It never stops. Because now...we expand the real numbers with imaginary square roots of negative numbers. These are numbers we can't picture, numbers that normal human consciousness cannot comprehend. And when we add the imaginary numbers to the real numbers, we have the comples number system...'"

Recommended reading - Mystery: Above quotation from *Smilla's Sense of Snow* by Peter Høeg, or the movie, *Smilla's Sense of Snow* starring Julia Ormond

OBJECTIVE 4.2
Solve logarithmic equations algebraically.

DISCUSSION

An equation such as $\ln(x + 1) - \ln(x - 1) = 0.693$ or $\log(x + 4) = 2$ which involves a logarithmic function is called a **logarithmic equation**. The problem addressed in this Discussion is to find all of the numbers which satisfy a given logarithmic equation.

Some logarithmic equations, such as $\log x = 1$, can be solved by inspection (here $x = 10$). Others, such as $\log_5(x + 1) - 2\log_2 x = 1$, can only be solved by numerical (rather than algebraic) methods. The equations we will study fall between these two extremes. They are solved algebraically by using the properties of exponential and logarithmic functions, algebra and a calculator. The key to solving one of these equations is to rewrite it as an exponential equation and solve that equation by algebra. The resulting numbers include all of the solutions to the original equation and, quite possibly, some extraneous solutions. Solutions can be identified only by checking them in the original equation. Substituting an extraneous solution into the equation will always result in an undefined term which comes from applying a logarithm to a negative number. There may even be no solutions.

Logarithmic equations are not all solved in exactly the same way. The logarithmic equations in this book, however, can be solved by following these general steps.

Step 1. Change the form of the equation so it has a single logarithmic term on one side and a constant on the other. The Properties of Logarithms and algebra are used to do this. Sometimes the original equation is replaced by two equations at this step.

Step 2. Write an exponential equation with the same meaning. Evaluate the numerical powers involved, using a calculator as necessary.

Step 3. Solve the equation from Step 2 by algebra to obtain the possible solutions (including the extraneous solutions).

Step 4. Distinguish between solutions and extraneous solutions by substituting into the original equation.

SUMMARY

To solve a logarithmic equation follow these steps:

1. Rewrite the equation so it has one logarithmic term on the left and a constant on the right.
2. Write the equivalent exponential equation.
3. Solve the equation from step 2.
4. Distinguish between solutions and extraneous solutions by substituting into the original equation.

EXAMPLES

Example 1:   Solve the logarithmic equation $\log_5(7x + 6) - 3 = 0$.

Solution 1:   *Step 1.*   Write the equation with the logarithmic term on the left and a constant on the right.

$$\log_5(7x + 6) = 3$$

Step 2. Write the equivalent exponential equation.

$$5^3 = 7x + 6 \quad \text{or} \quad 7x + 6 = 125$$

Step 3.   Solve for x.

$$7x = 119$$
$$x = 17$$

Step 4.   Check by substituting $x = 17$ into the original equation.

$$\log_5\left[7(17) + 6\right] = \log_5 125 = \log_5 5^3 = 3$$

The solution to this equation is $x = 17$.

Example 2: Solve the logarithmic equation $\log_2(x - 2) + \log_2(x + 1) = 2$.

Solution 2:   *Step 1.*   Write the equation with one logarithmic term on the left and a constant on the right. By the Product Property for Logarithms we have

$$\log_2(x - 2)(x + 1) = 2.$$

Step 2. Write the equivalent exponential equation.

$$2^2 = (x - 2)(x + 1) \quad \text{or} \quad x^2 - x - 2 = 4$$

Step 3.   Solve for x.

$$x^2 - x - 6 = 0$$
$$(x - 3)(x + 2) = 0$$
$$x = 3 \quad \text{or} \quad x = -2$$

Step 4. Substitute $x = 3$ into the original equation.

$$\log_2(3 - 2) + \log_2(3 + 1) = \log_2 1 + \log_2 2^2 = 0 + 2 = 2$$

Thus, $x = 3$ is a solution. Substitute $x = -2$ into the original equation.

$$\log_2(-2 - 2) + \log_2(-2 + 1) = \log_2(-4) + \log_2(-1)$$

These expressions are not defined. Thus, $x = -2$ is not a solution.
The solution to this equation is $x = 3$.

Example 3: Solve $\ln(3x + 5) - \ln(x - 1) = 1.609438$.

Solution 3: *Step 1.* Write the left side as one logarithmic term.

$$\ln \frac{3x + 5}{x - 1} = 1.609438$$

Step 2. Write an exponential equation.

$$e^{1.609438} = \frac{3x + 5}{x - 1} \quad \text{or} \quad \frac{3x + 5}{x - 1} = 5$$

Step 3. Solve for x.

$$3x + 5 = 5(x - 1)$$
$$3x + 5 = 5x - 5$$
$$2x = 10$$
$$x = 5$$

Step 4. Substitute $x = 5$ into the original equation. Rounded to six decimal places,

$$\ln\left[3(5) + 5\right] - \ln\left[5 - 1\right] = \ln 20 - \ln 4 = 1.609438.$$

The solution to this equation is $x \cong 5$.

Example 4: Solve $\log_2\left[\log_3(5 - 4x)\right] = 2$.

Solution 4: *Step 1.* Not needed.

Step 2. Write an exponential equation.

$$2^2 = \log_3(5 - 4x) \quad \text{or} \quad \log_3(5 - 4x) = 4$$

The result is another logarithmic equation. Write this equation as an exponential equation.

$$3^4 = 5 - 4x \quad \text{or} \quad 5 - 4x = 81$$

Step 3. Solve for x.

$$4x = -76$$
$$x = -19$$

Step 4. Substitute $x = -19$ into the original equation.

$$\log_2\left[\log_3\left(5 - 4(-19)\right)\right] = \log_2\left[\log_3 81\right]$$

$$= \log_2\left[\log_3 3^4\right] = \log_2 4$$

$$= \log_2\left[2^2\right] = 2$$

The solution to this equation is $x = -19$.

Example 5: Solve the logarithmic equation $(\ln x)^2 + \ln x^2 - 8 = 0$.

Solution 5: The Properties of Logarithms cannot be used to combine the logarithmic terms on the left. Additional algebraic manipulations are needed in Step 1 to transform this equation into the desired form.

Step 1. Use the Power Property for Logarithms to write the equation as
$$(\ln x)^2 + 2\ln x - 8 = 0.$$

This is a quadratic equation in $\ln x$. Replace $\ln x$ with z and write the equation as
$$z^2 + 2z - 8 = 0 \quad \text{or} \quad (z + 4)(z - 2) = 0.$$

From the factored form of the equation we see that $z = -4$ or $z = 2$. Replace z by $\ln x$ to get the logarithmic equations of the desired form.
$$\ln x = -4 \quad \text{or} \quad \ln x = 2$$

Step 2. Write the exponential equations.
$$e^{-4} = x \quad \text{or} \quad e^2 = x$$

Step 3. Compute x from the equations in Step 2.
$$x = e^{-4} = 0.0183156389 \quad \text{and} \quad x = e^2 = 7.389056099$$

Step 4. Substitute $x = e^{-4} = 0.0183156389$ into the original equation.

$$\left(\ln e^{-4}\right)^2 + \ln\left(e^{-4}\right)^2 - 8 = (-4)^2 + \ln\left(e^{-8}\right) - 8 = 16 - 8 - 8 = 0$$

Substitute $x = e^2 = 7.389056099$ into the original equation.

$$\left(\ln e^2\right)^2 + \ln\left(e^2\right)^2 - 8 = (2)^2 + \ln e^4 - 8 = 4 + 4 - 8 = 0$$

The solutions to this equation are

$$x = e^{-4} = 0.0183156389 \quad \text{and} \quad x = e^2 = 7.389056099.$$

PRACTICE PROBLEMS

Solve the following logarithmic equations.

Problems 1 - 3 are similar to Example 1.

1. $\log_2(x - 1) = 4$ **2.** $2\log_3(2x - 4) = 2$ **3.** $\log_5(x^2 - 6x - 2) = 1$

Problems 4 - 9 are similar to Examples 2 and 3.

4. $\log_6(x + 4) + \log_6(x - 1) = 1$ **7.** $\log(4x + 1) - \log(5x - 2) = 0$

5. $\log_5(2x + 1) + \log_5(x - 2) = 2$ **8.** $2\log_3(x + 1) - \log_3(x^2 - 3x - 4) = -1$

6. $\log(x - 4) + \log(x + 2) = 0.845098$ **9.** $\log_{81}(5x - 1) - \log_{81}(x + 2) = \dfrac{1}{2}$

Problems 10 - 12 are similar to Example 4.

10. $\log\left(\log_2(3x + 7)\right) = 0.4771213$

11. $\log_3\left(\log_8(2x - 7)\right) = -1$

12. $\log_5\left(\log_2(4x + 3)\right) = 1$

Problems 13 - 15 are similar to Example 5.

13. $(\log_2 x)^2 - \log_2 x = 6$ **14.** $2(\log_4 x)^2 + \log_4 x^3 = 5$ **15.** $3(\ln x)^2 - 7(\ln x) = 6$

16. $\log(x - 1) + \log(x - 3) = 1.1760913$ **21.** $3(\log x)^2 - 8\log x^2 = -5$

17. $\log_2\left(\log_{16}(9x - 5)\right) = -2$ **22.** $\ln(5x + 2) + \ln(x - 1) = 2.484907$

18. $(\log_5 x)^2 - 7 = -2\log_5 x^3$ **23.** $\log_2\left(\log_{25}(3x - 1)\right) + 1 = 0$

19. $\ln(5x + 2) = 3$ **24.** $\log_2(2x - 3) - \log_2(x - 5) = -2$

20. $2\log_3(x + 3) - \log_3(x^2 + 8x + 15) = 2$ **25.** $\log(x^2 - x - 15) = 0.69897$

OBJECTIVE 4.3

Solve exponential equations algebraically.

DISCUSSION

An equation such as $2^x + 3 \cdot 2^{-x} = 5$ or $3^{(2x - 5)} = 7$ which has variables in exponents is called an **exponential equation**. The problem addressed in this Discussion is to find all numbers x which satisfy a given exponential equation.

Some exponential equations, like $2^x = 8$, can be solved by inspection. Others, such as $2^x + 3^{-x} = 2x + 1$, can only be solved by numerical (rather than algebraic) methods. Our concern is with the exponential equations that fall between these two extremes — too complicated to be solved by inspection, but not so complicated that numerical methods are needed. These equations can be solved algebraically by using the properties of logarithmic and exponential functions, algebra and a calculator.

Because exponentials and logarithms are inverse functions, one would expect the procedure for solving exponential equations to be analogous to that for logarithmic equations. We would expect to solve an exponential equation by rewriting it with a single exponential term on one side and a constant on the other, writing the equivalent logarithmic equation and, finally, finding the unknown from this logarithmic equation. This procedure will work, but it is computationally difficult. It requires evaluating logarithms with arbitrary bases. Calculators are designed to compute arbitrary exponentials, but they only compute logarithms base 10 and base e. Consequently, we modify the procedure for solving exponential equations to avoid evaluating logarithms with arbitrary bases.

Our procedure for solving exponential equations will be to write the equation so it has one exponential term or a constant on each side of the equality and then take a logarithm of both sides of the equation. The simplified equation can then be solved by algebra. To solve exponential equations, follow these steps.

Step 1. Change the form of the equation so it has a single exponential term on one side of the equality and either only a constant or only an exponential term on the other side. Use the Laws of Exponents and algebra to do this. Sometimes the original equation is replaced by two equations at this step.

Step 2.   Apply a logarithmic function to both sides of the equation. Use a logarithmic function with a base that makes evaluation easy (usually e or 10). The best choice of base depends on the numbers that appear in the problem.

Step 3.   Use the Properties of Logarithms to eliminate logarithms of exponentials and simplify the equation. Evaluate the logarithms of numbers, using a calculator as necessary.

Step 4.   Solve the equation from Step 3 by algebra.

Extraneous solutions to logarithmic equations arise because logarithms cannot be applied to negative numbers. This does not happen with exponential functions which are defined for all numbers x. It is usually not necessary to check for extraneous solutions to exponential equations. Checking solutions by substitution, however, is an excellent way to detect errors in your work.

The details of applying this step by step procedure will vary among equations. With some equations, the first step will require the most ingenuity. For others, the last step will be the most challenging. Reading examples and doing problems are the best ways to learn to solve equations. Several Examples and many Practice Problems follow the discussion.

CALCULATOR COMMENTARY

A solution to an equation is a set of numerical values for the variables involved having the property that using these values to evaluate the expression on the left side of the equal sign produces the same result as using these values to evaluate the expression on the right side. To solve an equation means to find all such sets of numerical values — *i.e.,* to find all solutions.

The calculator is an ideal tool for determining whether a particular set of values for the variables is a solution to a given equation. To illustrate, let's use the TI-83® to determine whether the numerical values $r = \dfrac{1 + \sqrt{34}}{5}$, $s = 0.4$ are a solution to the logarithmic equation

$$\log(r - 2s) + \log(r + s) = 0.$$

Enter the left member of the equation as **Y1** under the **Y=** menu using the ALPHA key to enter the variables **R** and **S**. Store $\dfrac{1 + \sqrt{34}}{5}$ in memory **R** and 0.4 in memory **S**. Press VARS , then the right arrow key to highlight **Y-VARS**. Then press 1 , 1 to recall **Y1**. Press ENTER and the calculator will evaluate the expression **Y1** using the values stored in memories **R** and **S**. The result is 0. (Because of rounding some other calculators may give a small number, not zero, as the result.) Thus, the numerical values $r = \dfrac{1 + \sqrt{34}}{5}$, $s = 0.4$ are a solution to the logarithmic equation . To determine if the values $r = 2$, $s = 0.5$ are a solution, store 2 in memory **R** and 0.5 in memory **S**. Recall **Y1** and press ENTER to find that the value of **Y1** for these values of r and s is not zero. Thus, the values $r = 2$, $s = 0.5$ are not a solution to this logarithmic equation. Use this technique to check your solutions to equations from the Practice Problems for Objectives 4.2 and 4.3.

Because possible solutions can be checked easily with a calculator, it might seem feasible to solve an equation by a "guessing and checking" procedure like this:

Step 1. Guess values for the unknowns.

Step 2. Evaluate the expressions on the two sides of the equation using the values for the unknowns selected in Step 1.

Step 3. If evaluating the two expressions yields the same results, accept these values as a solution. Otherwise, reject them.

Step 4. Continue until all solutions are found.

Random guessing and checking is neither effective nor efficient. However, systematic guessing and checking can be effective and efficient and is the basis for some numerical routines for solving equations. Numerical routines for solving equations are pre-programmed into the TI-83®. Look in the *TI-83 Graphing Calculator Guidebook* under **solve**, **root** and **intersect** to learn what these programs do and how to use them.

Instead of using pre-programmed numerical routines, we'll use the graphing capabilities of the TI-83® to solve equations. We will focus on logarithmic and exponential equations, but these graphical procedures can be used just as well with any equation in one unknown whose left and right members can be entered under the **Y =** menu.

The equation $2^x - 3^{-x} = 0.5x + 3$ can't be solved algebraically, but by using graphical means we can approximate the solutions with accuracy limited only by the capacity of the calculator. The solutions to this equation are the x-coordinates of the points where the graphs of $y = 2^x - 3^{-x}$ and $y = 0.5x + 3$ intersect. Since any intersection points lie on both graphs, its coordinates satisfy both of the equations $y = 2^x - 3^{-x}$ and $y = 0.5x + 3$. Thus, the x-coordinate of the intersection point produces the same y-value when substituted into either of the two expressions $2^x - 3^{-x}$ and $0.5x + 3$. That makes this x-value be a solution to the original equation! Our goal, then, is to find all of the points where the graphs intersect.

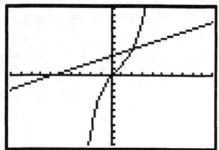

Figure 4CC.1 Graphs of **Y1** = $2^x - 3^{-x}$ and **Y2** = $0.5x + 3$

To begin, enter $2^x - 3^{-x}$ as **Y1** and $0.5x + 3$ as **Y2** on the **Y =** screen. Press ⌊ZOOM⌋ , ⌊ 6 ⌋ to generate the graphs in the standard viewing window as shown in Figure 4CC.1.

The graphs *appear* to intersect at only one point, but do they also intersect at other points outside this viewing window? To gain some assurance that there are no other intersection points, press ⌊ZOOM⌋ , scroll to **MEMORY** and press ⌊ 4 ⌋ to choose **Set Factors**.

Enter **2** for both **XFact** and **YFact**. Press ZOOM and press ⎡ **3** ⎤ to choose **Zoom Out**. Now each time you press ENTER , the graphs will be generated in a new viewing window covering twice the range of x-values and twice the range of y-values as the previous one. Press ENTER several times, pausing to observe the graphs as they are regenerated. The two curves appear to continue on their original courses, so it is unlikely that they intersect at any other points. We are confident there is only one intersection point and, hence, only one solution. Our task now is to find that solution to several decimal places from the graph.

Press ZOOM again and choose **Standard** to return to the graphs shown in Figure 4CC.1. Press the arrow keys several times and observe the display. A cursor (+) appears and moves one cell (pixel) horizontally or vertically each time an arrow key is pressed. The coordinates of the cursor's position are shown at the bottom of the screen. Move the cursor as nearly as possible to the point where the graphs intersect. Because the cursor can only be positioned at the cells (pixels) of the calculator screen, it can't be positioned exactly at the point where our eye tells us the graphs intersect. Nevertheless, we can see that the coordinates of the point of intersection are about $(2, 4)$.

We can also use TRACE to estimate the intersection point. Press this key. A special flashing cursor appears on the graph of **Y1** $= 2^x - 3^{-x}$. Press the up and down arrow keys. Each time either key is pressed, the cursor moves from one of the graphs to other. If there were more graphs displayed, the cursor would cycle through all those that are turned on in the order they are listed on the **Y** = screen. The equation in the upper left corner of the screen identifies the graph the cursor is following. Position the cursor on the graph of **Y1** $= 2^x - 3^{-x}$. Now, press the left and right arrow keys and observe how the cursor moves along the graph. The coordinates of its position are displayed at the bottom of the screen. The x-coordinate is the position in the coordinate system of the pixel where the cursor is located, just as in the case of free cursor movement. But now the y-coordinate is computed from the x-coordinate using the equation of the curve from the **Y** = screen. As a result, the y-coordinate assigned to a cursor position reached by **TRACE**ing along **Y1** is probably different from the y-coordinate assigned to the same cursor position by **TRACE**ing along **Y2**. Both of these y-coordinates are probably different from that assigned to this position by free cursor movements. By **TRACE**ing along either the graph of **Y1** or along the graph of **Y2** to the intersection point, we also estimate that the coordinates of the intersection point are about, but not exactly, $(2, 4)$. Find the y-coordinates assigned to the point where the graphs appear to intersect by each of these procedures (*i.e.,* **TRACE**ing **Y1**, **TRACE**ing **Y2**, and free cursor movement) and note the different y-coordinates obtained. To leave the **TRACE** mode, press GRAPH .

We **Zoom In** to take a closer look at the graph and improve our estimate of the coordinates of the intersection point. Press ZOOM , scroll to **MEMORY**, press 4 to choose **Set Factors**, and set **XFact** and **YFact** both to **10**. (Any zoom factors greater than 1 could be used, but with zoom factors **10** with each **ZOOM** we can expect to gain one decimal place of accuracy in our estimation of the intersection point.) Use TRACE (or the cursor movement keys) to position the cursor as close as possible to the point where the graphs intersect. Press ZOOM again, then 2 to choose **Zoom In**. When ENTER is pressed, a new viewing window centered at the location of the cursor and with the interval of x- and y-values reduced in length by a factor of **10** will appear. This window will show a much smaller section of the graphs, but in it the graphs are magnified by a factor of **10**. Press ENTER and watch as the graphs are regenerated. (To see the range of x- and y-values in this new viewing window, press WINDOW . Press GRAPH to return to the graph.)

In this new window, press TRACE and move the cursor as close as possible to the point where the graphs intersect. Rounded to the nearest tenth, we now estimate the coordinates of the point of intersection to be $(2.0, 4.0)$.

Leave the cursor at the intersection point and press ZOOM , 2 and ENTER to again **Zoom In** on the point of intersection. After zooming in this second time, estimate the coordinates of the point of intersection to be $(2.02, 4.02)$. Continue this procedure until zooming again produces no change in the fifth decimal place of the estimation for the x-coordinate of the intersection point. Expect this to occur after zooming five times (with zoom factors of **10**). After zooming in 5 times, we estimate that the coordinates of the point of intersection expressed to five decimal places are $(2.04561, 4.02281)$. **Zoom In** one more time to see whether the estimate changes in the fifth decimal place. From this work we conclude that the equation has one solution and, expressed to five decimal places, it is $x = 2.04561$.

To determine the solution to greater accuracy, continue this process of **ZOOM**ing and **TRACE**ing. To how many decimal places can you determine the solution before the resolution of the calculator screen is exceeded and you get an error message?

The shapes of the graphs determine how easily an equation can be solved by **ZOOM**ing and **TRACE**ing. To solve

$$\ln(11x + 5) = 3 \ln 5$$

graphically, we adapt the previous procedure to cope with characteristics of the graphs of logarithmic functions.

As before, begin by entering the expression $\ln(11x + 5)$ as **Y1** and the expression $3 \ln 5$ as **Y2** on the **Y =** screen and generate their graphs in the standard viewing window. As Figure 4CC.2

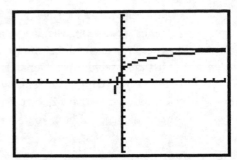

shows, the graphs do not intersect in the standard viewing window. **Zoom Out** to look for intersection points in larger windows. Press ZOOM , scroll to **MEMORY**, press 4 to choose **Set Factors**, and enter **2** for both **XFact** and **YFact**.

Figure 4CC.2 Graphs of **Y1** = $\ln(11x + 5)$ and **Y2** = $3\ln 5$

Press ZOOM , 3 to choose **Zoom Out**. Move the cursor to a point on the *x*-axis half way between the origin and the right edge of the screen. Then press ENTER to **Zoom Out**. Again move the cursor to a point on the *x*-axis half way between the origin and the right edge of the screen and press ENTER to **Zoom Out** a second time. The graphs that appear after **Zoom**ing **Out** twice are so close together that it is difficult to recognize intersection points. We are not gaining much information about the global behavior of these graphs by **Zoom**ing **Out**!

The graphs are close together in larger viewing windows because the logarithmic function increases very slowly as *x* increases. We can visually separate the graphs by **Zoom**ing **Out** more rapidly in the horizontal direction than in the vertical direction. Change the **ZOOM** factors to **XFact = 2** and **YFact = 1**. Press ZOOM again and choose **Standard** to return to the original graphs. Now **Zoom Out** as before, each time designating the point on the *x*-axis half way between the *y*-axis and the right side of the screen as the center of the new window. After **Zoom**ing **Out** once, notice that the two graphs appear to intersect some place to the right of $x = 10$. (They didn't intersect in the standard viewing window, so they don't intersect to the left of 10.) After **Zoom**ing **Out** several times, we see that the two graphs appear to continue on their original courses, so it is unlikely that they intersect at any other points. We are now convinced that the equation has only one solution. Our task is to find it accurately.

Since the solution is not to be found within the standard viewing window, first establish a window that includes the intersection point. Press WINDOW . Set **Xmin = -1, Xmax = 17.8, Ymin = -.1, Ymax = 6.1**. Press GRAPH . Since the graphs intersect within this window, we can use these graphs to begin the procedure for finding the solution.

As before, set **XFact** and **YFact** both to **10**. Locate the cursor as near as possible to the intersection point. **Zoom In** on the point of intersection by pressing ZOOM , 2 , ENTER . Reposition the cursor on the intersection point and press ENTER again to **Zoom In** on the intersection point a second time. After **Zoom**ing twice the graphs are so close together that it is difficult to see intersection points. If we **Zoom In** again, the graphs will be even closer. The graphs are close together in a smaller viewing window because the graph of logarithmic function is nearly horizontal near the x-value we are seeking. We can separate the graphs by **Zoom**ing **Out** more rapidly in the vertical direction than in the horizontal direction. Set **XFact = 10** and **YFact = 15**. Also, reset the **WINDOW** values to **Xmin = -1, Xmax = 17.8, Ymin = -.1, Ymax = 6.1**. Now **Zoom In** and estimate repeatedly as before to find the solution to several decimal places. Check your solution by substituting into **Y1**.

The equation $\ln(11x + 5) = 3\ln 5$ can also be solved algebraically. Solve the equation algebraically. Compare the exact solution you obtain algebraically with the approximate solution obtained from analyzing the graphs. Could you have guessed the exact solution from the approximate solution?

SUMMARY

To solve an exponential equation follow these steps:

1. Rewrite the equation so it has one exponential term on the left and either an exponential term or a constant on the right.

2. Apply a logarithmic function to both sides of the equation.

3. Use Properties of Logarithms to simplify the equation.

4. Solve the equation from Step 3.

EXAMPLES

Example 1: Solve the exponential equation $7^x - 31 = 0$. Round off the answer to five decimal places.

Solution 1: *Step 1.* Rewrite the equation so it has an exponential term on the left and a constant on the right.
$$7^x = 31$$
Step 2. Apply the function log (or ln) to both sides of the equation.
$$\log\left(7^x\right) = \log 31$$
Step 3. Simplify.
$$x \log 7 = \log 31$$
Step 4. Solve for x. Rounded to five decimal places
$$x = \frac{\log 31}{\log 7} = 1.76472.$$

Note 1. In Example 1, any logarithmic function, $\log_b$, could be used in Step 2. Use log or ln because these functions can be evaluated on a calculator. Try Example 1 again using ln instead of log.

Note 2. In Objective 3.2 we considered the problem of finding the numerical value of x when $x = \log_b a$. We could find x only when we could recognize a as a power of b. Now we can compute x from this equation for all bases b and all $a > 0$. To do this, rewrite the logarithmic equation $x = \log_b a$ as the exponential equation $a = b^x$. Solve this exponential equation by the methods of Example 1 and find that $\log_b a = \dfrac{\ln a}{\ln b}$ or $\log_b a = \dfrac{\log a}{\log b}$. These equations are called the **Change of Base Formulas**.

Example 2: Solve the exponential equation $9^{\left(x^2 - \frac{3}{2}x + \frac{1}{2}\right)} = 27$.

Solution 2:   *Step 1.*   Not needed.

Step 2.   The constant and the base of the exponential are powers of 3. We can find their logarithm base 3. Apply the function $\log_3$ to both sides of the equation.

$$\log_3 9^{\left(x^2 - \frac{3}{2}x + \frac{1}{2}\right)} = \log_3 27$$

Note that log or ln could also be used in this step. If we use log or ln, however, the numbers in Step 3 will not be integers.

Step 3.   Simplify $\log_3 9^{\left(x^2 - \frac{3}{2}x + \frac{1}{2}\right)} = \log_3 27$.

$$\left(x^2 - \frac{3}{2}x + \frac{1}{2}\right)\log_3\left(3^2\right) = \log_3\left(3^3\right)$$

$$\left(x^2 - \frac{3}{2}x + \frac{1}{2}\right) \cdot 2 = 3$$

$$2x^2 - 3x + 1 = 3$$

Step 4. Solve for x.

$$2x^2 - 3x - 2 = 0$$

$$(2x + 1)(x - 2) = 0$$

$$x = -\frac{1}{2} \quad \text{or} \quad x = 2$$

Example 3: Solve $5^{(3x - 2)} - 3 \cdot 2^{(x + 1)} = 0$. Round off the answer to four decimal places.

Solution 3:   *Step 1.*   Rewrite the equation so it has one exponential term on each side of the equality.
$$5^{(3x - 2)} = 3 \cdot 2^{(x + 1)}$$

Step 2. Apply the function ln (or log) to both sides of the equation.
$$\ln\left[5^{(3x - 2)}\right] = \ln\left[3 \cdot 2^{(x + 1)}\right]$$

Step 3. Simplify.
$$(3x - 2)\ln 5 = \ln 3 + \ln\left[2^{(x + 1)}\right]$$

$$(3x - 2)\ln 5 = \ln 3 + (x + 1)\ln 2$$

Step 4. Solve for x. Round to four decimal places.
$$(3\ln 5)x - 2\ln 5 = \ln 3 + \ln 2 + (\ln 2)x$$
$$(3\ln 5 - \ln 2)x = \ln 3 + \ln 2 + 2\ln 5$$
$$x = \frac{\ln 3 + \ln 2 + 2\ln 5}{3\ln 5 - \ln 2} = 1.2117$$

Example 4: Solve $5^x - 4\left(5^{-x}\right) = 3$. Round the answer to four decimal places.

Solution 4:   The Laws of Exponents cannot be used to combine the exponentials on the left. Additional algebraic manipulations are needed in Step 1 to transform the equation into the desired form.

Step 1. Multiply each term of the equation by 5^x.
$$5^{2x} - 4 = 3\left(5^x\right) \quad \text{or} \quad 5^{2x} - 3\left(5^x\right) - 4 = 0$$

Rewrite this equation as a quadratic equation in 5^x.
$$\left(5^x\right)^2 - 3\left(5^x\right) - 4 = 0$$

Replace 5^x by z and write the equation as
$$z^2 - 3z - 4 = 0 \quad \text{or} \quad (z - 4)(z + 1) = 0.$$

From the factored form of the equation we see that
$$z = 4 \quad \text{or} \quad z = -1.$$

Replace z by 5^x to get exponential equations of the desired form.
$$5^x = 4 \quad \text{or} \quad 5^x = -1$$

Steps 2 - 4. Solve each exponential equation.

From $5^x = 4$

we find $x \ln 5 = \ln 4$

and, rounded to four decimal places, $x = \dfrac{\ln 4}{\ln 5} = 0.8614.$

The equation $5^x = -1$ has no solution since for every real number

$x, 5^x > 0$. The only solution to this equation is $x = \dfrac{\ln 4}{\ln 5} = 0.8614.$

PRACTICE PROBLEMS

Solve the following exponential equations. Problems 1 - 5 are similar to Examples 1 and 2.

1. $4^x = 15$

2. $3 \cdot 5^x = 57$

3. $3^{(2x + 1)} = 108$

4. $8^{\left(x^2 + \frac{13}{3}x - \frac{8}{3}\right)} = 4$

5. $e^{\left(x^2 + 5x + 6\right)} = 7.38906$

Problems 6 - 9 are similar to Example 3.

6. $5^{(3x - 8)} = 4^{(2x + 7)}$

7. $4 \cdot 2^{(3x + 1)} = 8^{(2x - 5)}$

8. $7 \cdot 3^{(8x - 1)} = 5^{-x}$

9. $\left(\dfrac{1}{7}\right)^{(3x - 4)} = 49^{(5x + 10)}$

Problems 10 - 12 are similar to Example 4.

10. $2^x + 4\left(2^{-x}\right) = 5$

11. $2e^x - 5e^{-x} = 9$

12. $2\left(3^{2x}\right) = -3^x$

13. $25^{\left(x^2 - x - \frac{5}{2}\right)} = \dfrac{1}{5}$

17. $\dfrac{1}{3} \cdot 27^{(3x - 6)} = 9^{(x + 3)}$

14. $e^{(4x + 3)} = 5^{(x - 7)}$

18. $10^{\left(x^2 - 7x + 8\right)} = 0.01$

15. $e^x + 6 = 27e^{-x}$

19. $5^{2x} + 10 = -7\left(5^x\right)$

16. $5^x = e$

20. $32^{(x - 1)} = \left(\dfrac{1}{4}\right)^{(3x + 2)}$

21. $31^{(2x-11)} = 5\left[11^{(3x+8)}\right]$

22. $10^x = 24.54709$

23. $\dfrac{5^{(x+1)}}{7^{(x-3)}} = 3$

24. $4\left(3^x\right) - 5 = 24\left(3^{-x}\right)$

25. $10^{\left(5x^2 + 8x - 2\right)} = 100$

26. Choose some equations from the Examples and Practice Problems for Objectives 4.2 and 4.3 and solve them graphically.

27. **(a)** Determine how many solutions the equation $(\ln x)^2 + \ln x^2 - 8 = 0$ has by examining the graph.
   (b) Compare your conclusion with the solution to Objective 4.2, Example 5.
   (c) Explain why it is difficult to determine the number of solutions this equation has by examining the graph.
   (d) Find the smallest solution of this equation by analyzing the graphs.

OBJECTIVE 4.4

Given an applied problem described by a given exponential or logarithmic equation, solve the problem.

DISCUSSION

Exponential and logarithmic functions are used to give a mathematical description of a phenomenon or situation. Such a mathematical description is called a **mathematical model**. A mathematical model is analogous to an engineer's scale model of a bridge used to test the effects of wind and loading or to a map that describes some features of the earth's surface. Frequently a mathematical model consists of a function that is specified by an equation relating the variables in the situation.

Exponential functions are used as mathematical models of the biological phenomenon of population growth. The fruit fly, *Drosophila melanogaster,* is well suited for laboratory studies of population growth. It breeds rapidly and an entire generation from adult to adult offspring passes in about 10 days. In one laboratory study an experimenter lined the bottom of a large bottle with mashed banana, introduced a population of 10 fruit flies and closed the bottle with fine mesh netting. She then observed the growth of the *Drosophila* population and recorded the population at three-day intervals. The data are recorded in the following table.

Days, t	Observed population, N
0	10
3	15
6	27
9	39
12	105
15	152
18	225

Table 4.1 Observed population of *Drosophila melanogaster*

The exponential function

$$P(t) = 10e^{(0.18)t},$$

where t denotes time in days since the beginning of the study and P denotes the population at time t, is a mathematical model of the fruit fly population in this study. From this model we can compute a population for each of the recorded times. The observed and computed populations are given in Table 4.2.

Day, t	Observed population, N	Computed population, P
0	10	10
3	15	17
6	27	29
9	39	51
12	105	87
15	152	149
18	225	255

Table 4.2 Observed and Computed Populations

The observed and computed populations are not identical. The mathematical model does not describe the growth of the population exactly. It does, however, describe the situation accurately enough to answer many questions without repeating the experiment. For instance, we can estimate the fruit fly population on the 16th day of the experiment by evaluating $P(16)$. Our estimate is $P(16) = 10e^{(0.18)16} = 178$.

We can predict when the population will reach 700 by solving the equation $700 = 10e^{(0.18)t}$. Divide by 10. Rewrite the resulting exponential equation as the logarithmic equation $\ln 70 = 0.18t$. We predict that the population will reach 700 individuals when $t = \dfrac{\ln 70}{0.18} = 24$ days. This population model, as most mathematical models, is not perfect. Many factors, such as limited food supply and space, influence the development of the population but are not incorporated into the model. The model predicts that on day 100 the population will be $P(100) = 10e^{(0.18)100} = 656,600,000$. Surely food supply and physical space would be exhausted before then! Nevertheless, exponential models of population growth are useful within their limits and provide understanding and insight that can be used to devise additional experiments and develop more comprehensive mathematical models.

Another application uses logarithms to transform numerical data that varies between very small and very large values to a narrower, more manageable, range. The concentration of hydrogen ions in a solution, for example, is expressed in moles per liter (one mole is 6.02×10^{23} molecules) and is denoted $[H+]$. The range of values for $[H+]$ for common solutions is from 10^{-14} to 10^{4}. In most settings (especially graphical) it is impractical to work with such a wide range of numbers and especially the very small numbers which are included. This difficulty is overcome by working instead with a logarithm of $[H+]$. The pH of a solution is defined to be the negative of the common logarithm of the hydrogen ion concentration so, $pH = -\log[H+]$. The range of values for the pH of common solutions is from -4 (when $[H+] = 10^4$) to 14 (when $[H+] = 10^{-14}$). Working with numbers between -4 and 14 is more convenient than working with numbers between 10^{-14} and 10^4.

To illustrate the use of the pH scale, suppose that the concentration of hydrogen ions in a particular solution is $[H+] = 0.000243$ moles/liter. Then the pH of this solution, computed with a calculator and rounded to the nearest tenth, is

$$pH = -\log[H+] = -\log(0.000243) = 3.6.$$

Conversely, suppose that the pH of another solution is $pH = 2.602$. Then $[H+]$, the concentration of hydrogen ions, is found by substituting $pH = 2.602$ into the equation $pH = -\log[H+]$ and solving the resulting equation, $2.602 = -\log[H+]$, for $[H+]$. From rewriting this logarithmic equation as an exponential equation we find that when $pH = 2.602$,

$$[H+] = 10^{-2.602} = 0.0025 \text{ moles/liter.}$$

Logarithms are also used in similar ways in the scales for loudness of sound in physics, intensity of earthquakes in geology and magnitude of stars in astronomy. These logarithmic scales are examined in the Practice Problems.

PRACTICE PROBLEMS

1. The population of the United States in 1970 was 205 million. The rate of increase in the population at any time is proportional to the population at that time. A mathematical model for the population of the United States is given by the function

    $$P(t) = 205 e^{(0.018)t}$$

    where t is the number of years since 1970 and P is the population in millions.

    (a) As predicted by this mathematical model, what will be the population of the United States in the year 2001?

    (b) The area of the United States is about $101,000,000$ million square feet. According to this model, when will the population of the United States reach standing room only, *i.e.*, one person per square foot?

2. Uranium -238 is radioactive and decays into lead -206 at a rate proportional to the amount of uranium -238 present. A mathematical model for the decay of uranium -238 is given by the function

    $$F(t) = 100 e^{(-0.154)t},$$

    where t is time in **billions of years** and F is the percent of the original amount of uranium -238 remaining in the sample at time t.

(a) The rate of decay of a radioactive substance is usually described by giving the **half-life** of the substance. This is the time it takes for half of a sample to decompose. Show that the half-life of uranium – 238 is 4.5 billion years.

(b) In a volcanic eruption the lead is removed from the lava by the intense heat. Uranium – 238 remaining in the lava decomposes into lead – 206 and slowly a quantity of lead accumulates in the cooled lava. In a sample of lava, 99 percent of the uranium remains (1 percent had decomposed into lead). Approximately how many years ago was the volcanic eruption that produced the lava?

3. Nitrogen pentoxide is a solid that decomposes into the gases nitrogen dioxide and oxygen. The function

$$N(t) = 17 e^{(-0.0005)t},$$

where t is the time in seconds and N is the number of grams of nitrogen pentoxide remaining in the sample at time t, is a mathematical model for the decomposition of a sample of 17 grams of nitrogen pentoxide.

(a) According to this model, how much nitrogen pentoxide remains after 1000 seconds?

(b) How long does this model predict it will take for 15 grams of nitrogen pentoxide to decompose from the sample (so 2 grams remain)?

4. Performance tests showed that the probability P that an electronic component of a particular kind will fail within t months after it is installed is given by the function

$$P(t) = 1 - e^{(-0.0186)t}.$$

(a) According to this model, what is the probability that the component will fail within 15 months after it has been installed?

(b) As part of scheduled maintenance, components are replaced before the probability that they will have failed exceeds 0.05. Within how long after installation should the component described be routinely replaced?

5. The function

$$D(t) = \frac{1035}{\left[1 + e^{(4.296 - 0.166t)}\right]},$$

where t is time in days and D is population, is a mathematical model for the fruit fly population described in the Discussion that accounts for the limited environment.

(a) According to this model, what is the population of the fruit fly colony on day 18? Compare this number with the data given in Table 4.1.

(b) According to this model, when will the fruit fly population reach 700? Compare this number with the prediction in the Discussion.

(c) According to this model, what is the population of the fruit fly colony on day 100? Compare this number with the prediction in the Discussion.

6. The concentration of hydrogen ions in a solution is expressed in moles per liter (one mole is 6.02×10^{23} molecules) and is denoted $[H+]$. The pH of a solution is defined by the equation
$$pH = -\log[H+].$$

(a) A solution with hydrogen ion concentration $[H+] = 1 \times 10^{-7}$ is called a **neutral solution**. What is the pH of a neutral solution?

(b) Acidic solutions have pH values less than 7. A sample of freshly pressed apple juice is an acidic solution with a pH value of 3.76. Calculate $[H+]$.

(c) Basic solutions have pH values greater than 7. A sample of sea water is a basic solution with a pH value of 8.24. Calculate $[H+]$ for this solution.

(d) The hydrogen ion concentration in a sample of saliva is $[H+] = 2.93 \times 10^{-7}$. Calculate the pH value for this sample.

7. The concentration of hydroxide ions in a solution is expressed in moles per liter (one mole is 6.02×10^{23} molecules) and is denoted $[OH-]$. The pOH of solution is defined by the equation
$$pOH = -\log[OH-].$$

(a) The hydrogen ion concentration $[H+]$ and the hydroxide ion concentration $[OH-]$ in a solution are related by the equation $[H+][OH-] = 1.0 \times 10^{-14}$. For a neutral solution the equation is $[H+][OH-] = 1.0 \times 10^{-7}$. What is the pOH of a neutral solution?

(b) For acidic solutions pOH is greater than 7. A cup of coffee has a pOH value of 9.07. Calculate $[OH-]$.

(c) The hydroxide ion concentration in a sample of household ammonia is $[OH-] = 7.94 \times 10^{-3}$ moles per liter. Calculate pOH.

(d) For basic solutions pOH is less than 7. A sample of blood has pOH of 6.62. What is the hydroxide ion concentration?

8. The human ear is sensitive to sounds over a wide range of intensities. Sounds of intensity 10^{-12} watts per square meter are at the threshold of hearing. Sounds of intensity 1 watt per square meter cause pain for most people. Because of this wide range of intensities and because the sensation of loudness seems to increase as a logarithm of intensity, the loudness D (in decibels) of a sound of intensity I is defined by the equation

$$D = 120 + 10 \log I.$$

(a) What is the loudness of a sound of intensity $I = 10^{-12}$ watts per square meter, which is the threshold of human hearing?

(b) Constant exposure to sound of 90 decibels (or greater) endangers hearing. What is the intensity of sounds of loudness $D = 90$ decibels?

(c) A large rocket engine generates sounds of loudness 180 decibels. What is the intensity of the sound generated by such an engine?

(d) How loud (in decibels) is the sound of a rock band that produces sounds of intensity 0.83 watts per square meter?

9. The magnitude M of an earthquake on the Richter scale is defined by the equation

$$M = 0.67 \log (0.37E) + 1.46,$$

where E is the energy of the earthquake in kilowatt hours.

(a) The Mexico City earthquake of 1978 had magnitude 7.85 on the Richter scale. What was the energy of the Mexico City earthquake?

(b) What is the magnitude on the Richter scale of an earthquake with energy 3000 kilowatt hours?

10. A casual glance shows that stars differ from one another in apparent brightness. Astronomers assign a number, called the magnitude, to each star to quantify its perceived brightness. The system now in general use to assign magnitudes to stars was developed by N. Pogson in 1856. The magnitude M of a star is defined by the function

$$M = -2.5 \log I,$$

where I is a dimensionless number that indicates the intensity of the light received from the star. In this system, numerically **smaller** magnitudes are associated with **brighter** stars; a numerically **large** magnitude refers to a **faint** star.

(a) The bright star Aldebaran has magnitude $M = 1.0$. What is the intensity I of the light received from Aldebaran?

(b) A star which is barely visible on a dark night has magnitude 6.5. What is the intensity of the light received from a barely visible star?

(c) Sirius is the brightest star in the night sky. The intensity of the light received from Sirius is 3.7. What is the magnitude of Sirius?

(d) The intensity of the light received from a full moon is 100,000. What is the magnitude of a full moon?

(e) The second nearest star to the earth is Barnard's Star. The intensity of light received from Barnard's Star is 0.00015. Is Barnard's Star visible to the naked eye?

UNIT 4

SAMPLE EXAMINATION

1. In simplest form, $(2x - y)\, e^{\left[\ln(x + 2y) - 3\ln(2x^2 + 3xy - 2y^2)\right]} =$

A) $\dfrac{1}{3}$

B) $(2x - y)(x + 2y - 6x^2 - 9xy + 9y^2)$

C) $\dfrac{1}{(2x - y)^2(x + 2y)^2}$

D) $(2x - y)\left[(x + 2y) - (2x^2 + 3xy - y^2)^3\right]$

E) $\dfrac{(2x - y)(x + 2y)}{(2x + y)^3(x - 2y)^3}$

2. In simplest form, $\dfrac{1}{2}\log_6\left(\dfrac{6^{(x^2 + 3x)}}{6^{(-3x - 9)}}\right) =$

A) $-\dfrac{1}{6}$ B) $-\dfrac{1}{3}$ C) $x + 3$ D) $\dfrac{1}{2}(x + 3)^2$ E) $\dfrac{1}{2}(x + 3)(x - 3)$

3. Which interval(s) contain(s) a solution of $2^{\left(x^2 + 4x + 3\right)} = \dfrac{1}{4}$? There is at least one correct response. Choose all correct responses.

    A) $-7 \leq x < -4$ **B)** $-4 \leq x < -1$ **C)** $-1 \leq x < 2$

    D) $2 \leq x < 5$ **E)** There is no solution.

4. Which interval(s) contain(s) a solution to $\log(3x + 1) + \log(x + 4) = 1.14613$? There is at least one correct response. Choose all correct responses.

    A) $-6 \leq x < -3$ **B)** $-3 \leq x < 0$ **C)** $0 \leq x < 3$

    D) $3 \leq x < 6$ **E)** There is no real number solution.

5. The radioactive substance durillium – H $\left(DU^H\right)$ decays with time. The amount of DU^H currently present in a laboratory sample is given by the formula $A = A_0 e^{(-0.02)t}$ where A denotes the amount of DU^H currently present in the sample, A_0 denotes the amount of DU^H originally present in the sample, and t denotes the age of the sample in days. Suppose a sample that contained 6.8 milligrams of DU^H when it was first created in the lab now contains 1.7 milligrams of DU^H. To the nearest day, what is the age of the sample?

    A) 13 days   **B)** 30 days   **C)** 44 days   **D)** 69 days   **E)** 81 days

UNIT 5

APPLICATIONS OF SEMI-LOG GRAPHS

OBJECTIVE 5.1

    (a) Given an exponential function $f(t) = Ae^{kt}$, where A is positive and k is not 0, sketch its graph.

    (b) Given an equation of the form $y = Ae^{kt}$, where A is positive and k is not 0, transform it into a linear equation in t and $y* = \ln y$.

    (c) Given a linear equation in t and $y* = \ln y$, rewrite it as an exponential equation in t and y.

OBJECTIVE 5.2

    (a) Given an exponential function $f(t) = Ae^{kt}$, where A is positive and k is not 0, sketch its semi-log graph.

    (b) Given a straight line in a semi-log coordinate system, write an equation for the corresponding exponential function.

OBJECTIVE 5.3

Given a number of data points, find the slope and y-intercept of the least squares line of best fit for this data. Write an equation for this line in slope intercept form.

OBJECTIVE 5.4

Given data from observation of a phenomenon described by an exponential function $f(t) = Ae^{kt}$,

    (a) estimate A and k by transforming the data logarithmically and computing a least squares line of best fit for the transformed data,

    (b) estimate $f(t)$ for a given value of t, and

    (c) estimate t for a given value of $f(t)$.

UNIT 5

APPLICATIONS OF SEMI-LOG GRAPHS

OVERVIEW

In Unit 4 we examined functions, called mathematical models, that describe phenomena we see in the world around us. We then used these functions to obtain information and make predictions about the phenomena they describe. In Unit 5 we will investigate methods for constructing models like those we used in Unit 4. We will construct exponential functions that model the natural phenomena of growth and decay from data obtained by observing these phenomena. Then, as in Unit 4, we will use the exponential model we constructed to obtain information about the phenomenon the model describes.

APPLICATIONS OF SEMI-LOG GRAPHS

OBJECTIVE 5.1

    (a) **Given an exponential function** $f(t) = Ae^{kt}$, **where** A **is positive and** k **is not** 0, **sketch its graph.**

    (b) **Given an exponential equation** $y = Ae^{kt}$, **where** A **is positive and** k **is not** 0, **transform it into a linear equation in** t **and** $y* = \ln y$.

    (c) **Given a linear equation in** t **and** $y* = \ln y$, **transform it into an exponential equation in** t **and** y.

DISCUSSION

It is often easier to extract information from a mathematical model by looking at a graph rather than an equation. The function $f(t) = 2e^{1.2t}$ is a mathematical model of a growth phenomenon. It is not easy to see from the equation just how rapidly this population is growing at different times, but the graph shows this information dramatically. To graph $f(t)$, make a table of values of the function for different values of t. Because we cannot plot fractions very precisely, round off the function values. We obtain the following table.

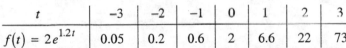

t	−3	−2	−1	0	1	2	3
$f(t) = 2e^{1.2t}$	0.05	0.2	0.6	2	6.6	22	73

Table 5.1

Next, plot some of these points in a rectangular coordinate system and draw a smooth curve through them as in Figure 5.1.

We see more dramatically from the graph than from the equation that the population increases more and more rapidly as time passes and that the population quickly (depending on the units of time) becomes overwhelmingly large.

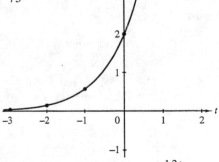

Figure 5.1 Graph of $f(t) = 2e^{1.2t}$

The function $g(t) = 1.5e^{-0.76t}$ models a decay phenomenon. To graph $g(t)$, make a table of values of the function for different values of t. As in the previous case, for easy plotting round off the function values. We obtain the following table.

t	-3	-2	-1	0	1	2	3
$g(t) = 1.5e^{-0.76t}$	14.7	6.9	3.2	1.5	0.7	0.3	0.2

Table 5.2

Next, plot some of these points in a rectangular coordinate system and draw a smooth curve through them as in Figure 5.2.

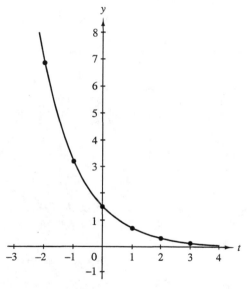

Figure 5.2 Graph of $g(t) = 1.5e^{-0.76t}$

Skill in interpreting graphs of exponential functions makes analyzing growth and decay models easier. It's worth using some of our time to examine the graphs of general exponential functions. Figures 5.1 and 5.2 show the general shapes of graphs of exponential functions of the form $f(t) = Ae^{kt}$ where A is positive and k is not 0. Notice that the graph of $f(t) = 2e^{1.2t}$ (Figure 5.1) has y-intercept 2 and the graph of $g(t) = 1.5e^{-0.76t}$ (Figure 5.2) has y-intercept 1.5. The graph of every exponential function $f(t) = Ae^{kt}$ has y-intercept A because for every k,

$$f(0) = Ae^{k0} = A \cdot 1 = A.$$

The sign of the number k in the exponent determines whether the function $f(t) = Ae^{kt}$ is increasing or decreasing. When k is positive the function is increasing. When k is negative the function is decreasing. The magnitude of k determines how rapidly the function changes. The larger the absolute value of k, the faster the function increases or decreases.

The graph of $f(t) = Ae^{kt}$ is very similar to the graph of $y = b^x$ discussed in Objective 1.4. In particular, the graph of $y = Ae^{kt}$, where A is positive and k is not 0, has the following properties.

- The y-intercept is A.
- Domain is all real numbers. Range is all positive numbers.
- Increasing when $k > 0$. Decreasing when $k < 0$.
- Negative t-axis (horizontal axis) is an asymptote when $k > 0$.
  Positive t-axis (horizontal axis) is an asymptote when $k < 0$.

Using these properties, one can sketch an accurate graph of a function $f(t) = Ae^{kt}$ after plotting only a few points. Two exponential functions are plotted by this method in Examples 1 and 2.

To be most useful, the graph of a function which is used as a mathematical model of a real situation must satisfy some practical requirements. First, the graph must show the values of the function for those values of the variables that are of interest. Second, from the graph it must be possible to estimate accurately the values of the function for the values of the independent variable of interest. Finally, the graph must be of reasonable physical size.

Figure 5.1 illustrates the fact that exponential functions used to model growth phenomena, *i.e.*, those with $k > 0$, usually increase so rapidly that a coordinate system with an unreasonably long vertical axis is needed to show their graphs for a reasonable interval of values for the independent variable. Exponential functions which model decay phenomena, *i.e.*, those with $k < 0$, usually decrease so rapidly that from a reasonably sized graph it is impossible to estimate accurately function values for even modest sized values of the independent variable. To see this, try to estimate $g(3.75)$ from the graph in Figure 5.2. Because most exponential functions take on extremely large or extremely small values over a rather short interval, their graphs usually do not meet these requirements for practicality.

We saw a similar situation in the discussion of pH in Objective 4.4. The range of numerical values for hydrogen ion concentrations is unwieldy because it extends from very small to very large numbers. The way out of that practical problem is to transform the data logarithmically by defining pH to be the negative of the common logarithm of the hydrogen ion concentration.

The technique that works so well to tame hydrogen ion concentrations also subdues the graphs of exponential functions. Transform the equation $y = Ae^{kt}$ by applying the natural logarithm function to both sides of the equation. This gives the new equation

$$\ln y = \ln\left[Ae^{kt}\right] = \ln A + \ln\left[e^{kt}\right] = \ln A + kt.$$

Let $b = \ln A$ and replace $\ln y$ by $y*$ (read y *star*). The resulting equation, $y* = b + kt$, represents a straight line with slope k and intercept b in a $t - y*$ coordinate system. By taking the natural logarithm we transformed an unmanageable exponential equation into a simple linear equation whose graph meets the practical requirements above. The graph of $y* = b + kt$ in a standard rectangular coordinate system is called the semi-log graph of the associated exponential function.

The process of transforming an exponential equation into a linear equation can be reversed. Begin with the linear equation $y* = b + kt$ where $y* = \ln y$. Apply the exponential function $E(x) = e^x$ to both sides of this linear equation and carry out the simplifications.

$$E(y*) = e^{y*} = e^{\ln y} = y = E(b + kt) = e^{(b + kt)} = e^b e^{kt} = Ae^{kt}$$

From this chain of equalities, extract the exponential equation $y = Ae^{kt}$ where $A = e^b$. Notice that since $A = e^b$ we also have $\ln A = b$. Thus, this exponential equation can be transformed back into the linear equation by applying the natural logarithm function. Examples 3 and 4 illustrate the processes for transforming between exponential and linear equations.

SUMMARY

1. The graph of $f(t) = Ae^{kt}$, where A is positive and k is not 0, has the following properties.
    - The y-intercept is A.
    - Domain is all real numbers. Range is all positive numbers.
    - Increasing when $k > 0$. Decreasing when $k < 0$.
    - Negative horizontal axis is an asymptote when $k > 0$.
      Positive horizontal axis is an asymptote when $k < 0$.

2. Transform $y = Ae^{kt}$ into a linear equation in t and $y* = \ln y$ by applying the natural logarithm function to both sides of the equation. The resulting equation is $y* = b + kt$ where $b = \ln A$.

3. Transform $y* = b + kt$ (where $y* = \ln y$) into an exponential equation in t and y by applying the exponential function $E(x) = e^x$ to both sides of the equation. The transformed equation is $y = Ae^{kt}$ where $A = e^b$.

EXAMPLES

Example 1: Sketch the graph of $h(t) = 3.4e^{0.5t}$.

Solution 1: Use the properties of the graphs of exponential functions $f(t) = Ae^{kt}$ from the Summary. The function $h(t)$ is of this form with $A = 3.4$ and $k = 0.5$.

Properties:

1. Since $A = 3.4$, the y-intercept is 3.4. Plot the point $(0, 3.4)$.
2. The domain is all numbers. The range is all positive numbers.
3. Since $k = 0.5 > 0$, the function is increasing. Plot a point with positive first coordinate, *e.g.*, $t = 1$, to see how rapidly the function is increasing. Since $h(1) = 3.4e^{(0.5)(1)} = 5.6$ (rounded), the point $(1, 5.6)$ is on the graph.
4. Since $k = 0.5 > 0$, the negative *t*-axis is an asymptote.

Draw a smooth curve with these properties through the two points plotted. The graph constructed in this way is shown in Figure 5.3.

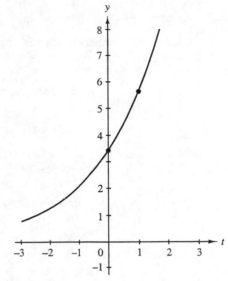

Figure 5.3

Example 2: Sketch the graph of $g(t) = 0.67e^{-2.3t}$.

Solution 2: Use the properties of the graphs of exponential functions $f(t) = Ae^{kt}$ from the Summary. The function $g(t)$ is of this form with $A = 0.67$ and $k = -2.3$.

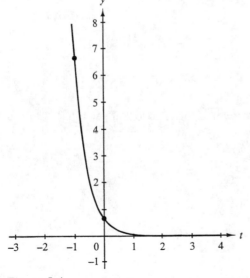

Figure 5.4

Properties:

1. Since $A = 0.67$, the y-intercept is 0.67. Plot the point $(0, 0.67)$.
2. The domain is all numbers. The range is all positive numbers.
3. Since $k = -2.3 < 0$, the function is decreasing. Plot a point with negative first coordinate, *e.g.*, $t = -1$, to see how rapidly the function is decreasing. Since $g(-1) = 0.67e^{(-2.3)(-1)} = 6.68$ (rounded), the point $(-1, 6.68)$ is on the graph.
4. Since $k = -2.3 < 0$, the positive *t*-axis is an asymptote.

Draw a smooth curve with these properties through the two points plotted. The graph constructed in this way is shown in Figure 5.4.

Example 3: Transform the equation $y = 4.81e^{-1.36t}$ into a linear equation in t and $y* = \ln y$.

Solution 3:   Apply the natural logarithm function to both sides of the equation.

$$y* = \ln y = \ln 4.81e^{-1.36t}$$

By the Product Property and the Composition Property for logarithm functions we have

$$\ln 4.81e^{-1.36t} = \ln 4.81 + \ln e^{-1.36t} = 1.57 - 1.36t.$$

Since the numerical coefficients in the original equation are given to two decimal places, $\ln 4.81$ is rounded to two decimal places.
Thus, the given equation can be rewritten as

$$y* = 1.57 - 1.36t.$$

Example 4: Transform the equation $y* = 6.31t - 1.31$, where $y* = \ln y$, into an exponential equation in t and y.

Solution 4:   Replace $y*$ by $\ln y$ and write the equation as

$$\ln y = 6.31t - 1.31.$$

Apply the exponential function $E(x) = e^x$ to both sides of this equation.

$$e^{\ln y} = e^{(6.31t - 1.31)}$$

Now,

$$e^{\ln y} = y \quad \text{and} \quad e^{(6.31t - 1.31)} = e^{-1.31}e^{6.31t} = 0.27e^{6.31t}.$$

Since the coefficients in the original equation are given to two decimal places, $e^{-1.31}$ is rounded to two decimal places.
Thus, the given equation can be rewritten as the exponential equation

$$y = 0.27e^{6.31t}.$$

PRACTICE PROBLEMS
In problems 1 - 6, sketch the graph of each exponential function.

1. $f(t) = 3.7e^{0.42t}$

2. $y = 0.39e^{3.1t}$

3. $y = 5.1e^{2.6t}$

4. $g(t) = 0.57e^{-0.77t}$

5. $y = 3e^{-2t}$

6. $F(t) = 0.50e^{-1.9t}$

In problems 7 - 12, transform each exponential equation into a linear equation in t and $y* = \ln y$. Round the constant term to five decimal places.

7. $y = 2.41 e^{2.23t}$

8. $y = 0.16 e^{-1.59t}$

9. $y = 3.92 e^{0.19t}$

10. $y = 20.08 e^{-4t}$

11. $y = 0.025 e^{-0.26t}$

12. $y = 0.36 e^{6.22t}$

In problems 13 - 18, transform each linear equation in t and $y*$ into an exponential equation in t and y. Round to five decimal places.

13. $y* = 7.38t + 2.91$

14. $y* = 6.11 - 2.17t$

15. $y* = -5.06t - 1.68$

16. $y* = 2.61 - 0.92t$

17. $y* = 1.46t - 3.04$

18. $y* = 4.37 + 3.84t$

19. If x and y are related by the equation $y = 5e^{2x}$, what equation relates x and $y* = \ln y$?

20. Suppose t and W are related as $W = 0.5 e^{-0.2t}$. How are t and $W* = \ln W$ related?

21. If $\ln y = -3 + 0.5x$, what equation relates x and y?

22. Suppose $\ln W$ and t are related as $\ln W = 0.35t + 5.2$. How are t and W related?

OBJECTIVE 5.2

(a) **Given an exponential function** $f(t) = Ae^{kt}$, **where** A **is positive and** k **is not 0, sketch its semi-log graph.**

(b) **Given a straight line in a semi-log coordinate system, write an equation for the corresponding exponential function.**

DISCUSSION

Any exponential equation $y = Ae^{kt}$ can be transformed into a linear equation $y* = b + kt$ in t and $y* = \ln y$. The graph of this linear equation in the $t - y*$ coordinate system is called the **semi-log graph** of the exponential function. The $t - y*$ coordinate system is called the semi-log coordinate system. The semi-log graph of an exponential function is always a straight line. The semi-log graph of an exponential function can be constructed by rewriting the exponential equation as a linear equation in t and $y* = \ln y$ and graphing this line in a $t - y*$ (semi-log) coordinate system. This process is illustrated in Example 1.

A semi-log graph can also be constructed without explicitly rewriting the equation by using specially ruled semi-log graph paper. This paper is designed so the transformation of the equation is accomplished as the points are plotted. Most semi-log graph paper is ruled to transform the equation by the common logarithm (base 10) instead of the natural logarithm (base e). Although semi-log graph paper is convenient and useful, it is not used in this book.

Every straight line which is not parallel to an axis in the semi-log ($t - y*$) coordinate system is the semi-log graph of some exponential function. An equation for an exponential function can be recovered from its semi-log graph. First, determine the $y*$-intercept b and the slope k of the line from the graph. Next, write the equation for the line in the form $y* = b + kt$. Finally, transform this linear equation in t and $y* = \ln y$ into an exponential equation in t and y as in Objective 5.1. This process is illustrated in Example 2.

SUMMARY

1. To sketch the semi-log graph of an exponential function $f(t) = Ae^{kt}$, transform $y = Ae^{kt}$ into a linear equation in t and $y* = \ln y$ by applying the natural logarithm. The graph in the $t - y*$ coordinate system of the resulting linear equation is the semi-log graph of $f(t) = Ae^{kt}$.

2. The semi-log graph of an exponential function is a straight line in the $t - y*$ coordinate system. To obtain the equation for an exponential function from its semi-log graph, find the slope m and the $y*$-intercept b of the semi-log graph. The equation for the semi-log graph is $y* = mt + b$. Replace $y*$ with $\ln y$. Finally, rewrite the resulting logarithmic equation in exponential form.

EXAMPLES

Example 1: Sketch the semi-log graph of $f(t) = 90e^{-3t}$.

Solution 1: Transform the exponential equation $y = 90e^{-3t}$ into a linear equation in t and $y* = \ln y$ by applying the natural logarithm function. This gives

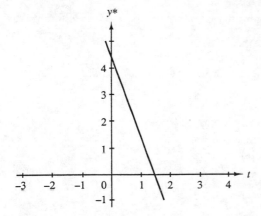

$$y* = \ln y = \ln 90e^{-3t}$$
$$= \ln 90 + \ln e^{-3t}$$
$$= 4.5 - 3t.$$

The graph of the linear equation

$$y* = 4.5 - 3t$$

is the semi-log graph of $y = 90e^{-3t}$.
This graph is shown in Figure 5.5.

Figure 5.5 Semi-log graph of $f(t) = 90e^{-3t}$

Example 2: Find an equation for the function whose semi-log graph is shown in Figure 5.6.

Solution 2:   The graph is a straight line in the $t - y*$ coordinate system. Therefore, this is the semi-log graph of an exponential function $f(t) = Ae^{kt}$.

This line has $y*$-intercept -2.5 and slope 0.5. An equation for it is

$$y* = -2.5 + 0.5t.$$

Recall that $y* = \ln y$. Rewrite the equation $\ln y = -2.5 + 0.5t$ as an exponential equation in t and y by applying the exponential function $E(x) = e^x$. This gives

$$y = e^{(-2.5 + 0.5t)} = e^{-2.5}e^{0.5t} = 0.082e^{0.5t}.$$

The function whose semi-log graph is shown in Figure 5.6 is

$$f(t) = 0.082e^{0.5t}.$$

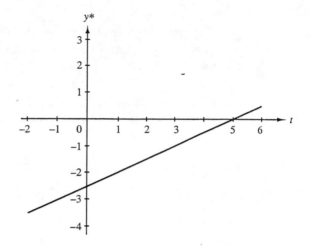

Figure 5.6

PRACTICE PROBLEMS

In problems 1 - 6, sketch the semi-log graphs of the given functions.

1. $f(t) = 20.1e^{-t}$

2. $y = 7.34e^{\frac{2}{3}t}$

3. $y = e^{5x}$

4. $g(t) = 0.17e^{0.33x}$

5. $h(t) = 0.061e^{-4.1t}$

6. $y = e^{-\frac{3}{4}t}$

In problems 7 - 12, find an equation in t and y for the exponential functions whose semi-log graphs are shown in Figures 5.7 - 5.12.

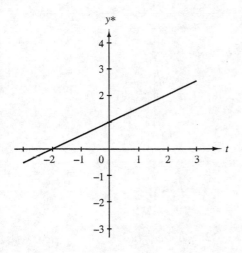

7. *Figure 5.7*

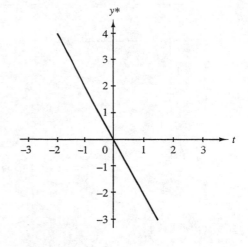

8. *Figure 5.8*

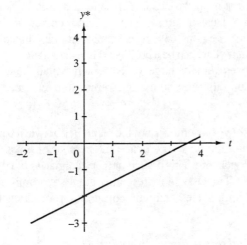

9. *Figure 5.9*

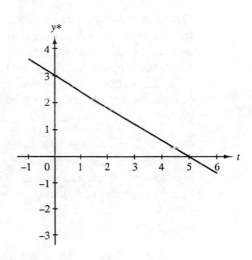

10. *Figure 5.10*

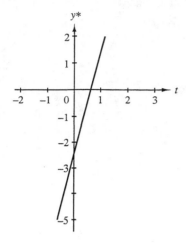

11. *Figure 5.11*

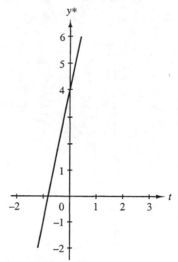

12. *Figure 5.12*

AUTHOR'S NOTE

Computers have a limited number of 'slots' for storing the digits representing a number. Each number used in a calculation or resulting from a calculation must fit in the number of slots available. Thus, the accuracy with which a number can be entered or manipulated is limited by the number of digits that can be used to represent it. This can be a problem when calculations such as multiplication or subtraction result in an extremely large or extremely small number. Mathematicians and computer scientists are studying ways to use logarithms to overcome this problem.

One idea is to repeatedly take the natural logarithm of a number until the result lies between 0 and 1 and then represent the original number by two numbers. The first is the number of times the logarithm was taken and the second is the final logarithm. This particular pair of digits would then be used to perform calculations in the computer. This way of representing numbers promises to achieve greater accuracy, but to require more complicated and time-consuming procedures for calculating.

Recommend reading - Historical Novel: *The Difference Engine* by William Gibson.

OBJECTIVE 5.3

Given a number of data points, find the slope and *y*-intercept of the least squares line of best fit for this data. Write an equation for this line in slope-intercept form.

DISCUSSION

We have previously considered the problem of finding an equation for a function from its graph. When the graph is a straight line, an equation for the function can be found from the *y*-intercept and the slope of the graph. When the graph is known to be an exponential function $f(x) = b^x$ or a logarithmic function $f(x) = \log_b x$, we need only find the base *b* of the exponential or logarithm to recover the equation. The base is found from the coordinates of a judiciously chosen point on the graph. To solve these problems we need to recognize the general form of the equation for the function given by the graph. It is very difficult to recover an equation for a function from its graph without this additional information.

Investigators must often infer an equation for a function, not from its graph, but from a scattered collection of data points near the graph. To solve this problem, too, one must recognize the general form of the function whose graph the data points approximate. As an illustration consider the following situation.

The number of eggs laid by a fish depends upon the size of the fish. The bigger the fish, the more eggs spawned. A fisheries biologist collected the following data for a particular species. The number of eggs spawned is tabulated for fish of various lengths.

length (centimeters)	x	26	29	34	36	40
number of eggs (thousands)	y	2.0	1.9	3.1	4.8	5.0

Table 5.3

The investigator wishes to find a function $y = f(x)$ to use as a mathematical model for this phenomenon. From the length x of an individual female fish, she wants to be able to calculate the (approximate) number y of eggs that this fish will spawn by evaluating the function f at x.

The biologist first constructs a **scatter plot** by graphing the pairs of data points from Table 5.3. It appears that the points in the scatter plot fall along a straight line, so the investigator seeks a linear function as the mathematical model. Intuitively, the graph of this function should be the straight line that lies **closest** to the points in the scatter plot. She draws such a straight line and obtains the graph shown in Figure 5.13.

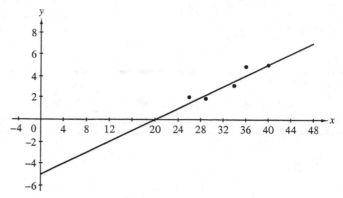

Figure 5.13   A straight line that fits the data

To obtain an equation for the function, the biologist observes that the line which she drew has y-intercept -5. She also notes that the line passes through the point $(40, 5)$. Since the points $(0, -5)$ and $(40, 5)$ are on the line, the slope of the line is

$$m = \frac{\left(5 - (-5)\right)}{(40 - 0)} = 0.25.$$

Using these values for the y-intercept and the slope, the biologist writes $f(x) = 0.25x - 5$ as an equation for a function which models spawning in this fish species.

Every non-vertical straight line is given by an equation of the form $y = mx + b$ where m is the slope and b is the y-intercept of the line. To find the line which best fits given data points we must choose the slope m and the intercept b so the line is as close to the data points as possible. In practice, especially when the data points are nicely positioned, this is done by using the fisheries biologist's method in the previous illustration. The line is "eyeballed" and the equation is found by reading the slope and the y-intercept from the graph. This visual method has serious disadvantages. If the data is scattered considerably it is not at all clear which line is best. Even when the data is not widely scattered, different artists may have different opinions about which line best fits the data. It is desirable to have an unambiguous criterion for **best**, and a procedure for computing the slope and the y-intercept of the best line from the data.

Some notation is needed to describe the least squares criterion for a line of best fit and to explain how to calculate this line. Suppose we are investigating a phenomenon we believe is modeled by an unknown linear function $y = f(x) = mx + b$. We believe that the graph of f is the straight line which best fits the data obtained from observing the phenomenon. Our problem is to find an equation for this function.

Suppose we have n data points (x_1, y_1), (x_2, y_2), (x_3, y_3), ... , (x_n, y_n). The numbers $x_1, x_2, x_3, ... , x_n$ are presumed to be known exactly. The corresponding observed values $y_1, y_2, y_3, ... , y_n$ of the dependent variable are approximations which may differ from the **true** (but unknown) values $z_1, z_2, z_3, ... , z_n$ of the dependent variable. The **true** values lie on the graph of $y = f(x) = mx + b$, *i.e.*, on the line which best fits the data. Therefore,

$$f(x_1) = mx_1 + b = z_1,$$
$$f(x_2) = mx_2 + b = z_2,$$
$$f(x_3) = mx_3 + b = z_3,$$
$$\vdots$$
$$f(x_n) = mx_n + b = z_n.$$

For each of the values $x_1, x_2, x_3, ... , x_n$ the difference between the **observed** value y_i and the **true** value z_i of the dependent variable is

$$
\begin{aligned}
y_i - z_i &= y_i - f(x_i) \\
&= y_i - (mx_i + b) \\
&= y_i - mx_i - b.
\end{aligned}
$$

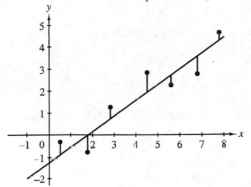

Figure 5.14

Graphically, this difference is the vertical distance between the observed value and the line of best fit. This difference is positive when the observed point lies above the line of best fit and negative when the observed point lies below the line of best fit, as shown in Figure 5.14.

The differences $y_i - z_i$ are the deviation of each data point from the line of best fit. Combinations of these differences measure how closely a line fits all of the data points. Different combinations lead to different criteria for a line to **best** fit the data. Because of various statistical considerations, the sum of the squares of these deviations

$$(y_1 - mx_1 - b)^2 + (y_2 - mx_2 - b)^2 + ... + (y_n - mx_n - b)^2$$

is the combination most frequently used. The **least squares line of best fit** makes this sum of squares as small as possible.

Methods from calculus can be used to find formulas that express the slope m and the y-intercept b of the least squares line of best fit in terms of the coordinates of the data points. Formulas for m and b are expressed more easily in terms of the auxiliary quantities defined below.

Let n denote the number of data points. Let
$$S_x = x_1 + x_2 + x_3 + \dots + x_n$$
be the sum of the first coordinates of the data points (the values of the independent variable)
and let
$$X = \frac{S_x}{n}$$
be the average of the first coordinates of the n data points. Let
$$S_y = y_1 + y_2 + y_3 + \dots + y_n$$
be the sum of the second coordinates of the n data points (the values of the dependent variable)
and let
$$Y = \frac{S_y}{n}$$
be the average of the second coordinates of the n data points. Let
$$S_{xx} = (x_1)^2 + (x_2)^2 + (x_3)^2 + \dots + (x_n)^2$$
be the sum of the squares of the first coordinates of the n data points and let
$$S_{xy} = x_1 y_1 + x_2 y_2 + x_3 y_3 + \dots + x_n y_n$$
be the sum of the products of the coordinates of each of the n data points.

The slope m and the intercept b of the least squares line of best fit are given in terms of these
quantities by
$$m = \frac{nS_{xy} - S_x S_y}{nS_{xx} - S_x S_x} \quad \text{and} \quad b = Y - mX.$$

Notice that in these formulas x denotes the independent variable and y denotes the dependent
variable. In many applications symbols other than x and y are used for the variables. To use
these formulas in such situations, replace x by the symbol for the independent variable in your
problem and replace y by the symbol for the dependent variable.

To obtain the most accurate equation for the least squares line of best fit , do not round the
numerical values computed for $S_x, S_y, S_{xx}, S_{xy}, Y$ and X. Use all the decimal places your
calculator displays to calculate m and b. Finally, as the last step, round m and b to be
compatible with the accuracy of the original data.

The least squares line of best fit has some appealing properties. First,
$$(y_1 - z_1) + (y_2 - z_2) + (y_3 - z_3) + \dots + (y_n - z_n) = 0.$$

This equation says that the errors in which the observed value of the dependent variable is larger than the true value exactly balance the errors in which the observed value is smaller than the true value. Second,

$$Y = mX + b.$$

This equation says that the least squares line of best fit passes through the average of the data points. One might expect a line which is **closest** to the data points to have these two properties.

For most data the least squares line of best fit is very close to the line that one would draw by visually fitting the data as closely as possible. This is illustrated in Example 2 and the Practice Problems.

CALCULATOR COMMENTARY

The TI-83® Graphing Calculator and other graphics calculators are designed to make scatter plots and present data in other graphical ways and to perform statistical calculations on lists of data. Examples 1 and 2 below illustrate how to use the TI-83® to calculate the least squares line of best fit and to present data graphically. Read the *TI-83® Guidebook* for more information about statistical calculations on the TI-83®.

SUMMARY

1. The **least squares line of best fit** for a set of data points minimizes the sum of the squares of the vertical distances between the data points and the line.

2. The least squares line of best fit for n data points

$$(x_1, y_1), (x_2, y_2), (x_3, y_3), \dots, (x_n, y_n)$$

is given in terms of the following quantities:

$$S_x = x_1 + x_2 + x_3 + \dots + x_n, \quad X = \frac{S_x}{n},$$

$$S_y = y_1 + y_2 + y_3 + \dots + y_n, \quad Y = \frac{S_y}{n},$$

$$S_{xx} = (x_1)^2 + (x_2)^2 + (x_3)^2 + \dots + (x_n)^2 \quad \text{and}$$

$$S_{xy} = x_1 y_1 + x_2 y_2 + x_3 y_3 + \dots + x_n y_n.$$

3. The slope m and the y-intercept b of the least squares line of best fit for n data points are given by

$$m = \frac{n S_{xy} - S_x S_y}{n S_{xx} - S_x S_x} \quad \text{and} \quad b = Y - mX.$$

EXAMPLES

Example 1: The following table, copied from the Discussion, shows the number of eggs spawned by fish of various lengths of a certain species. Find the least squares line of best fit for this data. Compare the conclusions reached graphically in the Discussion with the conclusion reached numerically here.

length (centimeters) x	26	29	34	36	40
number of eggs (thousands) y	2.0	1.9	3.1	4.8	5.0

Table 5.4

Solution 1: First, evaluate the quantities used to compute the slope and y-intercept of the least squares line of best fit. The length of the fish is the independent variable, so the lengths in the table are used for the x values. The number of eggs spawned is the dependent variable, so the numbers of eggs from the table are used as the y values. We have, then,

$$S_x = x_1 + x_2 + x_3 + x_4 + x_5 = 26 + 29 + 34 + 36 + 40 = 165,$$

$$X = \frac{S_x}{n} = \frac{165}{5} = 33,$$

$$S_y = 2.0 + 1.9 + 3.1 + 4.8 + 5.0 = 16.8,$$

$$Y = \frac{S_y}{n} = \frac{16.8}{5} = 3.36 \text{ and}$$

$$S_{xx} = \left(x_1\right)^2 + \left(x_2\right)^2 + \left(x_3\right)^2 + \left(x_4\right)^2 + \left(x_5\right)^2$$

$$= \left(26\right)^2 + \left(29\right)^2 + \left(34\right)^2 + \left(36\right)^2 + \left(40\right)^2 = 5569,$$

$$S_{xy} = x_1y_1 + x_2y_2 + x_3y_3 + x_4y_4 + x_5y_5$$

$$= \left(26\right)\left(2.0\right) + \left(29\right)\left(1.9\right) + \left(34\right)\left(3.1\right) + \left(36\right)\left(4.8\right) + \left(40\right)\left(5.0\right) = 585.3.$$

It follows from the expressions for the slope m and the y-intercept b of the least squares line of best fit that

$$m = \frac{nS_{xy} - S_x S_y}{nS_{xx} - S_x S_x} = \frac{\left(5\right)\left(585.3\right) - \left(165\right)\left(16.8\right)}{\left(5\right)\left(5569\right) - \left(165\right)\left(165\right)} = 0.2491935484$$

and that

$$b = Y - mX = \left(3.36\right) - \left(0.24919355\right)\left(33\right) = -4.863387097.$$

After rounding to two decimal places, which seems compatible with the data, we have $m = 0.25$ and $b = -4.86$, and

$$y = 0.25x - 4.86$$

as an equation for the least squares line of best fit. Compare this result with the conclusion reached from graphical considerations in the Discussion.

Calculator Solution 1:

Data for statistical analysis is stored in the TI-83® as lists. There are several ways to create, store, and edit lists, but the **STAT** list editor is especially convenient.

To access the **STAT** list editor, press | STAT | (row 3, column 3) and then choose **Edit** by pressing | 1 | or | ENTER | . The first line of the **STAT** list screen shows the names of the first three of six pre-programmed lists. Press the left and right arrow keys to move between lists and access the remaining three lists. The center portion of the display shows up to seven entries of three lists displayed as completely as space allows. The bottom line shows the location of the cursor and the full value of the entry at that location. All six lists should be blank. Clear lists that contain entries by using the arrow keys to move the cursor to the name of the list on the top line and pressing | CLEAR | , | ENTER | .

To enter the data from the first line of Table 5.4 as list **L1**, use the arrow keys to move the cursor to the first line of this list. Enter the first number from the top row of Table 5.4 and then press | ENTER | or the down arrow key to move the cursor to the next line. Continue in this way until all of the numbers from the first row of Table 5.4 are entered in order. Use the right arrow key to move to list **L2**. Enter the numbers from the second row of Table 5.4 as **L2**. List entries can be corrected in the same way as entries on the home screen. Read the *TI-83® Guidebook* for information on editing lists.

Now we are ready to calculate the least squares line of best fit, which, in statistical terminology, is called a **linear regression**. Press | STAT | again. Scroll to **CALC** to display the calculate menu and press | 4 | to choose **LinReg (ax + b)** (linear regression). Press | 2nd | , [**L1**] (row 9, column 2), | **,** | , | 2nd | , [L2] (row 9, column 3) to instruct the calculator to use list **L1** as the independent variable and list **L2** as the dependent variable in calculating least squares line of best fit. When this information is entered correctly, the display will show

```
LinReg (ax + b) L1,
L2
```

Press ENTER . The calculator will soon display

> **LinReg**
> **y=ax+b**
> **a=.2491935484**
> **b=-4.863387097**

The equation for the least squares line of best fit is
$$y = ax + b = (0.2491935484)x - 4.863387097$$
or, rounding to two decimal places,
$$y = 0.25x - 4.86.$$

Example 2: (a) Construct a scatter plot of the data given in Table 5.5 below by plotting it in a rectangular coordinate system.

(b) Draw the line which, in your judgment, is **closest** to the data points plotted.

(c) Find the equation $y = b + mt$ for the least squares line of best fit for this data.

(d) Draw the graph of the line found in (c).

(e) Compare the lines drawn in (b) and (d).

t	1	3	5	6
y	4	2	1.5	1

Table 5.5

Solution 2: (a) The scatter plot of data points (t, y) is shown in Figure 5.15.

(b) In Figure 5.15 draw the line which you think best fits the data.

(c) Evaluate the quantities used to compute the slope and y-intercept of the least squares line of best fit. In this Example the independent variable is t rather than x. We have, then,

$$S_t = t_1 + t_2 + t_3 + t_4 = 1 + 3 + 5 + 6 = 15,$$

$$T = \frac{S_t}{n} = \frac{15}{4} = 3.75,$$

$$S_y = 4 + 2 + 1.5 + 1 = 8.5,$$

$$Y = \frac{S_y}{n} = \frac{8.5}{4} = 2.125,$$

$$S_{tt} = (t_1)^2 + (t_2)^2 + (t_3)^2 + (t_4)^2$$

$$= (1)^2 + (3)^2 + (5)^2 + (6)^2 = 71$$

and
$$S_{ty} = t_1y_1 + t_2y_2 + t_3y_3 + t_4y_4$$

$$= (1)(4) + (3)(2) + (5)(1.5) + (6)(1) = 23.5.$$

It follows from the expressions for the slope m and the y-intercept b of the least squares line of best fit that

$$m = \frac{nS_{ty} - S_tS_y}{nS_{tt} - S_tS_t} = \frac{(4)(23.5) - (15)(8.5)}{(4)(71) - (15)(15)} = -0.5677966102$$

and
$$b = Y - mT = (2.125) - (0.5678)(3.75) = 4.254237288.$$

After rounding to two decimal places, which seems compatible with the original data, we have

$$y = -0.57t + 4.25$$

as an equation for the least squares line of best fit.

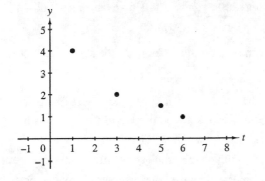

Figure 5.15

(d) Graph the line $y = -0.57t + 4.25$ from (c) in the coordinate system in Figure 5.15. The y-intercept of this line is 4.25. The t-intercept, found by solving $0 = -0.57t + 4.25$, is 7.46. To sketch the graph, plot the points $(0, 4.25)$ and $(7.46, 0)$ and draw a straight line through them.

(e) In your opinion, does the line "eyeballed" in part (b) or the least squares line of best fit graphed in part (d) more closely fit the data?

Calculator Solution 2:

Follow the procedure given in Example 1 to enter the data from Table 5.5 into lists **L1** and **L2**.

(a) Press [2nd], [STAT PLOT] (row 1, column 1) to access the menu used to tell the calculator what data to use to construct a statistical plot. As you see from the **STAT PLOT**'s menu, the machine can produce three statistical plots at the same time. Plots 2 and 3 should be **Off**. If they are not, press [4], [ENTER] to turn all plots off and then press [2nd], [STAT PLOT] to again display the **STAT PLOT**'s menu. Press ⌷ 1 ⌷ to access the menu for **Plot 1**. On the first active line of this menu, choose **On** and press ⌷ENTER⌷. On the second active line, highlight the first icon and press ⌷ENTER⌷ to choose a scatter plot. On the third line, type ⌷ **2nd** ⌷, [**L1**] (row 9, column 2) and press ⌷ENTER⌷ to indicate that the independent variable comes from **List 1**. On the fourth line, type ⌷ **2nd** ⌷, [**L2**] (row 9, column 3) and press ⌷ENTER⌷ to indicate that the dependent variable comes from **List 2**. On the fifth line, highlight the mark that you wish to use to identify points in the scatter plot and press ⌷ENTER⌷.

Press ⌷ **Y=** ⌷ to access the **Y** = editor. Turn off all expressions on this screen.

Establish a viewing window that will include all the points in the scatter plot. **Xmin** must be smaller than the smallest entry in **List 1**, **Xmax** must be larger than the largest entry in **List 1**, **Ymin** must be smaller than the smallest entry in **List 2**, and **Ymax** must be larger than the largest entry in **List 2**. In a later part of this example you will want to graph the least squares line of best fit in this window, so you may wish to choose **Xmin ≤ 0 ≤ Xmax** and **Ymin ≤ 0 ≤ Ymax** so the origin is within the window. You can have the TI-83® set a window which will include all point of the scatter plot by choosing ⌷ **ZOOM** ⌷, ⌷ **9** ⌷. However, this window will not include the origin.

Finally, press ⌷**GRAPH**⌷ to generate the scatter plot. Compare the scatter plot on the TI-83® with Figure 5.15.

(b) You can use the TI-83® to draw the line which you feel best fits the data. Estimate the *y*-intercept and slope of a line that you think will fit the points in the scatter plot well. Enter the expression for this line as **Y1** on the **Y** = screen. Press ⌷**GRAPH**⌷ to generate both the scatter plot and the graph of the line. If the line does not fit the data as closely as you expected, revise your estimates of the slope and *y*-intercept, change the expression for **Y1**, and generate the graph again. Continue revising your line until you are satisfied that it fits the points in the scatter plot closely.

(c) Now we are ready to calculate the least squares line of best fit. Press ⌷ **STAT** ⌷ again. Scroll to **CALC** to display the calculate menu and press ⌷ **4** ⌷ to choose **LinReg(ax + b)**. Press ⌷ **2nd** ⌷, [**L1**] (row 9, column 2), ⌷ **,** ⌷, ⌷ **2nd** ⌷, [**L2**] (row 9, column 3) to instruct the calculator to use list **L1** as the independent variable and list **L2** as the dependent variable in calculating least squares line of best fit.

When this information is entered correctly, the display will show

```
LinReg(ax+b) L1,
L2
```

Press ENTER . The calculator will soon display

```
LinReg
y=ax+b
a=-.5677966102
b=4.254237288
```

The equation for the least squares line of best fit is
$$y = ax + b = (-.5677966102)x + 4.254237288$$
or, rounding to two decimal places,
$$y = -0.57x + 4.25.$$

(d) & (e) Enter the equation $y = -0.57x + 4.25$ for the least squares line of best fit as **Y2** on the **Y=** screen. Press GRAPH to generate the scatter plot, the graph of the line you devised in (b), and the graph of the least squares line all in the same viewing window. In your opinion, does the line you constructed in part (b) or the least squares line of best fit graphed in (d) more closely fit the points in the scatter plot?

PRACTICE PROBLEMS

In problems 1 - 10:

(a) Construct a scatter plot of the given data;
(b) In the same coordinate system as used for the scatter plot, draw the straight line which, in your judgment, is closest to the data points plotted;
(c) Calculate, either manually or using the TI-83®, the equation for the least squares line of best fit; and
(d) Graph the line from (c) and compare it with the line of best fit found visually in (b).

1.

x	1	2	3
y	1	2	1

The dependent variable is *y*.

3.

x	1	2	5
y	1	2	1

The dependent variable is *y*.

2.

x	1	2	3
y	1	1	2

The dependent variable is *y*.

4.

t	1	2	3	4
y	1	2	2	1

The dependent variable is *y*.

5.

t	1	2	3	4
y	1	1	2	2

The dependent variable is y.

6.

x	1	3	4	6.5	7
y	−2.0	−3.0	−2.6	−4.0	−3.2

The dependent variable is y.

7.

t	0	1	3	4	5	6
z	4	1	−2	−3	−6	−8

The dependent variable is z.

8.

t	1	3	4	6	7	8
w	2.0	3.0	2.8	3.5	3.5	4.5

The dependent variable is w.

9.

t	0.5	1.5	4.5	5.0	5.5	6.0
y	−8.1	−5.3	4.8	4.2	7.6	10.3

The dependent variable is y.

10.

x	1	2	4	6	7	8	10
y	4.5	3.6	2.9	1.7	0.8	0	−1.2

The dependent variable is y.

In problems 11 and 12:
(a) Construct a scatter plot of the given data;
(b) Calculate, either manually or using the TI-83®, the equation for the least squares line of best fit; and
(c) In the same coordinate system as used for the scatter plot, draw the graph of the least squares line of best fit.

11.

Speed (miles per hour)	s	30	40	50	60	70
Gas mileage (miles per gallon)	m	18.3	20.8	16.3	15.8	13.6

Speed is the independent variable.

12.

Viscosity,	v	43	47	49	50	54	56
Horsepower,	h	16.3	17.0	17.5	16.7	18.1	17.7

Viscosity is the independent variable.

OBJECTIVE 5.4

Given data from observation of a phenomenon described by an exponential function $f(t) = A e^{kt}$,

(a) estimate A and k by transforming the data logarithmically and computing a least squares line of best fit for the transformed data,

(b) estimate $f(t)$ for a given value of t and

(c) estimate t for a given value of $f(t)$.

DISCUSSION

The problem of inferring a linear equation $y = mx + b$ from data points near its graph was discussed in Objective 5.3. In that Discussion we followed the lead of statisticians and computed the least squares line of best fit as an approximation for the unknown linear equation. The analogous problem for functions of the form $f(t) = A e^{kt}$ is important because exponential functions model so many natural phenomena.

The technique developed in Objective 5.3 fits a line, not an exponential curve, to a set of data points. It is sensible to use the least squares line of best fit only when we believe, either from examining the data or from theoretical considerations, the data lie along a straight line. A scatter plot of data arising from observing a growth or decay phenomena, for instance, will not appear to lie along a line. Computing a least squares line of best fit would not be a good approach. The following (completely fanciful) scenario illustrates the situation.

Doctors Priscilla Precise and Seymour Snarff, the notorious research team, are investigating the chemical compound U_2Gh. The compound is very unstable. When a sample of U_2Gh is prepared, decay begins immediately. Snarff prepared a sample of U_2Gh. Precise observed the decay of the sample and recorded the data below. In her table, t denotes time in minutes since the sample was prepared and y denotes the number of grams of the compound remaining at time t.

Time (minutes) since preparation t	2	4	6	8	10
Grams remaining at time t y	12.182494	4.481690	1.648721	0.606531	0.223130

Table 5.6

To get a clearer picture of the relation among data points, Precise and Snarff plotted the pairs (t, y) in a rectangular coordinate system to make a scatter plot of their data. Figure 5.16 shows their graph. Snarff and Precise briefly contemplated the scatter plot, and decided that their data is not distributed along a straight line.

When, as in the situation faced by Snarff and Precise, data are distributed along a curved path rather than a straight line, finding a function $y = f(x)$ whose graph fits the data can be difficult. An alternative to fitting a curve is to transform the data by applying some function to the independent variable, the dependent variable, or both, so that points in the scatter plot of the transformed data are distributed along a straight line. Then, construct the least squares line of best fit for the transformed data.

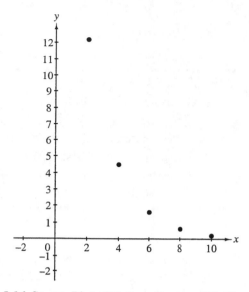

Figure 5.16 Scatter Plot of Data on Decay of U_2Gh

Finally, reverse the transformation process to obtain a function whose graph approximates the original data. The functions statisticians use to transform data include squaring, cubing, taking square or cube roots, taking reciprocals and taking logarithms. Sometimes a transformation is suggested by a theoretical model of the relation between the variables, but frequently the investigator must rely on the data to suggest a transformation.

Snarff and Precise observed that the data in their scatter plot appeared to be distributed along a decay curve and then remembered that exponential functions $f(t) = A e^{kt}$ often provide good models of decay processes. Precise suggested that since the semi-log graph of an exponential function is a straight line, a semi-log graph of these data should also lie along a line. The investigators decided to transform their data by taking the logarithm of the dependent variable. They calculated $y* = \ln y$ for each of the data points and got this table.

t	2	4	6	8	10
y	12.182494	4.481690	1.648721	0.606531	0.223130
$y* = \ln y$	2.5	1.5	0.5	−0.5	−1.5

Table 5.7

Encouraged by the information added to their table, the team constructed another scatter plot, this time showing t and $y*$. This plot is shown in Figure 5.17.

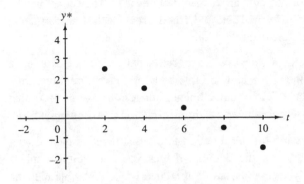

Precise and Snarff were pleased to see that the points in the semi-log plot of the data lay along a straight line, so they did not need to compute the least squares line of best fit. They observed that the line has $y*$-intercept $b = 3.5$. They computed the slope from the points $(2, 2.5)$ and $(10, -1.5)$ and found

$$m = \frac{-1.5 - 2.5}{10 - 2} = \frac{-4}{8} = -0.5.$$

Figure 5.17 Semi-log Plot of Data on Decay of U_2Gh

Thus, the equation for the line in the $t - y*$ coordinate system is $y* = -0.5t + 3.5$. Points in the scatter plot of the **transformed** data lie along this straight line. To get the relationship between y and t, Snarff expressed $y*$ in terms of y and t, and wrote

$$\ln y = -0.5t + 3.5.$$

Then, Precise rewrote this equation as an exponential equation which expresses y in terms of t.

$$y = e^{(-0.5t + 3.5)} = e^{3.5}e^{-0.5t} = 33.1155e^{-0.5t}$$

The chemists were confident this function gives a good mathematical model of the process of decay of U_2Gh.

If Priscilla had been less precise in measuring the amount of U_2Gh in the sample, the transformed data would not have lain perfectly along a straight line. In that case, instead of drawing the straight line through all of the data points the team would have computed the least squares line of best fit for the transformed data. The point is, one device for inferring a mathematical model from data that are not arrayed along a line is transforming the data. If the data are arrayed along an exponential curve, use a logarithmic transformation.

SUMMARY

1. When data is distributed along a straight line, use the least squares line of best fit to infer a linear function that fits the data.

2. When data are distributed along a curve rather than a straight line, statisticians sometimes transform the data by applying some function to the independent variable, the dependent variable, or both, so that the transformed data are distributed linearly. They construct the least squares line of best fit for the transformed data and, finally, reverse the transformation process to obtain a function that fits the original data.

3. To obtain an exponential function $f(t) = A e^{kt}$ that fits data distributed along a growth or decay curve, transform the dependent variable by taking its natural logarithm. Compute the least squares line of best fit to obtain a linear equation $\ln y = mt + b$ that fits the transformed data. Finally, rewrite this logarithmic equation in exponential form.

4. To obtain the most accurate expression for the function that best fits given data, do not round the transformed data. Use all of the decimal places your calculator displays throughout the calculations. Finally, as the last step, round in a way compatible with the accuracy of the original data.

EXAMPLES

Example 1: Prof. Snarff is also investigating methods for producing another compound, Ar_3Gh, for industrial use. Snarff has discovered a reaction that produces large quantities of Ar_3Gh very quickly. As long as adequate quantities of the reactants are present, the number of grams of the compound that had been produced t minutes after the reaction began is given by a function of the form $f(t) = A e^{kt}$. Snarff recorded the following data from an experiment designed to study means for controlling this reaction.

Time (minutes) since reaction began t	10	20	30	40	50
Amount (grams) of Ar_3Gh produced y	2.7	5.5	6.1	13.5	20.1

Table 5.8

(a) What is an equation for the function $f(t) = A e^{kt}$ that models this reaction?
(b) According to the model from (a), how many grams of Ar_3Gh had been produced when Snarff stopped the reaction after 60 minutes?
(c) According to the model, after how many minutes had 10 grams of the compound been produced?

Solution 1: (a) To find numerical values for A and k, first, find the natural logarithm $\ln y$ of each of the observed values y.

Time (minutes) since reaction began	t	10	20	30	40	50
Amount (grams) Ar_3Gh produced	y	2.7	5.5	6.1	13.5	20.1
	$y* = \ln y$	0.993251773	1.704748092	1.808288771	2.602689685	3.000719815

Table 5.9

Next, plot $y* = \ln y$ for each value of t. These points do not lie exactly along a straight line. Compute the least squares line of best fit for this data.

Evaluate the quantities used to compute the slope and $y*$-intercept of the least squares line of best fit. We have

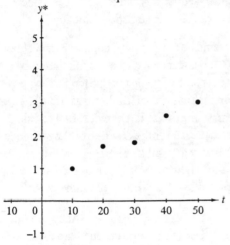

$$S_t = 10 + 20 + 30 + 40 + 50 = 150$$

$$T = \frac{150}{5} = 30$$

$$S_{y*} = \ln(2.7) + \ln(5.5) + \ln(6.1) + \ln(13.5)$$

$$+ \ln(20.1) = 10.109698137$$

$$Y* = \frac{10.10969814}{5} = 2.021939627$$

$$S_{tt} = (10)^2 + (20)^2 + (30)^2 + (40)^2 + (50)^2 - 5500$$

$$S_{ty*} = 10\ln(2.7) + 20\ln(5.5) + 30\ln(6.1)$$

$$+ 40\ln(13.5) + 50\ln(20.1) = 352.419720881.$$

Figure 5.18

From these quantities we find that the least squares line of best fit has slope

$$m = \frac{(5)(352.419720881) - (150)(10.10969814)}{(5)(5500) - (150)(150)} = 0.0491287768$$

and $y*$-intercept

$$b = 2.021939627 - (0.0491287768)(30) = 0.5480763243.$$

An equation for the least squares line of best fit for the transformed data is

$$y* = 0.5480763243 + (0.0491287768)t.$$

This is the equation for the semi-log graph of the exponential function that models the reaction. By rewriting this linear equation in t and $y*$ as an exponential equation in t and y we obtain

$$y = 1.729922006\, e^{(0.0491287768)t}\,.$$

After rounding in a way compatible with the original data, we obtain

$$f(t) = 1.73 e^{0.05t}$$

as an exponential function that models this reaction.

Solution 1:   (a) *Calculator Commentary*

The tedious work required to calculate the equation for the least squares line of best fit manually can be avoided by using the TI-83's statistical functions.

Access the **STAT** list editor, by pressing $\boxed{\text{STAT}}$ (row 3, column 3) and choosing **Edit** by pressing either $\boxed{1}$ or $\boxed{\text{ENTER}}$. Clear all lists that contain entries by using the arrow keys to move the cursor to the name of the list on the top line and pressing $\boxed{\text{CLEAR}}$, $\boxed{\text{ENTER}}$. Enter the data from the first line of Table 5.8 as list **L1**. Use the arrow keys to move the cursor to the first line of list **L1**, enter the first number from the top row of Table 5.8, and then press $\boxed{\text{ENTER}}$ or the down arrow key to move the cursor to the next line. Continue in this way until all five numbers from the first row of Table 5.8 are entered in order. Use the right arrow key to move to list **L2**. Enter the numbers from the second row of Table 5.8 as **L2** in the same way.

When a function is applied to a list, the TI-83® generates a new list by applying the function to each entry of the original list. Use this feature to generate a list **L3** whose entries are the natural logarithms of the entries of list **L2**. On the **STAT** list screen, move the cursor to the name **L3** of list 3 on the top line of the screen. Press $\boxed{\text{LN}}$, $\boxed{\text{2nd}}$, [**L2**] (row 9, column 3), $\boxed{\text{ENTER}}$. Compare the resulting list **L3** with the third line of Table 5.9.

Now we are ready to calculate the least squares line of best fit. Press $\boxed{\text{STAT}}$ again. Scroll to **CALC** to display the calculate menu and press $\boxed{4}$ to choose **LinReg(ax + b)** (linear regression). Press $\boxed{\text{2nd}}$, [**L1**] (row 9, column 2), $\boxed{,}$, $\boxed{\text{2nd}}$, [**L3**] (row 9, column 4) to instruct the calculator to use list **L1** as the independent variable and list **L3** as the dependent variable in calculating least squares line of best fit. Press $\boxed{\text{ENTER}}$. The calculator will soon display

```
LinReg
y=ax+b
a=.0491287768
b=.5480763242
```

The equation for the least squares line of best fit is
$$y = ax + b = (0.0491287768)t + 0.5480763242$$
or, rounding to two decimal places,
$$y = 0.05t + 0.55.$$

Let's generate a scatter plot similar to that shown in Figure 5.18. Press ⎡2nd⎤ , [STAT PLOT] (row 1, column 1) to access the menu used to tell the calculator what data to use to construct a statistical plot. **Plots 2** and **3** should be **OFF**. If they are not, press ⎡4⎤ , ⎡ENTER⎤ to turn all plots off and then press ⎡2nd⎤ , [STAT PLOT] to again display the **STAT PLOT** menu. Press ⎡1⎤ to access the menu for **Plot 1**. On the first active line, highlight **On** and press ⎡ENTER⎤ . On the second active line, highlight the first icon and press ⎡ENTER⎤ to choose a scatter plot. On the third line, type ⎡2nd⎤ , [L1] and press ⎡ENTER⎤ to indicate that the independent variable comes from **List 1**. On the fourth line, type ⎡2nd⎤ , [L3] and press ⎡ENTER⎤ to indicate that the dependent variable comes from **List 3**. On the fifth line, highlight the mark that you wish to use to identify points in the scatter plot and press ⎡ENTER⎤ .

Press ⎡Y=⎤ to access the **Y=** editor. Turn off all expressions on this screen. Establish a viewing window similar to that in Figure 5.18 by setting **Xmin = -5, Xmax = 55, Xscl = 5, Ymin = -1, Ymax = 4, Yscl = 1.**

Finally, press ⎡GRAPH⎤ to generate the scatter plot. Compare the scatter plot on the TI-83® with Figure 5.18. To see how well the least squares line fits the data, enter the equation for this line as **Y1** on the **Y=** edit screen and press ⎡GRAPH⎤ . (Remember to use x as the variable.)

(b) The model predicts that when Snarff stopped the reaction after 60 minutes
$$f(60) = 1.73e^{0.05(60)} = 34.75$$
grams of Ar_3Gh had been produced.

(c) At the time t when 10 grams of the compound had been produced,
$$f(t) = 1.73e^{0.05t} = 10 \quad \text{or} \quad e^{0.05t} = 5.780346821.$$

Solve this exponential equation and find
$$0.05t = \ln(5.78034682) \quad \text{and} \quad t = 35.08927369.$$
In keeping with the accuracy of the initial data, we round to the nearest minute and conclude that 35 minutes after the reaction began, 10 grams of Ar_3Gh had been produced.

PRACTICE PROBLEMS

1. The key resource in the information society is not only renewable, but self-generating. Running out of information is not a problem, but drowning in it is! The following table gives estimates of the number of scientific and technical articles that had appeared in print at various times during the past few years.

Years (since 1960) t	5	10	15	20
Estimated number N of articles in print (millions)	2.1	3.5	6.6	12.1

    (a) From these data find a function $N(t) = Ae^{kt}$ that models the publication of scientific and technical information.
    (b) According to the model, how many printed scientific and technical articles were there in 1957 (a year often identified with the beginning of the information society)?
    (c) According to the model, when will there be 1 billion printed scientific and technical articles?
    (d) According to the model, how long does it take for the number of scientific-technical articles to double?

2. To assess how quickly a burn was healing under a new method of treatment, a burn research team estimated the area of the burn every four days and recorded the following data.

Time (days) t	0	4	8	12	16
Area (sq. cm.) A	88	75	62	51	42

    (a) From these data find an exponential function $A(t) = Ce^{kt}$ that models the progress of healing.
    (b) According to this model, what will the area of the burn be on day 30?
    (c) According to this model, what will the area of the burn be on day 10?
    (d) According to this model, when will the area of the burn be 1 sq. cm.?

3. According to an official of the World Bank, high rates of population growth in developing countries threaten their ability to become economically self-sufficient and improve the quality of life for their citizens. The following table shows population data for one of these countries from the recent past.

Years (since 1960) t	4	8	12	16	20	24
Population (in millions) P	9.6	11.1	12.2	13.9	17.3	19.7

(a) From these data find an exponential function $P(t) = Ae^{kt}$ that models the population of this country.
(b) According to the model, what was the population of the country in 1975?
(c) According to the model, when will the population of this country reach 50 million?
(d) According to the model, how many years does it take for the population of this country to double?

4. The air pressure P at altitude x feet above sea level decreases exponentially as x increases. A team of Colorado State University atmospheric science students measured the air pressure at several Colorado communities and recorded the following data.

Community	Elevation	Air pressure
Sterling	3900 ft.	1734 lbs./sq. ft.
Fort Collins	5000 ft.	1722 lbs./sq. ft.
Colorado Springs	6000 ft.	1638 lbs./sq. ft.
Aspen	7900 ft.	1548 lbs./sq. ft.
Leadville	10,100 ft.	1455 lbs./sq. ft.

(a) From these data, find a function $P(x) = Ae^{kx}$ that models the relation between air pressure and altitude.
(b) From this model, what air pressure would you predict in Silverton (elevation 9300 ft.) and at the summit of Mt. Elbert (elevation 14,400 ft.)?
(c) As of mid-1988, the record altitude achieved by an aircraft in horizontal flight was just over 85,000 feet. From this model, what air pressure would you predict at that altitude?
(d) According to this model, at what altitude is the air pressure equal to 1% of the air pressure at sea level?

5. In a laboratory study of population growth an experimenter lined the bottom of a large bottle with mashed banana, introduced a population of 10 fruit flies and closed the bottle with fine mesh netting. The growth of the fruit fly population was observed and the following data was recorded.

Time (days)	t	0	3	6	9	12	15	18
Population	N	10	15	27	39	105	152	225

(a) From these data, find a function $N(t) = Ae^{kt}$ which models the population of the fruit fly colony.
(b) According to the model, what was the population of the fruit fly colony on day 16 of the study?
(c) According to the model, when will the population be 750?

Note that this experiment was discussed in Objective 4.4. Compare these results with that Discussion.

6. The relationship between the concentration of a colored substance in a solution and the transmission of monochromatic light through the solution is modeled by an exponential function. This model is known as Beer's Law. An experimenter observed the transmission of light of wave length 340 nanometers through a solution of nicotinamide adenine dinucleotide (NADPH$_2$) and recorded the following data.

Concentration (NADPH$_2$ centimoles/liter) c	0.25	0.50	0.60	0.75	1.00	1.20
Intensity (transmitted light in lumens) I	6.68	4.95	4.05	3.36	2.19	1.65

(a) From these data, find a function $I(c) = Ae^{kc}$ that models transmission of light of wave length 340 nanometers through solutions of NADPH$_2$.

(b) What is the intensity of the light through a clear liquid with none of the compound in solution? What is the intensity of the light through a solution of concentration 2.00 centimoles/liter?

(c) What concentration of NADPH$_2$ will result in transmitted light of intensity 5 lumens?

(d) What concentration will result in a 90% reduction in intensity of the transmitted light?

UNIT 5
SAMPLE EXAMINATION

1. The equation $y = 0.21e^{20.08t}$ can be written as a linear equation in t and $y* = \ln y$ as

   A) $y* = 0.21 + 3t$ **B)** $y* = -1.56 + 3t$ **C)** $y* = -1.56 + 20.08t$

   D) $y* = 0.21 + 20.08t$ **E)** $y* = 20.08 + 0.21t$

2. Which exponential function has the straight line shown in Figure 5.19 as its semi-log graph?

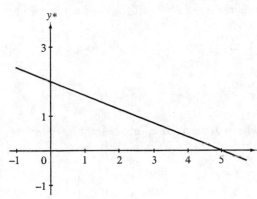

   A) $y = 0.7e^{-0.9t}$

   B) $y = 0.7e^{-0.4t}$

   C) $y = 2.0e^{-0.4t}$

   D) $y = 7.4e^{-0.4t}$

   E) $y = 7.4e^{-0.9t}$

Figure 5.19

3. What is the equation for the least squares line of best fit for the following data?

x	−1	1	2	4	7
y	12.6	14.5	14.8	16.6	18.5

   The independent variable is x. Round to two decimal places as the last step in the calculation of the slope and the y-intercept.

   A) $y = 0.73x + 13.50$ **B)** $y = 0.75 + 13.45$ **C)** $y = 0.83x + 12.91$

   D) $y = 1.20x + 12.28$ **E)** $y = 1.37x + 11.84$

Problems 4 and 5 are based on the following information.

The population of Mothbite, Minnesota has been declining since 1970. As part of a study commissioned by the city council, the consulting firm of Smith, Smith, and Grabowski prepared the following table showing the city's population for several selected years. In their table, t denotes the number of years since 1970 and p denotes the population of Mothbite in thousands.

t	0	5	8	13	16	20
p	40.8	38.9	36.5	31.5	30.3	28.8

Find an exponential function $p(t) = Ae^{kt}$ that models the population of Mothbite by transforming the data logarithmically and computing a least squares line of best fit for the transformed data.

4. Rounded to the nearest whole number, what is A in the exponential model found above for the population of Mothbite?

    A) 38   B) 39   C) 40   D) 41   E) 42

5. According to this model, to the nearest thousand what will the population of Mothbite be in the year 2000 (30 years after 1970)?

    A) 22,000   B) 23,000   C) 24,000   D) 25,000   E) 26,000

UNIT 6

COMPREHENSIVE REVIEW

OVERVIEW

In this book we considered the mathematical concept of function and studied the exponential and logarithmic functions as specific examples of functions. Functions are important because they are a fundamental tool for expressing and investigating mathematical ideas and because they can be used to describe, or model, events in the world around us.

In Unit 1 we defined a function as a procedure for determining exactly one number from each number in some collection and we explored a variety of procedures used to specify functions. In Unit 2 we investigated functions specified by procedures that can be reversed to obtain an inverse function and then defined the logarithmic functions as inverses of exponential functions. In Unit 3 we learned to manipulate expressions involving logarithmic functions and write them in different equivalent forms. In Unit 4 we concentrated on solving equations involving logarithmic or exponential functions to obtain information from mathematical models of phenomena we observe in the world around us. In Unit 5 we studied methods for constructing exponential functions that model growth and decay phenomena and used the functions we constructed to gain information about the phenomena they model.

No one understands completely how our brains work. But we do know that rote memorization, translating into a picture, and forming a web of interconnections among pieces of information are three of the ways the human mind sorts and recalls information. The brain didn't evolve to store and use isolated facts, so we tend to forget information learned by rote. We can pull many details out of pictures. We can retain and make new connections with facts that we have stored as part of a network of information. As you studied this book you may have learned some information by rote memorization and some by translating into pictures and graphs. The questions which follow can help you make connections and weave the many different facts you have learned into a whole fabric.

UNIT 6
COMPREHENSIVE REVIEW

OBJECTIVE 6.1

The purpose of Unit 6 is to give you an opportunity to integrate everything you have learned about exponential and logarithmic functions.

COMPREHENSIVE REVIEW

REVIEW QUESTIONS

1. According to the Discussion for Objective 1.1, a function has been specified when its **domain** and a **procedure** for determining exactly one number from each number in the domain have been given.
   (a) Describe three different ways commonly used to specify the procedure for a function.
   (b) What is meant by the domain of a function?
   (c) Describe two different ways commonly used to specify the domain of a function.

2. (a) What notation is used to denote a function?
   (b) Explain the distinction between an independent variable and a dependent variable.
   (c) What is meant by the range of a function?

3. Can every function be given by formula or equation? If not, how might such a function be specified?

4. (a) Explain what the graph of a function is and how it is constructed.
   (b) Explain how the graph of a function can be used to evaluate the function.
   (c) Give examples of graphs of functions.
   (d) Is every graph the graph of a function? If not, give examples of graphs that are not graphs of functions.
   (e) How do you distinguish the graph of a function from other graphs?

5. (a) Do all exponential functions have the same domain? Do all exponential functions have the same range?
   (b) Do all logarithmic functions have the same domain? Do all logarithmic functions have the same range?
   (c) Is it just a coincidence that the domain of the exponential functions is the same as the range of the logarithmic functions?
   (d) Is it just a coincidence that the range of the exponential functions is the same as the domain of the logarithmic functions?

6. (a) What is "common" about log, the common logarithm function?
   (b) What is "natural" about ln, the natural logarithm function?

7. Within the limits of the range of numbers your scientific calculator will accept, you can use it to evaluate any exponential. But you can only use it to evaluate the natural and common logarithms directly.
   (a) Why might the calculator be designed this way?
   (b) Is it possible to use your scientific calculator to evaluate other logarithmic functions? If so, how?

8. (a) How does the graph of an exponential function change as the size of the base is increased or decreased? How does it stay the same?
   (b) How does the graph of a logarithmic function change as the size of the base is increased or decreased? How does it stay the same?

9. Forming the composition of two functions is sometimes described as a kind of function multiplication. Compare the process of forming the composition of two polynomial functions with the process of multiplying them in the familiar way. Describe some similarities. Describe some differences.

10. A student suggested that the inverse of a function should be called the *reverse* of the function. Would this be reasonable terminology? Why or why not?

11. Does every function have an inverse? Explain.

12. In Units 1 and 2 we examined three different ways to specify a function; an equation, a graph, or a calculator. How might you specify the inverse function when the function itself is specified: (a) by an equation, (b) by a graph, (c) by a calculator?

13. List as many ways as you can think of for deciding whether two functions are a pair of inverse functions.

14. (a) How are an exponential function and a logarithmic function with the same base related?
    (b) How is this relationship reflected in the equations for these functions?
    (c) How is it reflected in their graphs?

15. What are the Product, Quotient, and Power Properties for Logarithms and how are they used? Are there corresponding properties for exponential functions? If so, what are they? If not, why not?

16. (a) Explain how to solve an equation involving an exponential function.

  (b) Are different techniques needed depending on whether the unknown appears as the base or as the power in the exponential?

17. (a) Explain how to solve an equation involving a logarithmic function.

  (b) Are different techniques needed depending on where the unknown appears in the logarithmic function?

18. (a) What is a mathematical model? How are mathematical models used?

  (b) Give an example of a mathematical model that involves an exponential function.

  (c) Give an example of a mathematical model that involves a logarithmic function.

19. (a) Explain how the least squares line of best fit is used to infer a mathematical model from observed data.

  (b) How can a least squares line of best fit, which is a **linear** function, be used to infer a mathematical model which involves an **exponential** function?

  (c) How might a least squares line of best fit be used to infer a mathematical model which involves a **logarithmic** function?

20. Who wrote *A Mathematician Reads the Newspaper*? There is only one correct response.

  (a) James Kilpatrick

  (b) John Allen Paulos

  (c) Martin Gardner

  (d) Howard W. Eves

ANSWER SECTION

UNIT 1
FUNCTIONS AND GRAPHS

OBJECTIVE 1.1

1. all real numbers except $x = 2$

2. the real numbers $x \leq \dfrac{5}{3}$

3. all real numbers

4. the real numbers $x > -\dfrac{9}{2}$

5. the real numbers x such that $-3 \leq x < 2$ or $2 < x \leq 3$

6. all real numbers except $x = 1$ or $x = 5$

7. (a) $f(-2) = -1$

   (b) $f(3) = 19$

8. (a) $h(4) = -\dfrac{6}{5}$

   (b) -1 is not in the domain of h

   (c) 19.51767367

9. (a) $\dfrac{-19}{4}$ is not in the domain of g

   (b) $g(-1) = \dfrac{1}{\sqrt{5}} = \dfrac{\sqrt{5}}{5}$

   (c) 0.3772644883

10. (a) 2 is not in the domain of F

    (b) $F(4) = 1$

    (c) $F(1)$ is not defined

11. (a) $\dfrac{1}{2}$ is not in the domain of H

    (b) $H(5) = \dfrac{5}{9}$

    (c) $H(1) = 5$

    (d) -1.921354594

12. (a) $R(5)$ is not defined

    (b) $R\left(\dfrac{1}{2}\right) = 0$

    (c) $R(-2) = -\dfrac{5}{7}$

13. 16

14. -5

15. not defined

16. $\dfrac{1}{2}$

17. -10

18. not defined

19. -7638.905065

20. -1.090278458

OBJECTIVE 1.2

1. is a function

2. is not a function

3. is a function

4. is a function

5. is a function

6. is a function

7. Domain: the interval from $-2\frac{1}{2}$ to $2\frac{1}{2}$
   Range: the interval from -4 to 4

8. Domain: the interval from -3 to 5
   Range: the interval from 0 to 2

9. Domain: the interval from -4 to 4
   Range: $\{-4, -1\}$

10. Domain: the interval from -3 to $4\frac{1}{2}$
    Range: the interval from -4 to -1

11. Domain: the interval from -4 to -1
    unioned with the interval from 1 to 4
    Range: the interval from -4 to -1
    unioned with the interval from 1 to 4

12. Domain: the interval from -4 to 3
    Range: $\left\{\frac{1}{2}, 1, 1\frac{1}{2}, 4\right\}$

13. (a) $f(-3) = 0$
    (b) $f(0) = -2$

14. (a) $h(-1)$ is not defined
    (b) $h(4) = -1$

15. (a) $F(3) = 2$
    (b) $F\left(-4\frac{1}{2}\right)$ is not defined

16. (a) $-4,\ 1,\ 4$
    (b) $-3\frac{1}{2},\ -1$

17. (a) 2 is not in the range of g
    (b) -3 and 3

18. (a) 3
    (b) $\dfrac{1}{3}$

19. (a) Use **TRACE**
    (b) Domain: the interval from 0 to 18.75
        Range: the interval from 0 to 2
    (c) $G(1) = 1.35$; $G(5.75) = 1$; $G(14.5) = 1.8$
        (approximately)
    (d) (*i*) 3.25, 9.5, 15.75 (approximately)
        (*ii*) no such values

        (*iii*) .5, 5.75, 7, 12, 13.25, 18.25
        (approximately)

20. (a) Use **TRACE**
    (b) Domain: the interval from -1.61 to 1.85 (approximately)
        Range: the interval from -0.16 to 3 (approximately)
    (c) 0.469: 0.973; 1.098 (approximately)
    (d) (*i*) $a = 1.55$ (*ii*) $a = -1.4$ (approximately)

OBJECTIVE 1.3

1. 256
2. 3.85403
3. 18.19771
4. 0.47120
5. 403.42879
6. 0.45186
7. 0.04321
8. 281.50735

9. 3.81904
10. 271.22044
11. 1.87354
12. 5.02583
13. 0.69897
14. 0.85399
15. −0.21266
16. 4.98703

17. 0.77739
18. 2.23607
19. −0.08569
20. not defined
21. 78.11916
22. 4.07151
23. 1.36195
24. −173.43863
25. 8.65817

OBJECTIVE 1.4

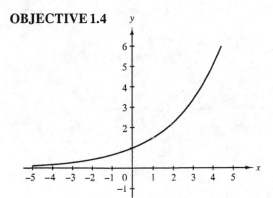

1. *Figure 1.40A* $y = \left(\dfrac{3}{2}\right)^x$

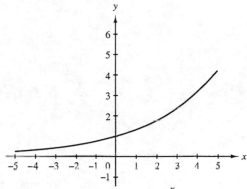

2. *Figure 1.41A* $f(x) = \left(\dfrac{4}{3}\right)^x$

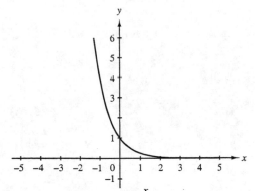

3. *Figure 1.42A* $y = \left(\dfrac{1}{4}\right)^x$

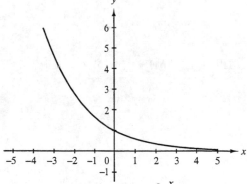

4. *Figure 1.43A* $f(x) = \left(\dfrac{3}{5}\right)^x$

6. $f(x) = \left(\dfrac{1}{4}\right)^x$ **7.** $y = 2^x$ **8.** $y = \left(\dfrac{3}{2}\right)^x$ **9.** $f(x) = \left(\dfrac{2}{7}\right)^x$

OBJECTIVE 1.5

1. (a) –5

(b) –1

2. (a) undefined

(b) –7

3. (a) 4

(b) –2

4. (a) 0

(b) 4

5. (a) $\sqrt{6}$

(b) undefined

6. (a) $g \circ f(x) = 4x^2 + 4x + 3$

(b) $6x^2 - 8x + 5$

7. (a) $S \circ T(x) = \dfrac{17x^2 - 8x + 2}{9x^2}$

(b) $T \circ S(x) = \dfrac{4x^2 + 1}{6x^2 + 3}$

8. (a) $h \circ k(x) = x$

(b) $k \circ h(x) = x$

9. (a) $G\big(H(x)\big) = \dfrac{2x + 1}{4x}$

(b) $H\big(G(x)\big) = \sqrt[5]{\dfrac{6x^5 + 9}{11x^5 + 3}}$

10. (a) $g\big(k(x)\big) = \dfrac{14x + 55}{6x + 21}$

(b) $k\big(g(x)\big) = \dfrac{9}{4x + 35}$

11. $\dfrac{27x + 44}{6x - 8}$

12. $\dfrac{29x - 52}{5x + 4}$

13. $4 + x$

14. $\dfrac{1}{6} - \sqrt[5]{\dfrac{6x^5 - 4}{-39x^5 - 6}}$

15. undefined

SAMPLE EXAMINATION

1. B)   **2.** B), D), and E)   **3.** D)   **4.** C)   **5.** A)

UNIT 2
INVERSE FUNCTIONS

OBJECTIVE 2.1

5. **(a)** $g(-2) = 3$

(b) 5 is not in the domain of g

1. has an inverse

6. **(a)** $q(-3)$ is not defined

2. has an inverse

(b) $q(1) = \dfrac{3}{2}$

3. does not have an inverse

7. **(a)** $R(2) = 1$

4. does not have an inverse

(b) -4 is not in the domain of R

8. **(a)** $f(-1) = 2$

(b) $f(0) = \dfrac{7}{2}$

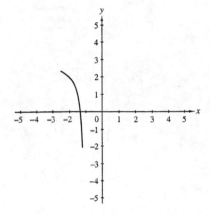

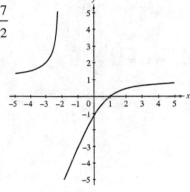

11. *Figure 2.27A*

9. *Figure 2.25A*

10. The graph in Figure 2.26 does **not** have an inverse function

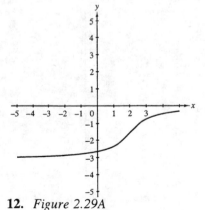

13. reflected graph is a function

14. reflected graph is not a function

15. reflected graph is a function

16. reflected graph is not a function

17. reflected graph is a function

18. reflected graph is not a function

12. *Figure 2.29A*

OBJECTIVE 2.2

1. $T(x) = 2x - 4$

2. $G(x) = 2 + \sqrt[3]{x}$

3. $g(x) = \dfrac{x}{1 - x}$

4. $q(x) = \sqrt[3]{x^3 - 1}$

5. $P(x) = \left(1 - \dfrac{1}{x}\right)^3$

6. $g(x) = \sqrt[3]{\dfrac{x + 4}{7}}$

7. $k(x) = \dfrac{4x - 5}{7x - 2}$

8. $q(x) = \dfrac{x^3 + 7}{3}$

9. $s(x) = \dfrac{\sqrt[5]{x} - 3}{2}$

10. $T(x) = \dfrac{x^3 - 8}{x^3}$

11. $s(x) = (3x + 1)^7$

12. $t(x) = \sqrt[5]{\dfrac{7 + 3x}{10x}}$

13. $y = \left(\dfrac{3x}{4 + 5x}\right)^3$

14. $G(x) = 5x^7 + 4$

15. $y = \dfrac{-4\sqrt[3]{x} - 1}{3\sqrt[3]{x} - 2}$

16. $k(x) = \dfrac{(\sqrt[3]{3})x}{\sqrt[3]{8 + x^3}}$

17. $f(x) = \sqrt[7]{\dfrac{4}{2x - 3}}$

18. $s(x) = \sqrt[5]{\dfrac{x + 15}{2}}$

19. $y = \sqrt[7]{x + 1} + 5$

20. $F(x) = -12x + 7$

OBJECTIVE 2.3

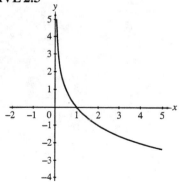

1. *Figure 2.42A* $y = \log_{1/2} x$

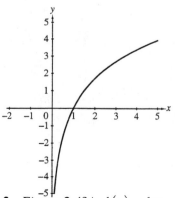

2. *Figure 2.43A* $h(x) = \log_{3/2} x$

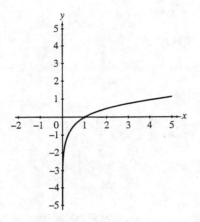

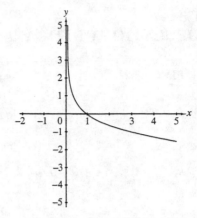

3. *Figure 2.44A* $y = \log_4 x$

4. *Figure 2.45A* $g(x) = \log_{1/3} x$

5. $y = \log_{1/3} x$ **6.** $y = \log_{5/2} x$ **7.** $y = \log_{3/2} x$ **8.** $y = \log_{1/2} x$

OBJECTIVE 2.4

1. are not inverses
2. are inverses
3. are not inverses
4. are inverses
5. are inverses

6. are not inverses
7. are inverses
8. are inverses
9. are not inverses
10. are inverses

11. are not inverses
12. are inverses
13. are inverses
14. are not inverses
15. are inverses

SAMPLE EXAMINATION

1. B) and C)   **2. A)**   **3. E)**   **4. D)**   **5. A)**

UNIT 3
MANIPULATION OF LOGARITHMIC FUNCTIONS

OBJECTIVE 3.1

1. $\log_b c = 0.5$

2. $\log_3 c = a$

3. $\log_b 7 = a$

4. $\log_x 5 = a$

5. $\log_s 11.3 = 4.2$

6. $\log_{1/2} K = 0.517$

7. $\log_w y = z$

8. $\log_b c = (p + q)$

9. $\log_{(x + y)} B = k$

10. $\log_{(u/v)} t = s$

11. $\log_x (S + R) = 1 + kt$

12. $\log_R (s - t) = \dfrac{p}{q}$

13. $3^a = c$

14. $b^{2.319} = c$

15. $b^a = 12$

16. $R^S = T$

17. $5^{1.573} = q$

18. $x^3 = 64$

19. $10^w = 238$

20. $e^{0.7513} = r$

21. $b^{(s + r)} = p$

22. $(uv)^z = Q$

23. $p^y = 4 + x^2$

24. $(a + b)^{n/k} = B$

25. B, D
26. A, E
27. not same meaning

28. same meaning
29. not same meaning
30. not same meaning

31. not same meaning
32. not same meaning

OBJECTIVE 3.2

1. $x = 2401$

2. $x = 5$

3. $x = 5$

4. $x = 65536$

5. $x = 144$

6. $x = \dfrac{7}{3}$

7. $x = 4.94609$

8. $x = 36.48287$

9. $x = -\dfrac{1}{2}$

10. $x = -3$

11. $x = 2.35913$

12. $x = 2.0000$

OBJECTIVE 3.3

1. $\log_b xy = \log_b x + \log_b y$

4. $\log_b\left(x^p\right) = p\log_b x$

2. $p\log_b x = \log_b x^p$

5. $\log_b\left(\dfrac{x}{y}\right) = \log_b x - \log_b y$

3. $\log_b x - \log_b y = \log_b\left(\dfrac{x}{y}\right)$

6. $\log_b x + \log_b y = \log_b xy$

7. not identity

11. not identity

16. not identity

21. identity

8. not identity

12. not identity

17. identity

22. identity

9. not identity

13. identity

18. not identity

23. not identity

10. not identity

14. not identity

19. not identity

24. identity

15. identity

20. not identity

OBJECTIVE 3.4

1. not identity

2. identity

9. $\ln(x - 5)(x + 1)^2$

3. $\log\left(\dfrac{x^5}{y^{2/3}z}\right)$

6. $\log_7 \dfrac{125(2s + 1)}{s^5(s - 1)^2}$

10. $\log_3(x + 1)(x - 2)^{7/2}$

4. $\log_2\left(\dfrac{u^{3/5}v^{1/4}}{8w^3}\right)$

7. $\log\dfrac{(s + r)^3(r + 1)^{3/2}}{s^{2/3}}$

11. $\log\dfrac{(x + 2y)^{7/3}}{x + 6y}$

5. $\ln\dfrac{3(t^2 + 2)}{(t - 1)(t - 2)^2}$

8. $\log_5 5$ which is 1

12. $\log_5(w + 1)^{5/2}$

13. $\dfrac{5}{3}\log x - 3\log y - 4\log z$

18. $\dfrac{2}{9}\log_3 a + \dfrac{8}{3}\log_3(a + b) + \dfrac{2}{3}\log_3 c - \dfrac{1}{3}$

14. $\dfrac{5}{3}\log_8 u + \dfrac{2}{3}\log_8 v + 2\log_8 w + 2$

19. $-\dfrac{9}{8}\log x - 3\log y + \dfrac{1}{2}\log z - \dfrac{3}{2}\log 2$

15. $-\dfrac{7}{8}\log_4 r - \dfrac{3}{10}\log_4 s - \dfrac{1}{2}\log_4 t + \dfrac{1}{2}$

20. $\dfrac{2}{9}\log_6 x - \dfrac{2}{3}\log_6 y - \dfrac{2}{9}\log_6 z + \dfrac{1}{3}\log_6 3$

16. $\dfrac{1}{3}\ln\left(2x^2 + x + 5\right) - \dfrac{2}{3}\ln(x + 5) + \dfrac{1}{9}\ln x$

21. $-10\ln r - 4\ln s + \dfrac{5}{3}\ln t - 10$

17. $-18\log r + 8\log s + \dfrac{12}{5}\log t + 6$

22. $-\dfrac{9}{40}\log_2 r + \dfrac{3}{2}\log_2 s + \dfrac{1}{2}\log_2 t + \dfrac{9}{10}$

SAMPLE EXAMINATION

1. A)   **2. E)**   **3. C) and D)**   **4. D)**   **5. A)**

UNIT 4
EXPONENTIAL AND LOGARITHMIC EQUATIONS

OBJECTIVE 4.1

1. $2t + 5$

4. $\dfrac{(x - y)^2}{(x + y)^{1/2}}$

7. $\dfrac{1}{y^2 + 1}$

2. $\left[x(x + 1)\right]^3$

5. $t^3 - 1$

8. $6y + 2$

3. $\dfrac{t + 3}{t - 2}$

6. $\dfrac{\left(y^2 + y - 6\right)^{3/2}}{y}$

9. 0

10. $\dfrac{1}{3}(a - b)^2$

11. $\dfrac{1}{7}(x + 2y)^2(x + y)$

12. $\dfrac{3a(b - c)}{b + c} + 1$

13. $x - 2y$

14. $t - 2$

15. $(2a - b)^{7/2}$

16. $\dfrac{(t + s)^2}{t - s}$

17. $\left(x^2 + xy + y^2\right)^2\left(x^2 - xy + y^2\right)$

18. $2y - 5x^2$

19. $(a + b)^{3/2}$

20. $(t - u)^{1/3}(t + u)^{5/3}$

21. $x + 2y$

22. $t^2 + 7st + s^2$

23. $\dfrac{7x + 3}{2x - 1}$

24. $4y(3 + y)$

OBJECTIVE 4.2

1. $x = 17$

2. $x = \dfrac{7}{2}$

3. $x = -1$ or $x = 7$

4. $x = 2$

5. $x = \dfrac{9}{2}$

6. $x - 5$

7. $x = 3$

8. no solution

9. no solution

10. $x = \dfrac{1}{3}$

11. $x = \dfrac{9}{2}$

12. $x = \dfrac{29}{4}$

13. $x = 2^{-2} = 0.25$ and $x = 2^3 = 8$

14. $x = 4^{-5/2} = 0.03125$ and $x = 4$

15. $x = e^{-2/3} = 0.513417119$ and $x = e^3 = 20.08553692$

16. $x = 6$

17. $x = \dfrac{7}{9}$

18. $x = 5^{-7} = 0.0000128$ or $x = 5$

19. $x = 3.617107385$

20. $x = -\dfrac{21}{4}$

21. $x = 10^{1/3} = 2.15443469$ and $x = 10^5 = 100000$

22. $x = 2$

23. $x = 2$

24. no solution

25. $x = -4$ and $x = 5$ (rounded)

OBJECTIVE 4.3

1. $x = 1.953445298$

2. $x = 1.8294828$

3. $x = 1.630929754$

4. $x = -5$ and $x = \dfrac{2}{3}$

5. $x = -4$ and $x = -1$

6. $x = 10.98375$ (rounded)

7. $x = 6$

8. $x = -0.081484$ (rounded)

9. $x = -1.230769$ (rounded)

10. $x = 0$ and $x = 2$

11. $x = 1.60944$ (rounded)

12. no solution

13. $x = -1$ and $x = 2$

14. $x = -5.96766$ (rounded)

15. $x = 1.098612$ (rounded)

16. $x = 0.621335$ (rounded)

17. $x = \dfrac{25}{7}$

18. $x = 2$ and $x = 5$

19. no solution

20. $x = \dfrac{1}{11}$

21. $x = -179.81089$ (rounded)

22. $x = 1.39$ (rounded)

23. $x = 18.8680$ (rounded)

24. $x = 1.04527$ (rounded)

25. $x = -2$ and $x = \dfrac{2}{5}$

OBJECTIVE 4.4

1. **(a)** 358 million
   (b) in the year 2698
2. **(a)** $50 = 100e^{-0.1546t}$, $t = 4.5$
   (b) 65,261,900 years
3. **(a)** 10.3 grams
   (b) 4280 seconds
4. **(a)** 0.24
   (b) 2.75 months
5. **(a)** 220
   (b) in 30 days
   (c) 1035

6. **(a)** 7
   (b) $[H+] = 1.74 \times 10^{-4}$
   (c) $[H+] = 5.75 \times 10^{-9}$
   (d) pH = 6.53
7. **(a)** 7
   (b) $[OH-] = 8.51 \times 10^{-10}$
   (c) pOH = 2.1
   (d) 2.4×10^{-7}

8. **(a)** 0 decibels
   (b) 10^{-3} watts/square meter
   (c) 10^{6} watts/square meter
   (d) 119.2 decibels
9. **(a)** 9.3×10^{9} kilowatt hours
   (b) 3.5
10. **(a)** $I = 0.398$
    (b) 0.0025
    (c) −1.42
    (d) −12.5
    (e) no

SAMPLE EXAMINATION

1. C)   2. D)   3. E)   4. C)   5. D)

UNIT 5
APPLICATIONS OF SEMI-LOG GRAPHS

OBJECTIVE 5.1

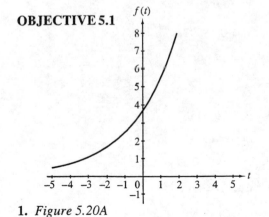

1. *Figure 5.20A*

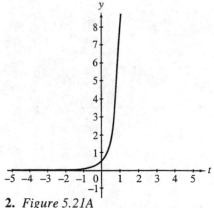

2. *Figure 5.21A*

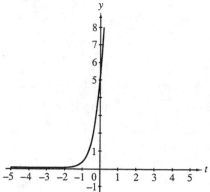

3. *Figure 5.22A*

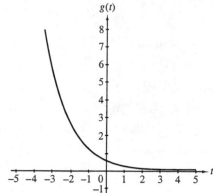

4. *Figure 5.23A*

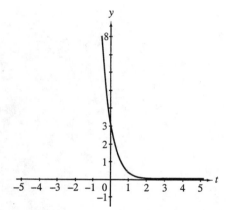

5. *Figure 5.24A*

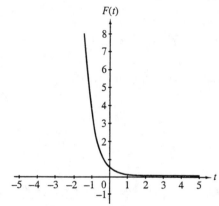

6. *Figure 5.25A*

7. $y* = 2.23t + 0.87963$

8. $y* = -1.59t - 1.83258$

9. $y* = 0.19t + 1.36609$

10. $y* = -4t + 2.99972$

11. $y* = -0.26t - 3.68888$

12. $y* = 6.22t - 1.02165$

13. $y = 18.35680e^{7.38t}$

14. $y = 450.33872e^{-2.17t}$

15. $y = 0.18637e^{-5.06t}$

16. $y = 13.59905e^{-0.92t}$

17. $y = 0.04783e^{1.64t}$

18. $y = 79.04363e^{3.84t}$

19. $\ln y = 2x + 1.60944$

20. $\ln W = -0.2t - 0.69315$

21. $y = 0.04979e^{0.5x}$

22. $W = 181.27224e^{0.35t}$

OBJECTIVE 5.2

1. line with slope -1, intercept $(0, 3)$

2. line with slope $\dfrac{2}{3}$, intercept $(0, 2)$

3. line with slope 5, intercept $(0, 0)$

4. line with slope 0.33, intercept $(0, -1.77)$

5. line with slope -4.1, intercept $(0, -2.8)$

6. line with slope $-\dfrac{3}{4}$, intercept (0.0)

7. $y = 2.71828 e^{0.5t}$

8. $y = e^{-2t}$

9. $y = 0.13534 e^{(4/7)t}$

10. $y = 20.08554 e^{-0.6t}$

11. $y = 0.08208\, e^{4t}$

12. $y = 54.59815 e^{5t}$

OBJECTIVE 5.3

Calculations were done without rounding. Final answers were rounded to three decimal places.

1. (c) $y = 0x + 1.333$

2. (c) $y = 0.5x + 0.333$

3. (c) $y = -0.077x + 1.538$

4. (c) $y = 0t + 1.5$

5. (c) $y = 0.4t + 0.5$

6. (c) $y = -0.248x - 1.892$

7. (c) $z = -1.888t + 3.646$

8. (c) $w = 0.299t + 1.771$

9. (c) $y = 3.192t - 9.985$

10. (c) $y = -0.623x + 5.137$

11. $m = -0.144s + 24.16$

12. $h = 0.119v + 11.274$

OBJECTIVE 5.4

Coefficients in the exponential equation found in (a) are rounded to a reasonable number of decimal places as the last step of the calculations. Later parts of the problem are answered from the model given in part (a).

1. (a) $N(t) = 1.129 e^{0.118t}$

   (b) $N(-3) = 792,000$ (approx.)

   (c) $t = 57.5$ years, or in year 2017

   (d) $t = 5.9$ years

2. (a) $A(t) = 89.2 e^{-0.047t}$

   (b) $A(30) = 21.8$ sq. cm.

   (c) $A(10) = 55.8$ sq. cm.

   (d) $t = 95.6$ days

3. (a) $P(t) = 8.17e^{0.036t}$

(b) $P(15) = 14.02$ million

(c) $t = 50.3$ years, or year 2010

(d) $t = 19.25$ years

4. (a) $P(x) = 1968e^{-0.00003x}$

(b) $P(9300) = 1489$ lbs. / sq. ft. (approx.)

$P(14,400) = 1277$ lbs. / sq. ft. (approx.)

(c) $P(85,000) = 154$ lbs. / sq. ft. (approx.)

(d) $x = 153,500$ ft. (approx.)

5. (a) $N(t) = 9.24e^{0.18t}$

(b) $N(16) = 165$

(c) $t = 24$ days

6. (a) $I(c) = 10.1e^{-1.5c}$

(b) $I(0) = 10.1$ lumens;

$I(2.00) = 0.5$ lumens

(c) $c = 0.47$ centimoles / liter

(d) $c = 1.54$ centimoles / liter

SAMPLE EXAMINATION

1. C)   **2.** D)   **3.** A)   **4.** E)   **5.** B)

APPENDIX

DIRECTORY OF PROGRAMS FOR THE TI-83®

GRAPHBX (Graph b^x)...Objective 1.4, page(s) 52-53
This program randomly chooses a number b between 0 and 5, stores b, and displays the graph of $y = b^x$.

GRAPHCX (Graph c^x)...Objective 1.4, page(s) 53-54
This program randomly chooses a number c between 0 and 1, stores c, and displays the graph of $y = c^x$.

DRWINVRS (Draw Inverse)...Objective 2.1, page(s) 73-75
This program graphs a function which is entered as **Y1**, and then draws the line $y = x$ and the reflection of the graph of the function through the line $y = x$ in a square viewing window.

REFLCTN (Reflection)..Objective 2.1, page(s) 84-85
This program plots the point (A, B), the line $y = x$ and the point (B, A) for numbers A and B in the viewing window specified by the operator.

GRPHLGBX (Graph $\log_b x$)..Objective 2.3, page(s) 100-102
This program randomly chooses a number b between 0 and 5, stores b, and displays the graph of $y = \log_b x$.

LOGIDNTY (Log Identity)...Objective 3.3, page(s) 129-130
This program invites the user to enter numerical values for x and y. If any of the expressions $\ln x$, $\ln y$, or $\ln xy$ are undefined, an error message is displayed. If all expressions are defined, the values of $\ln xy$ and $\ln x + \ln y$ are displayed.

INDEX

M124 Unit 1   Problem Set ID #:   1241.01
Problem Set #1

Name: Student ID#

1. Let $f(x) = \dfrac{-x + 1}{x^2 - 6x + 8}$. What is $f(-2) - f(3)$?

2. Let $g(x) = \dfrac{\sqrt{4x + 3}}{3x - 1}$. What is $g\left(-\dfrac{1}{2}\right) - g\left(\dfrac{1}{3}\right)$?

3.

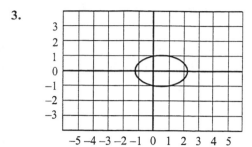

Figure 1241.01a

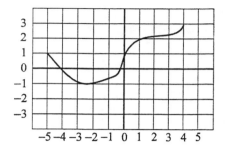

Figure 1241.01b

A) Which of the two graphs above is a function?

B) What is the function's domain?

C) What is the function's range?

D) Let the function be called G. Let a be the smallest number such that $G(a) = 1$. What is $a + G(4)$?

4. Let $f(x) = 0.459^x$ and $g(x) = \log x$.
Rounded to four decimal places, what is $f(-0.187) + g(1.235)$?

5. Let $h(x) = 10^x$ and $g(x) = \ln x$. Rounded to four decimal places, what is $h(2.14) + g(35)$?

Tutor signature:_____ Date:_____ Time:_____

M124 Unit 1
Problem Set #2

Problem Set ID #: 1241.02

Name: _____   Student ID# _____

1. The graph of a function of the form $f(x) = b^x$ is shown in the Figure 1241.02a. What is the equation for this function?

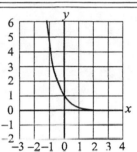

Figure 1241.02a

2. Using the grid provided at the right, graph the function $y = 4^x$.

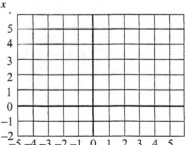

Figure 1241.02b

3. Let $f(x) = \dfrac{x^2 - 8}{2}$ and $g(x) = \sqrt{\dfrac{-2x}{x + 5}}$. What is $f \circ g(x) - g \circ f(-3)$?

4. Let $h(x) = \dfrac{2x + 4}{3}$ and $g(x) = \dfrac{x - 3}{-2x}$. What is $h \circ g\left(\dfrac{2}{3}\right) - g \circ h(x)$?

5. Let $f(x) = \dfrac{x^4 + 4}{5x^4}$ and $g(x) = \sqrt[4]{\dfrac{x + 20}{x}}$. What is $f \circ g(x) - g \circ f(2)$?

Tutor signature:_____ Date:_____ Time:_____

M124 Unit 2
Problem Set #1

Problem Set ID #:   1242.01

Name: _____   Student ID# _____

INSTRUCTIONS:

Student Managed Format: If you are eligible to take unit exams in this course, you can earn one participation credit by satisfactorily completing this problem set and submitting it for evaluation in the IMP Tutoring Center (Weber 136). You may only submit problem set number 1242.01 once for participation credit.

Instructor-led Format: You can get additional practice and feedback by writing complete answers to these problems and asking a tutor in the IMP Tutoring Center (Weber 136) to review your work with you. Students in the Instructor-led Format are not subject to the participation requirement and should not submit problem sets for participation credit. Problem sets do not earn homework credits and do not entitle you to additional testing opportunities.

1. The graph of a function $y = f(x)$ is shown in Figure 1242.01a. Graph the inverse function of f, using the grid in Figure 1242.01b, or state that f does not have an inverse function.

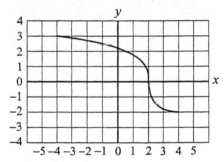

Figure 1242.01a

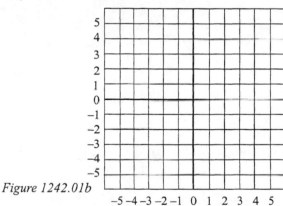

Figure 1242.01b

2. The graphs of two functions, $y = f(x)$ (Figure 1242.01c) and $y = g(x)$ (Figure 1242.01d), are shown below.

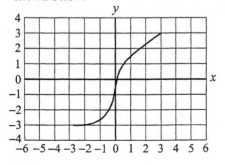

Figure 1242.01c

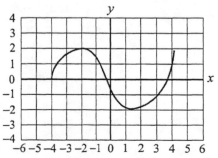

Figure 1242.01d

A)　Which of the two functions, f or g, has an inverse function?

B)　Let h denote the inverse function of the answer to **A)**. If $a = 3$ what is $h(a)$?

C)　$h(-2) =$

3.　Find an equation for the inverse function for $g(x) = \left(\dfrac{3x - 1}{x + 1}\right)^3$.

4.　Find and equation for the inverse function for $h(x) = \sqrt[3]{2x - 5} + 4$.

Tutor signature:_____Date:_____Time:_____

M124 Unit 2   **Problem Set ID #:   1242.02**
Problem Set #2

Name: _____   Student ID# _____

INSTRUCTIONS:

Student Managed Format: If you are eligible to take unit exams in this course, you can earn one participation credit by satisfactorily completing this problem set and submitting it for evaluation in the IMP Tutoring Center (Weber 136). You may only submit problem set number 1242.02 once for participation credit.

Instructor-led Format: You can get additional practice and feedback by writing complete answers to these problems and asking a tutor in the IMP Tutoring Center (Weber 136) to review your work with you. Students in the Instructor-led Format are not subject to the participation requirement and should not submit problem sets for participation credit. Problem sets do not earn homework credits and do not entitle you to additional testing opportunities.

1. The graph of a function of the form $y = \log_b x$ is shown in Figure 1242.02a.
    What is the equation for this function?

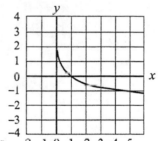

Figure 1242.02a

2. Graph the function, $y = \log_4 x$ using the grid in Figure 1242.02b.

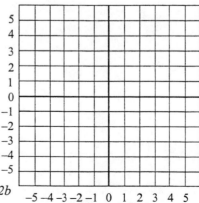

Figure 1242.02b

3. Let $F(x) = \left(\dfrac{x - 11}{3}\right)^3$ and $G(x)\ 3\sqrt[3]{x} + 11$. Are the functions F and G inverses? Verify.

4. Let $h(x) = \dfrac{7x - 3}{-x}$ and $k(x) = \dfrac{x + 3}{7}$. Are the functions h and k inverses? Verify.

Tutor signature:_____ Date:_____ Time:_____

M124 Unit 3
Problem Set #1

Problem Set ID #:   1243.01

Name: _____   Student ID# _____

---

1. For each of the following exponential equations, write a logarithmic equation with the same meaning.

    A) $y = 6^x$ **B)** $z^{11} = w$ **C)** $5 = a^b$

2. For each of the following logarithmic equations, write an exponential equation with the same meaning.

    A) $\log_b 8 = r$ **B)** $y = \log_i t$ **C)** $\log_r p = 23$

3. If $\log_x 2.45 = 0.43$, then, rounded to two decimal places,

$x =$

4. If $\log_{0.71} x = 6.97$, then, rounded to two decimal places,

$x =$

5. If $\log_3 81 = x$, then, rounded to two decimal places,

$x =$

Tutor signature:_____Date:_____Time:_____

M124 Unit 3   **Problem Set ID #:   1243.02**
Problem Set #2

Name: Student ID#

1. State the Product Property as it applies to the following:

    $\log_7 3x =$

2. State the Power Property as it applies to the following:

    $4\log_2 w =$

3. State the Quotient Property as it applies to the following:

    $\log_r 7 - \log_r q =$

4. Write the following in expanded form with no exponents or radicals:

$$\ln\left(\frac{3z^{-\frac{1}{4}}}{x^{\frac{2}{5}}y^3}\right)^4 =$$

5. Write the following as a single logarithm and simplify:

$$\frac{2}{5}\log_3(x - 5y) - \frac{1}{3}\log_3(x + 2y) - \log_3\left(x^2 - 3xy - 10y^2\right) =$$

Tutor signature: _____ Date: _____ Time: _____

M124 Unit 4   **Problem Set ID #:   1244.01**
Problem Set #1

Name: _____   Student ID# _____

INSTRUCTIONS:

Student Managed Format: If you are eligible to take unit exams in this course, you can earn one participation credit by satisfactorily completing this problem set and submitting it for evaluation in the IMP Tutoring Center (Weber 136). You may only submit problem set number 1244.01 once for participation credit.

Instructor-led Format: You can get additional practice and feedback by writing complete answers to these problems and asking a tutor in the IMP Tutoring Center (Weber 136) to review your work with you. Students in the Instructor-led Format are not subject to the participation requirement and should not submit problem sets for participation credit. Problem sets do not earn homework credits and do not entitle you to additional testing opportunities.

---

1. In simplest form, $e^{\left[\ln\left(x^2 - y^2\right) - 3\ln(x + y)\right]} =$

2. In simplest form, $\left(\dfrac{2}{x - 3y}\right)\log_5\left(\dfrac{5^{3x^2 - 10xy + 41y^2}}{5^{\left(-x^2 + 14xy + 5y^2\right)}}\right) =$

3. Solve the logarithmic equation $\log(x - 8) + \log(x - 4) = 1.07918$.

4. Solve the logarithmic equation $\log_3(x - 4) + \log_3(x + 4) = 2$.

Tutor signature:_____Date:_____Time:_____

M124 Unit 4
Problem Set #2

Problem Set ID #:   1244.02

Name: _____   Student ID# _____

1. Solve for x: $2^{x^2 + x - 7} = 32$.

2. Solve for x: $10^{2x - 1} = 3^{\frac{2}{3}x + 4}$.

3. In electrical engineering the voltage gain of an amplifier is defined by the logarithmic equation $D = 20\log\dfrac{E_O}{E_I}$ where D = the voltage gain in decibels, E_O = the output voltage of a device, and E_I = the input voltage of a device.

A) If the input to an amplifier is 1.2 volts and the output is 58 volts, what is the decibel voltage gain of the amplifier?

B) If the input to an amplifier is 1.5 volts and the decibel voltage gain of the amplifier is 35 decibels, what is the output voltage from the amplifier?

4. Newton's law of cooling states that an object's temperature will change at a rate proportional to the difference between the object's temperature and its surroundings. The formula describing this situation is $T = T_s + (T_o - T_s)e^{-kt}$ where T = the object's temperature at any time t, T_s = the surrounding temperature (assumed to be constant), T_o = the initial temperature of the object, k = a constant depending on the object, and t = time elapsed (in hours).

A) If a pot of coffee cools from a temperature of 180° to 110° in 30 minutes time, and the room temperature is 70°, find a value for the constant k.

B) What will be the temperature after 45 minutes?

C) How long will it be before the temperature of the coffee drops to 80°?

Tutor signature:_____Date:_____Time:_____

M124 Unit 5
Problem Set #1

Name: _____   Student ID# _____

1. Write the equation $y = 2.81e^{6.23t}$ as a linear equation in t and $y*$.

2. Write the equation $y* = 7.61 - 2.3t$, where $y* = \ln y$, as an exponential equation with base e.

3. Use the coordinate system in Figure 1245.01a to sketch
the semi-log graph of $f(t) = 2.34e^{-4.1t}$.

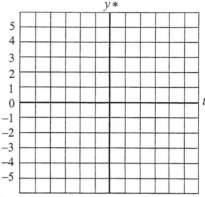

Figure 1245.01a

4. Find the exponential function that has the straight line
shown in Figure 1245.01b as its semi-log graph.

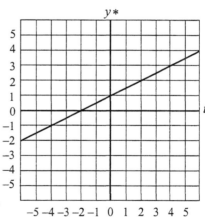

Figure 1245.01b

Tutor signature:_____ Date:_____Time:_____

M124 Unit 5   **Problem Set ID #:   1245.02**
Problem Set #2

Name: _____ Student ID# _____

1. What is the equation for the least squares line of best fit for the following data? The independent variable is x. Round to two decimal places as the last step in the calculation of the slope and the y-intercept.

x	-3	0	4	11
y	42	26	5	-21

2. Traffic in the city has increased dramatically in the 15 years since 1985. The city planning board collected the following data on the average number of cars to pass through a certain busy intersection each day:

time t since 1985 (years)	0	5	10	15
average number of cars c passing through the intersection (in thousands)	14.2	20.1	38.9	66.7

(See Over)

A) From this data, find an exponential function $c(t) = Ae^{kt}$ that models the average number of cars passing through the intersection each day. Round to three decimal places throughout the calculations.

B) According to this model, to the nearest one hundred cars, what will be the average number of cars passing through this intersection each day in the year 2015?

Tutor signature:_____Date:_____Time:_____